SOVIET TANKS
AND COMBAT VEHICLES
OF WORLD WAR TWO

SOVIET TANKS AND COMBAT VEHICLES OF WORLD WAR TWO

Steven J. Zaloga
and James Grandsen

ARMS AND ARMOUR PRESS
London - Melbourne - Harrisburg - Cape Town

1. Crewmen replace a track on a T34/85.

Contents

2. A column of T-37 amphibian scout tanks on manoeuvres. The lead vehicle is a T-37TU command vehicle with the early clothes-line antenna running around the hull (see page 76).

Published in 1984 by
Arms and Armour Press,
Lionel Leventhal Limited,
2–6 Hampstead High Street,
London NW3 1QQ.
Australasia: 4–12 Tattersalls Lane,
Melbourne, Victoria 3000.
South Africa: Sanso Centre, 8 Adderley Street,
P.O. Box 94, Cape Town 8000.
United States: Cameron and Kelker Streets,
P.O. Box 1831, Harrisburg, Pa. 17105.

1 2 3 4 5 6 7 8 9 0

British Library Cataloguing in Publication Data:
Zaloga, Steven J.
Soviet tanks of World War Two.
1. Tanks (Military science) – Soviet Union – History
I. Title II. Grandsen, James
623.74'752'0947 UG446.5

ISBN 0-85368-606-8

Layout by Anthony A. Evans.
Edited by Michael Boxall.
Typeset by Typsetters (Birmingham) Limited.
Camerawork by Chelmer Litho Reproductions, Maldon.
Printed and bound in Great Britain by
Robert Hartnoll Limited, Bodmin.

List of Diagrams

List of Tables

Preface

From 1941 to 1945 the dominant theatre of the European War was the Eastern Front, and the dominant land weapon there was the tank. Soviet tanks and armoured vehicles played a central role in the eventual victory, but the subject of Soviet armoured vehicle development has long been neglected and has not shared the attention paid to German armoured vehicles or the tanks of the other major powers. It is the aim of this book to fill that gap by tracing the development of tanks and armoured vehicles in Russia. The focus of the book is primarily the technical evolution of tanks and armoured vehicles in the USSR, though in order to properly understand the subject, it has also been necessary to examine the tactical organization of Soviet tank units, and their employment in combat. In order properly to appreciate the evolution of Soviet tanks during the Second World War, or the Great Patriotic War as the Russians prefer to call it, it is necessary to go back to the Tsarist roots of Russian armoured vehicles. Most published studies of this subject have ignored the important role played by early Russian armoured trains and armoured cars in the catalysing of interest in armoured vehicles in the Red Army. Special attention has been paid here as well to Soviet vehicle development during the 1930s, not only because the bulk of the tanks used during the first year of the war were manufactured during that period, but because it places the great success of Soviet tank development during the war into a proper perspective. The book does not pretend to be an exhaustive study of this complicated subject. Very little attention is paid to detailed descriptions of the various tank types, if only because of a lack of space. Instead, emphasis is placed on determining the reasons for the development of various types of tanks, their evolution once they reached production and, finally, their role in the armoured units of the Red Army. In a book of this size, it has been impossible to trace the use of the tank in every battle of the Second World War, and it has not been our intention to do so, but lessons drawn from the fighting are examined, especially when they had an impact on tank evolution. The interesting subject of the evolution of Soviet tank tactics is alluded to, but is so complex that nothing short of a full-length study could adequately treat of it. Where tactical problems influenced tank design, they have been dealt with. The scope of the book has been expanded to cover some vehicles normally outside the purview of armoured vehicle studies, notably the aerosans and Katyusha rocket launchers, because these vehicles were built as substitutes for more conventional armoured vehicles.

Research was hampered by the lack of detailed Soviet studies of the subject. No Russian study of Soviet tanks comparable to Shavrov's history of Soviet aircraft development has been published. This surely does not stem from any lack of Russian pride in their accomplishments, but from the fact that even at this late date many of the wartime projects are still hedged about with security restrictions, and there are of course a number of politically sensitive issues such as the effects of the purges on Soviet tank development. Nevertheless, over the years a partial picture of Soviet efforts in this field has emerged from hundreds of items appearing in disparate articles and books. This book has been based on Soviet material where available and where deemed reliable, and gaps have been filled from German, British and American archival sources. Special difficulty was encountered in finding photographs. The evacuation of the factories in 1941, and other war damage led to a loss of much Soviet historical material, and existing security restrictions do little to help matters. Although the Soviets have opened the Monino Aircraft Museum to the public, the extensive armoured vehicle collection at Kubinka is still restricted. We ask the readers' indulgence for the quality of some of the photographs which fall below the usual standard. Sadly, in too many cases, these are all that exist.

A few notes should be made concerning Russian designations and terms used in this book. A wealth of bogus tank designations have been applied to Soviet armoured vehicles, based in some cases on German or British wartime designations. Part of the problem stems from the fact that the Soviets, like the Americans (but unlike the British and Germans) do not generally take any special pains to identify their tank subtypes. The most common form of identification of subtypes is the traditional ordnance classification of model/year. This book uses Russian designations where available, and frequently appends the designation with further notes such as 'late production type' where relevant to some technical point. Certain peculiar Russian designations such as 'fast tanks' are used literally because of a lack of suitable English equivalents. Also, the Russian term *'samokhodnaya ustanovka'* has been rendered here as 'mechanized gun' rather than 'self-propelled gun' because it is closer in sense to the original. On the other hand, the Russian term for 'scout tanks' has been left as 'light tanks' rather than the literal, but awkward 'small tanks'. One of the more confusing features of Russian factory designation is the possibility of naming a factory in someone's honour in two fashions. An adjectival form can be used as in the case of the Kirovskiy Works named after S. M. Kirov. Or the honorific form *'imeni S. M. Kirov'* can be used. In this book, the latter form has been appended to the factory's military designation as (S. M. Kirov) to avoid confusion. The Soviet military designations for ordnance factories 'Zavod Nr.' has been transliterated rather than translated as this is already commonly the practice in other studies of Soviet war industries, notably in the aviation field. In data tables, where information was lacking, a blank space has been left, while in cases where the heading was not applicable, a dash (–) has been inserted. The scale drawings are to a modeller's constant scale of 1/76 except for the Tsar Tank. The convention of not illustrating the running gear on the far side of a vehicle with torsion bar suspension has been followed here for clarity.

As with any undertaking of this scope, the research of other specialists has proved vitally important. The authors would like to extend their special thanks to the foremost expert in this sphere, Janusz Magnuski, for his help on numerous matters. Thanks are also extended to James Loop, to Tom Jentz for help on matters relating to German vehicles, to David Fletcher and Peter Evans for aid on Lend-Lease subjects, and to Lee Ness, Professor James Goff and John Sloan for matters dealing with Soviet armoured unit organization. Special thanks must be extended to Just Probst for assistance with both photographic and historical research in the initial section on Tsarist armour. Many of the photographs used were collected with the help of Esa Muikku, George Balin, Ivan Bajtos, Jiri Hornat and Pierre Touzin. Thanks also go to Vika Edwards of the Sovfoto Office in New York for her patient help in finding TASS and Novosti photographs. Special appreciation also to Stephanie Doba for her help with the manuscript!

Steven Zaloga and James Grandsen, 1984.

Red Army Mechanization 1920–40

Armoured Vehicles of the Imperial Russian Army

The development of armoured vehicles in the Imperial Russian Army was inhibited by the lack of a mature automobile industry in Tsarist Russia. There were several small firms assembling cars from imported components, but it was not until the opening of the automotive facility at the Russo-Balt Wagon Factory (Russo-Baltiiskiy Zavod: RBVZ) in Riga, Latvia in 1908 that any significant number of cars or lorries were manufactured. Until 1915 when it was evacuated, RBVZ produced about 450 cars and lorries.

As early as 1900, an engineer named Dvinistkiy was given permission to begin work on a steam-powered armoured car, but eventually this project had to be abandoned because of a lack of sufficient engineering experience. In the wake of the 1904 Russo-Japanese War, an officer of the Siberian Cossack Corps of the Manchurian Army, M. Nakashidze, began design work on a turreted armoured car which won the favour of the War Ministry. The Ministry, however, was sceptical of the ability of Russian industry to manufacture such a vehicle and the French firm of Charron, Girardot & Voigt were contracted to build a prototype. Trials of the vehicle convinced the Imperial Russian Army of its utility, and consideration was given to initiating quantity production of the type at the Izhorskiy Factory (Admiralteyskiy Izhorskiy Zavod: AIZ) at Kolpino outside St Petersburg. Although the AIZ was well experienced in the manufacture of armour plate and was the chief supplier of armour and steel to the Tsarist Navy, the War Ministry decided to issue the contract for ten further vehicles to the French. These were completed in 1908, but only eight arrived in Russia because the Germans managed to 'lose' two of them while on rail transit through Germany. Curiously enough, they turned up later in Landwehr manoeuvres! The Nakashidze armoured car, despite its primitive design, inspired a number of young Russian officers, and opened their eyes to the potential for far more effective combat vehicles.

The Russian General Staff set up a Commission for Automotive Experimentation to investigate the utility of motor vehicles in the military role. The Commission was impressed with the Nakashidze armoured car, but further development of indigenous designs was hampered because they came under the direction of the fossilized Imperial Artillery Commission; many designs were rejected out of hand. Nevertheless, in 1914, the Automobile Corps was formed. This would subsequently play an important role in the formation of Tsarist, and later Soviet, armoured units through its efforts to build up cadres of drivers, mechanics and technically-trained officers in an empire where there were pitifully few technicians.

The Imperial Russian Army evinced a modest interest and in 1913 placed a number of foreign orders, mainly from Britain. The War Ministry also ordered from RBVZ fifteen light armoured cars armed with machine-guns and three gun-armed heavies based on the Type M lorry. The British armoured cars did not arrive in substantial numbers until after the outbreak of the war, so the first Russian armoured car unit to be formed was organized with the Russo-Balt armoured cars on 19 October 1914 and was assigned to the South-western Front. During the autumn and winter fighting around Lodz, the unit proved very effective and won over many officers who previously had been sceptical. As a consequence, the War Ministry increased the foreign orders and an Armoured Car Commission was formed as part of the Technical Administration of the General Staff (STAVKA) to consider indigenous designs.

As the British armoured cars began arriving and Russian armoured cars began to be manufactured, new units were formed, organized into detachments or companies. A detachment usually had two light cars with machine-guns (broneavtomobil) and one gun-armed heavy (pushechniy broneavtomobil or protivoshturmovoye orduiye: anti-assault gun). Each detachment numbered approximately 100 men with 21 lorries and support vehicles. The companies had twelve light cars and three heavies. Armoured car units were usually attached to rifle divisions or to corps and were employed in a wide range of defensive and offensive roles. Their main handicap was that they were virtually road-bound because of the high ground pressure of their narrow wheels, and were nearly useless in deep snow or during the muddy conditions of spring and autumn. To circumvent these problems, the War Ministry began promoting half-tracked armoured cars in 1916, but these numbered but a small fraction of the total inventory. The half-tracked armoured cars were popularly called 'Russian tanks'.

The Imperial Russian Army fielded no less than 30 different types of armoured car during the Great War, many of them in very small numbers. Initially, British armoured cars were the predominant type, but, by 1916 the War Ministry had become dissatisfied with some of the British vehicles, particularly the Armstrong-Whitworth and the Sheffield-Simplex. This prompted the Russians to promote the manufacture of armoured cars in quantity within the empire. In addition to RBVZ which was evacuated to Taganrog in 1915, there were three other firms closely connected with Russian armoured car production, all in the St Petersburg (Petrograd) area. These were the Obukhov Works (Staleliteyniy i Oruzheyniy Obukhovskiy Zavod: SOOZ) in Petrograd, the Izhorskiy Factory

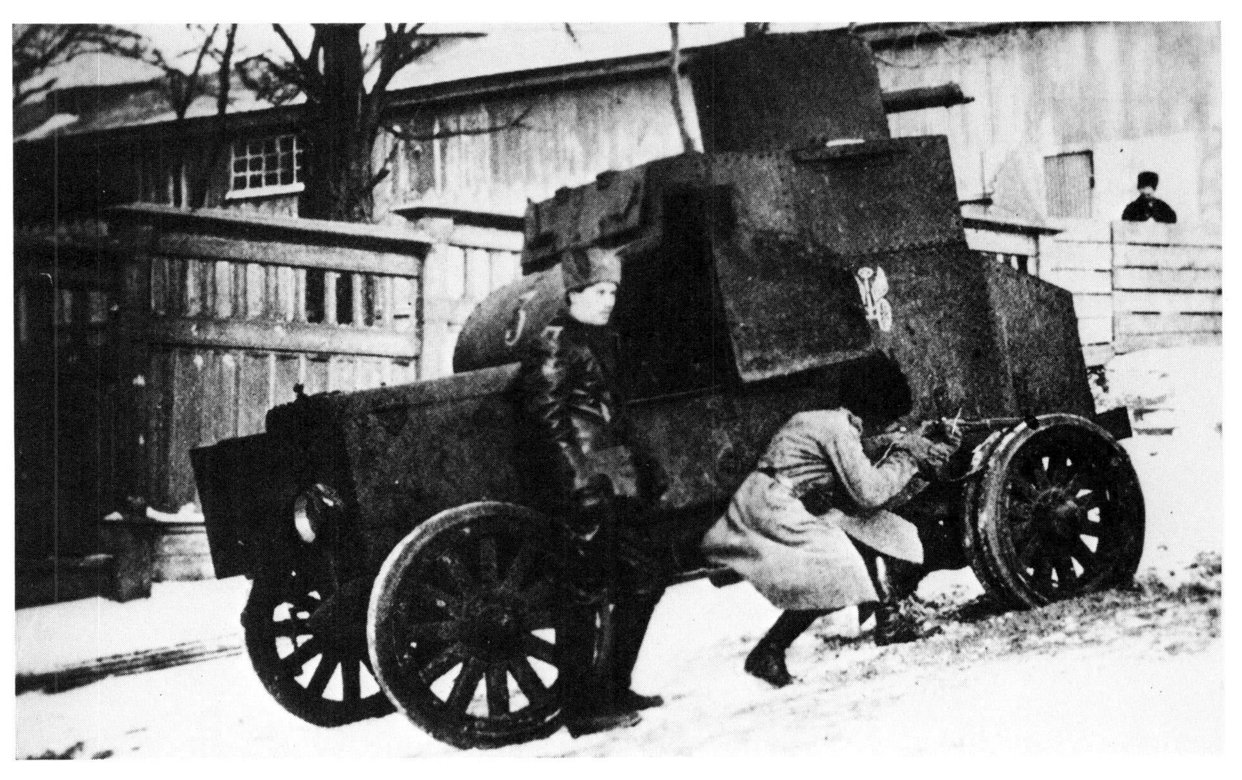

3. The Armstrong-Whitworth armoured car was one of the first British armoured cars to enter Russian service, but its performance was generally unsatisfactory.

△4

△5 ▽6

(AIZ) in Kolpino south of Petrograd, and the Putilov Works (Putilovskiy Zavod) also in Petrograd. The Izhorskiy Works built a total of 119 armoured cars up to 1919, mainly on Fiat, Pierce-Arrow and Peerless chassis, and a small number of half-tracked armoured cars on Palmers & Lombard agricultural tractor chassis. The Putilov Works was certainly the largest manufacturer, building more than 250 armoured cars and halftracks mainly on Austin and Packard chassis. The War Ministry had hoped to produce 200 armoured cars and 60 halftracks annually starting in 1916, but this goal was never met. The Russian industrial firms depended on imported parts which were always in short supply. By the war's end, the Imperial Russian Army fielded about 300 armoured cars in 52 armoured units. There were also three Allied units serving on the Eastern Front. The Belgian Corps des Auto-Canons-Mitrailleuses, which fought in Russia from 1915 to 1918, was equipped with 14 Mors armoured cars. The French sent the 10ème Groupe d'auto-canons, auto-mitrailleuses for use on the Roumanian Front, but most of its Renault armoured cars were destroyed in a fire in Archangel before seeing combat. The largest and most influential foreign group to serve in Russia was Locker-Lampson's Russian Armoured Car Division RNAS. When initially sent to Russia in 1916, it was equipped with 32 Lanchester armoured cars, two Pierce-Arrow and two Seabrook heavy armoured cars and a Rolls-Royce light armoured car. During later fighting, other types were employed including Ford light armoured cars and even Izhorskiy-Fiats.

In view of the large number of abortive projects, the following description of Russian armoured car types is limited to those which actually entered service with either the Imperial Russian Army or the later Red Army. The list is by no means comprehensive; photographs exist showing vehicle types of which no details are available.

Imported Light Armoured Cars

Nakashidze-Charron. This was the first Russian armoured car, designed in 1905 by M. Nakashidze and manufactured by the Société Charron, Girardot & Voigt at Puteaux near Paris. Following trials during the summer wargames of 1906, the War

4. Dissatisfaction with some of the imported British armoured cars such as this Sheffield-Simplex was one of the reasons that prompted the Russians to build most of their own armoured cars after 1916.
5. Undoubtedly the most successful of the British armoured cars purchased by the Imperial Russian Army was the Austin. This one Austin belonged to the Deniken Army during the civil war in 1919 as is evident from its Imperial cockade and chevron insignia.
6. One of the most distinctive Russian armoured cars was the Mgebrov-Renault with its wedge-shaped body. The original version used a single large turret like this one.
7. American and Russian troops listen to a military band in Obozerskaya on 27 September 1918, near a White-Russian Austin armoured car. The slogan on the Austin is 'Yedinaya Rossiya' (United Russia). (National Archives).
8. The more common version of the Mgebrov-Renault armoured car used twin rear turrets as on this vehicle being examined by German troops.

7△ 8▽

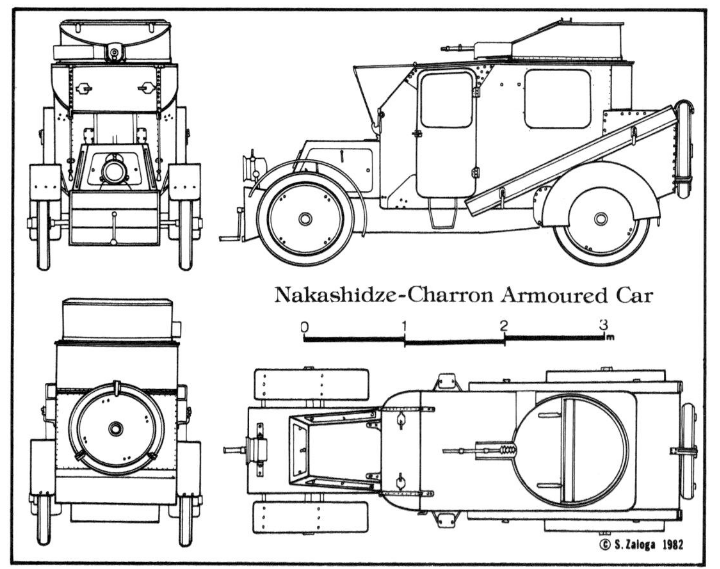

Nakashidze-Charron Armoured Car

Ministry ordered ten more vehicles but only eight arrived in Russia after the German Army stole two while in transit through Germany. This vehicle had a single turreted machine-gun and was armoured with 3mm steel plate.

Armstrong-Whitworth. This was one of the first foreign armoured car types ordered in 1913. It was accepted for service after trials of a prototype, and by the end of 1916 a total of 36 had been ordered. In service it was plagued with defects and was very critically received by its hapless crews.

Isotta-Fraschini (Jarrot). In 1914, Charles Jarrot & Letts Co was one of four firms selected by the Russian War Ministry to design an armoured car for use by the Imperial Russian Army. The design was based on an imported Isotta-Fraschini chassis and a total of 30 of the type were ordered.

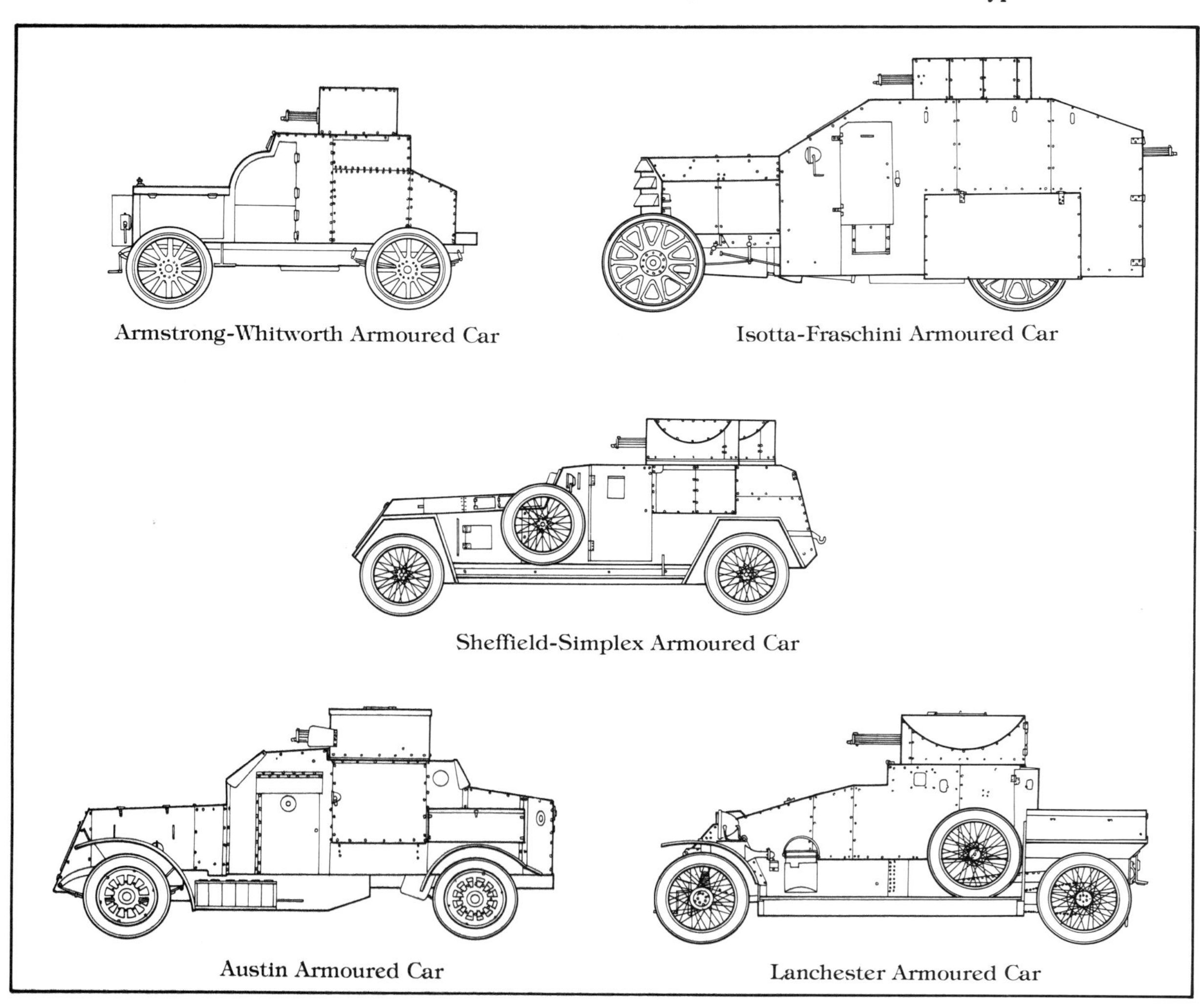
Armstrong-Whitworth Armoured Car

Isotta-Fraschini Armoured Car

Sheffield-Simplex Armoured Car

Austin Armoured Car

Lanchester Armoured Car

9. There were a number of different body styles on the Austins used by the Imperial Russian Army, this style being one of the more common.

Sheffield-Simplex Armoured Car. The Sheffield-Simplex Motor Works provided the Russian Army with lorries, ambulances and cars, and was selected to design an armoured car in 1914. It had an armoured body provided by the firm of T. Piggott & Co Ltd, and by 1916, the Russians had received 25. No further orders were placed because of deficiencies in the design. There were at least two distinct models of this car, differing mainly in details of the body design.

Austin. By far the most common imported type in Russian service. The Austin Motor Co Ltd was the largest single supplier of lorries and cars to the Imperial Russian Army and in 1913 won a contract to develop an armoured car. In contrast with many of the other cars supplied to Russia during this period, the Austin featured staggered twin machine-gun turrets. It proved the most satisfactory of the British armoured car types and 48 were ordered in 1914 alone. The majority of the Russian Austins were based on the 50hp Colonial chassis, and there were several distinct body types reflecting various improvements in the design as production continued. It is believed that about 100 Austins were shipped to Russia by which time the Putilov Works was building a close derivative based on imported Austin chassis.

Lanchester. About 20 Lanchester armoured cars were ordered from England in 1915. They were similar to the type used by the Locker-Lampson unit, but had a small cupola mounted on the turret roof.

Russian Light Armoured Cars

Russo-Balt. The second version was fully armoured and carried three Maxim machine-guns. About fifteen were manufactured and they were used to form the first Russian armoured car company in 1914.

Mgebrov-Renault. In 1915, Staff Captain Mgebrov designed an exotic, wedge-shaped armoured car on the basis of a Renault sedan. The heavily angled front was designed to better deflect machine-gun bullets. At least two versions were built, the initial type with a single large turret, and a later type with twin machine-gun turrets. The total number constructed is not known, but it would appear that after 1917, the Bolsheviks manufactured a number of vehicles on the same basic pattern with only minor changes in armour layout.

Mgebrov-Benz. In 1916, Captain Mgebrov designed another of his characteristically wedge-shaped armoured cars, but based on a German Benz chassis. The vehicle was completed days before Mgebrov's death in action in 1916, and there appears to have been no quantity production.

Poplavko-Jeffery. In 1915, Staff Captain Poplavko of the 7th Armoured Car Detachment on the South-western Front designed a very simple armoured car which was notable mainly for its thick, 16mm, armour. It was based on an American Jeffery-Quad lorry and as a result of its success in field trials, the War

△10

△11 ▽12

10. The Poplavko-Jeffery armoured car was one of the most heavily armoured vehicles of the period, and is distinctive in its lack of machine-gun turrets. These two vehicles served on the South-Western Front in 1916.
11. Apart from the Austin armoured car and its Putilov-built derivatives, the most common Russian armoured car was the Izhorskiy-Fiat, like this one seen in action in Galicia, Eastern Poland in 1916.
12. The Izhorskiy-Fiat had a number of design changes made during the course of production as is evident in comparing this late production version with the photograph of the Izhorskiy-Fiat in Galicia.

13. The twin-turret configuration and reliability of the Austin prompted the Russians to adopt this configuration as their standard armoured car design during the war. When further purchases of foreign cars was terminated in 1916, the Putilov Works built their own version of the Austin on imported chassis. This Putilov-Austin, named Stenka Razki, was captured by the Poles during the 1920 Russo-Polish war and renamed the Poznanczyk.

Ministry sanctioned the manufacture of about 30 in 1916 which were used to form independent armoured car detachments on the South-western Front.

Izhorskiy-Fiat. In 1915, the Izhorskiy Factory developed a derivative of the popular Austin armoured car based on imported Fiat 60×90 chassis. This was manufactured in relatively large numbers, and was the most common type in service aside from the Austin and its Putilov-built derivatives. As in the case of the Austin, there were several body variants which differed in minor details.

Putilov-Austin. Following the War Ministry's decision in 1916 to promote Russian manufacture of armoured cars in place of imports from Britain, the Putilov Works was assigned the task of developing a derivative of the popular Austin armoured car. This version had full front and rear driving controls and entered production in 1917. It was unofficially called the

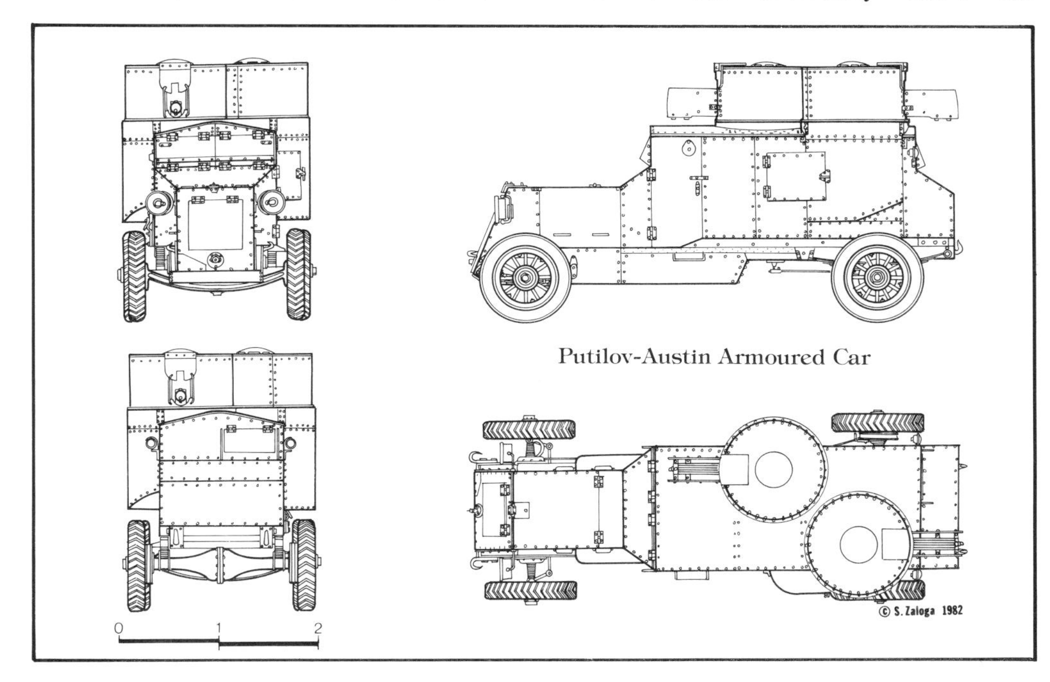

Putilov-Austin Armoured Car

Putilovsky-Ostin and about 200 were manufactured, excluding the half-tracked derivative.

Izhorskiy-White. From 1915 to 1917, the Izhorskiy Factory manufactured a small number of armoured cars based on the popular American White touring car. The configuration of these vehicles was very close to that of the Austin and they were sometimes very difficult to tell apart.

Putilov-Packard. In 1917, the Putilov Works built a small number of armoured cars on American Packard chassis which closely resembled the general layout of the Austin armoured car.

Izhorskiy-Peerless. Prior to the war's outbreak, the War Ministry ordered sixteen armoured cars based on the Peerless chassis from Wolseley Motors Ltd, which arrived in 1916. They were originally armed with 40mm Vickers pompom guns in an open rear compartment. After the 1917 Bolshevik Revolution, these were modified by the Izhorskiy Factory by the addition of a turret and three additional hull-mounted machine-guns.

Ford. A number of armoured Ford Model Ts were used by the RNAS squadron in Russia, having been designed by CPO L. Gutteridge and built by G. Allen & Sons. The Russians also used a number of armoured cars built on Ford chassis, but it is unclear if these were based on captured chassis, or chassis imported during the war.

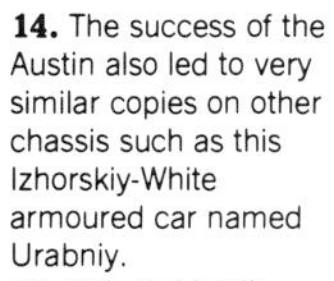

14. The success of the Austin also led to very similar copies on other chassis such as this Izhorskiy-White armoured car named Urabniy.
15. This Bolshevik armoured car company is equipped with a Ford (at the right), two Austins and an Izhorskiy-Fiat.
16. Another of the Austin look-alikes was the Putilov-Packard armoured car, in this case being followed by an Austin.

△14 ▽15

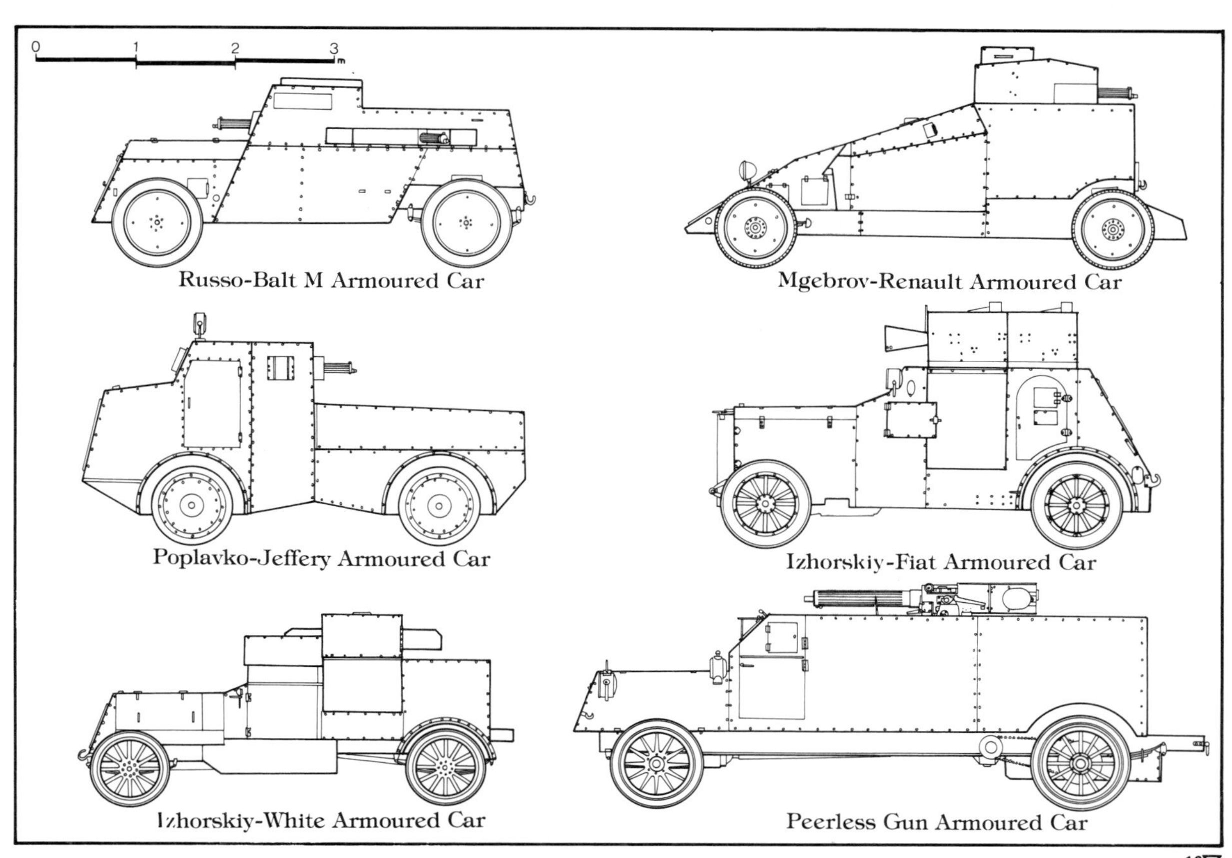
0
1
2
3
m
Russo-Balt M Armoured Car
Mgebrov-Renault Armoured Car
Poplavko-Jeffery Armoured Car
Izhorskiy-Fiat Armoured Car
Izhorskiy-White Armoured Car
Peerless Gun Armoured Car

16▽

Half-tracked Armoured Cars

Putilov-Austin. The French automobile designer, Adolphe Kégresse, headed the Tsar's personal automobile service from 1906, and in 1911 began work on a number of novel suspension systems to enable cars to drive on snow. His third system, a rubber reinforced band track suspension, could be placed on the rear axle instead of conventional wheels. In 1916, 200 suspension assemblies were ordered from the Putilov Works for both armoured cars and lorries. Sixty half-tracked armoured cars were ordered by the War Ministry, but only a few of them had been completed before the revolution. Nevertheless, about 60 were later completed on Austin and Packard chassis for the new Red Army. These vehicles were officially designated polugusenichniy broneavtomobil, but they were popularly called half-tanks (poltank) or 'Russian-type tanks'.

Gulkievich. In 1915, Colonel Gulkievich proposed to the Central Artillery Administration that a tracked armoured vehicle could be built which would be free of the mobility restrictions of the current armoured cars. In the absence of suitable tracked chassis in Russia, Gulkievich managed to have an American Lombard artillery tractor imported, and used the tracked suspension to provide the basis for a single armoured car built at the Putilov Works.

Putilov-Bullock. In view of the success of the Gulkievich concept, the Red Army ordered the Putilov Works to modify a number of Austin and Packard armoured cars with tracked suspensions taken from Lombard, Bullock and Holt half-tracked agricultural chassis which had been imported by the Imperial Russian Army for use as agricultural tractors. Only ten or so of these vehicles were actually built, but they proved infinitely superior to ordinary armoured cars in mud and snow.

17. From 1916, the Russians began to fit the track assembly designed by Kegresse on Putilov-Austins to improve their mobility in mud and snow. This particular Putilov-Austin half-track took part in the 1920 Russo-Polish War where both sides made extensive use of armoured cars for infantry support and for raiding.

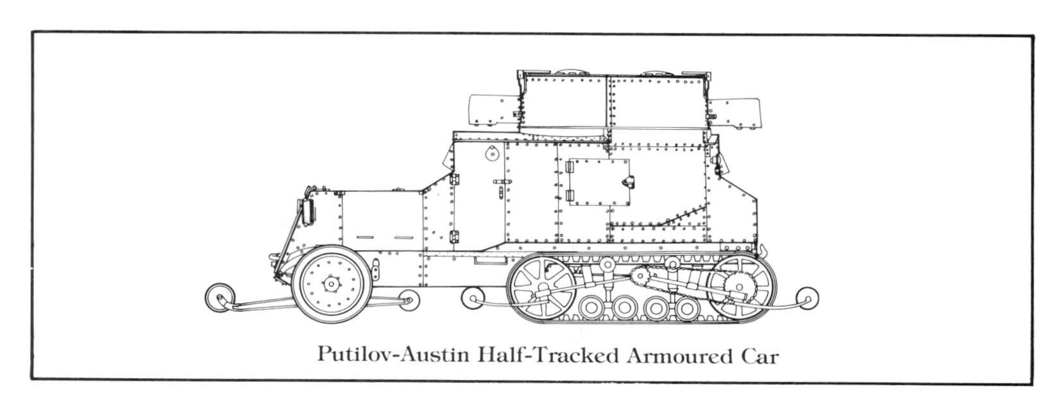
Putilov-Austin Half-Tracked Armoured Car

18. The shortage of the new Kegresse track assemblies led the Russian Army to consider expedient designs such as this Gulkievich half-track which was based on a Lombard agricultural tractor. The vehicle shown served with Wrangel's forces in the Crimea in 1919.
19. In addition to the Lombard, the Putilov Works used Bullock agricultural tractors to make armoured cars like this well-known 'Red Petersburg' which was armed with a machine-gun turret on the roof and a 76mm regimental gun in a rear-firing turret.

18△ 19▽

Heavy Armoured Cars

Putilov-Garford. In 1914, the Putilov Works began design of a heavy armoured car to provide fire support for machine-gun armed vehicles like the Russo-Balt armoured car. The new vehicle was based on imported American Garford Model 68/69 5-ton lorries and the main armament consisted of a 76.2mm regimental gun and two Maxim machine-guns in side sponsons. The configuration bears more than a passing resemblance to naval designs, which is not surprising because both the Putilov and Izhorskiy Factories had extensive experience in ship construction and armament. Production began in 1914 and total production probably amounted to several dozen vehicles. The Putilov-Garford proved quite successful in combat, and on a number of occasions became involved in engagements with both enemy armoured cars and armoured trains. It was among the most long-lived of the pre-revolutionary armoured cars; in the late

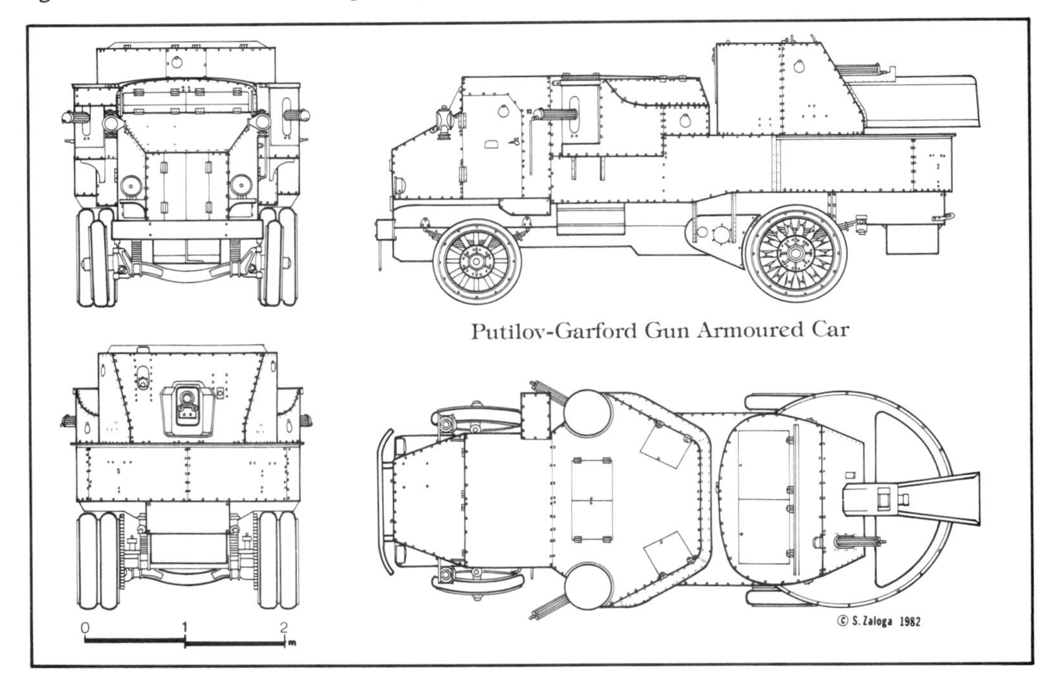

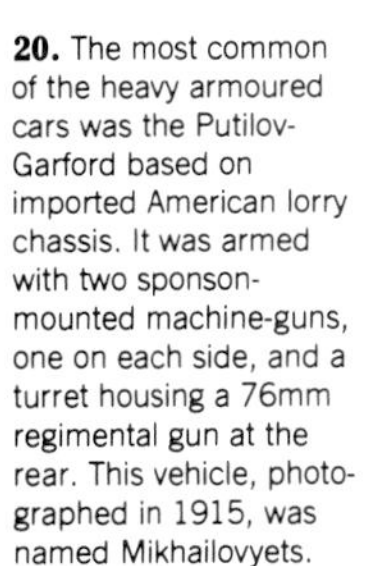

20. The most common of the heavy armoured cars was the Putilov-Garford based on imported American lorry chassis. It was armed with two sponson-mounted machine-guns, one on each side, and a turret housing a 76mm regimental gun at the rear. This vehicle, photographed in 1915, was named Mikhailovyets.

21. The ungainly Putilov-Packard heavy armoured car mounted imported Vickers pom-pom guns in a rear turret. It was used mainly for infantry support rather than air defence.
22. Many of the Russian built armoured cars were produced in very small numbers and with considerable variation in design as is evident by comparing this view of a Putilov-Packard with the other photograph.

1920s some were refurbished and used as rail patrol vehicles with special wheels for use on railway lines.

Packard. In December 1916, the Inter-Service Conference at Petrograd discussed the problem of the lack of anti-aircraft weapons and decided to develop an indigenous vehicle like the Peerless armoured car with pompom guns. In 1917, eleven Packards were modified as armoured cars and fitted with imported Vickers 40mm pom-poms. These were later used by the Red Army, mainly to provide fire support to infantry formations.

Renault 47mm. It would appear that among the vehicles brought to Russia with the French armoured car detachment were a small number of Renault 4×2 armoured cars equipped with Hotchkiss 47mm guns firing over the rear end. Apparently at least one fell into Russian hands.

Pierce-Arrow. The RNAS unit in Russia had several Pierce-Arrow heavy armoured cars armed with 3pdrs. Apparently, a few of

21△ 22▽

23. This frontal view of the Pierce-Arrow shows its very simple design compared to the Garford.
24. The Russian Pierce-Arrow bore no relation to the Pierce-Arrow armoured car used by the Locker-Lampson unit in Russia. It was armed with a short howitzer, and had two small machine-gun sponsons in the hull rear. This particular vehicle was used by communist revolutionaries in Berlin in 1919 after its capture by the German Army on the Eastern Front. The Germans made use of any armoured cars captured from the Russians.

△23 ▽24

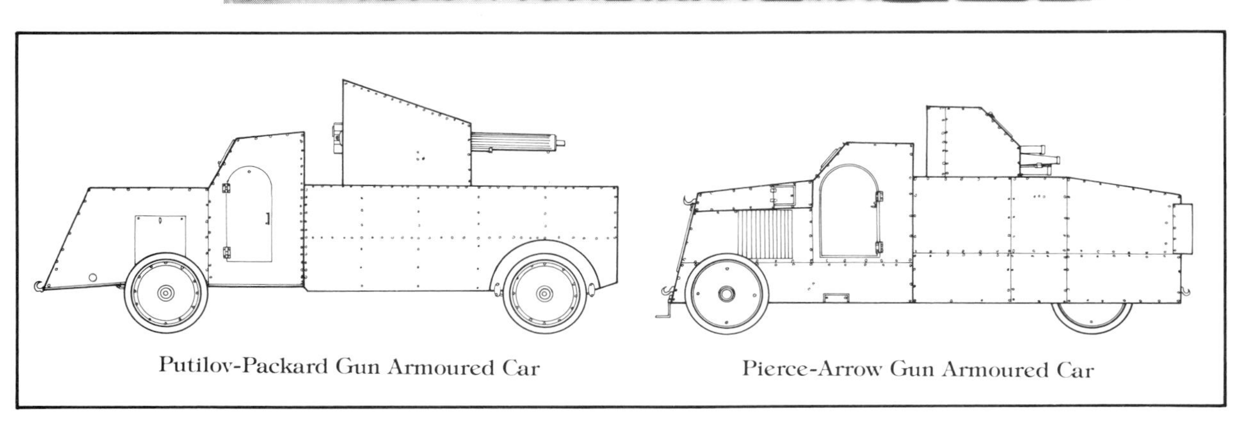

RUSSIAN ARMOURED CARS, 1905–20

Type	Weight (tonnes)	Crew	Armour (mm)	Dimensions (L×W×H in cm)	Armament (mm)	Engine (hp/cylinders)	Max road speed (km/h)
Nakashidze-Charron	3.2	3-4	3	480 × 170 × 240	7.62	35/4	45
Armstrong-Whitworth	3.8	3-4		390 × 240 × 230	2 × 7.62		
Isotta-Fraschini	6	3-6		562 × 285 × 280	2 × 7.62	120/4	65
Sheffield-Simplex	5.9	5		480 × 210 × 210	7.62	30/6	40
Austin	4.2	5	5-7.5	487 × 200 × 239	2 × 8	50/4	56
Lanchester	4.8	3-4	8	487 × 193 × 228	7.62	60/6	80
Russo-Balt	4.5	3-4		450 × 198 × 200	3 × 7.62	60/4	40
Mgebrov-Renault	3.5	2-3		510 × 232 × 230	2 × 7.62	18/4	15
Mgebrov-Benz	4	2-3			2 × 7.62		
Poplavko-Jeffery	8	4-5		452 × 200 × 214	2 × 7.62	40 + 40	32
Izhorskiy-Fiat	5.5	5	7	480 × 190 × 250	2 × 7.62	60/4	60
Putilov-Austin	5.2	5	8	490 × 190 × 240	2 × 7.62	50/4	50
Izhorskiy-White	6	3-4		445 × 190 × 202	2 × 7.62	35/4	45
Packard	5	3-4	5-9		40	33	50
Izhorskiy-Peerless	6	5-6	8	623 × 226 × 274	4 × 7.62	40/4	30
Ford	1.07	2	5.9		7.62	22/4	40
Putilov-Austin Halftrack	6	5	5-8	630 × 190 × 240	2 × 7.62	50/4	25
Putilov-Bullock Halftrack	7	6-7	8	700 × 285 × ?	76.2	100	8-10
Putilov-Garford	9-11	8	7-13	570 × 230 × 280	76.2	35/4	18-20
Pierce-Arrow	9	5	5-9	610 × 185 × 240	57		

25. One of the smaller heavy armoured cars was the Loyd which used a gun firing over the rear of the vehicle.
26. The Russo-Balt heavy armoured car was unusual in that its gun fired forward. In this view, the gun is missing from the front port.

these were captured and later rebuilt and re-armed in Petrograd by the Bolsheviks with 57mm guns.

Loyd. In 1916, a small number of Loyd lorries were converted to carry 76.2mm Model 1902 and Model 1910 guns which fired over the rear of the vehicle. These were not as successful as the Putilov Garfords, but they remained in service until 1920.

Russo-Balt. In 1915, the RBVZ built a small number of heavy armoured cars using a 76.2mm gun firing over the front of an armoured lorry chassis. Further production of this type was halted both by the evacuation of the factory and by the mixed results of the vehicle in combat use.

Armoured Trains

Armoured cars did not make the tremendous impact on the Eastern Front that tanks had on the Western Front. Their mobility was far more circumscribed than the early tanks, and indeed they were seasonal weapons of little value during the winter months or during the frequent muddy seasons. The Imperial Russian Army used them in larger numbers than any other army, and by the end of the war there were nearly enough to provide each front-line rifle division with an armoured car detachment. Far more successful were the armoured trains. In many ways, they can be regarded as the more important antecedents of later Soviet armoured formations than the armoured cars.

Armoured trains had first been used by the Imperial Russian Army in the 1904 Russo-Japanese War. Several factories manufactured the trains used in the 1914–1917 conflict. The Izhorskiy Works manufactured 43 armoured trains after 1917, and the Putilov Works manufactured more. There were two basic categories: light and heavy. Light armoured trains consisted of an armoured locomotive, two armoured artillery cars, each with two turreted 76.2mm guns and various machine-guns, and a number of support cars. The heavy trains differed in their use of a 4.2in or even a 6in gun in place of the 76.2mm. Each armoured train was usually supported by a supply train which also contained the sleeping-berths for the crew of the armoured train. Armoured trains could be used to provide fire support for infantry units, and eventually tactics were developed for even more dynamic employment. Eventually, armoured assault cars were carried, each containing a small infantry or cavalry unit which would be taken close to an enemy position and disgorged under heavy covering fire from the armoured train. These tactics reached fruition during the Russian Civil War. The Russian armoured train detachments were a primitive type of unit which today would be called a combined arms team. They combined armoured mobility, artillery firepower and infantry assault capability, but differed from later mechanized units because of the constraints imposed by the railway lines. Even so,

27. Another product of the Russo-Balt Works was this armoured anti-aircraft lorry mounting a 76.2mm anti-aircraft gun behind an armoured cab. Note the prominent outriggers for steadying the gun while firing.

28△ 29▽

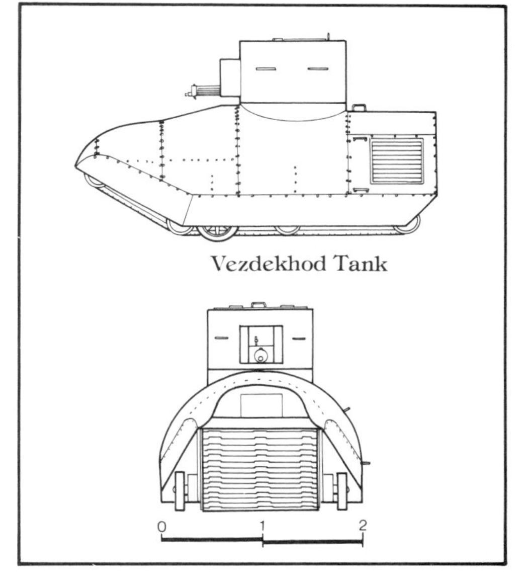

28. The Peerless armoured cars when originally purchased from Britain in 1914 were completely open in the rear. As is shown here, they were later partially enclosed with a shield around the front of their pom-poms. Some were also rebuilt with turrets. These vehicles belonged to the 2nd Armoured Battery in the Tsarskoye Selo area near Petrograd in March 1917.

29. The only serious Russian attempt at a true tank was the tiny Vezdekhod which is seen here with its designer. The armoured shell was never mated to the single-track chassis nor, it seems, was its turret ever added. A scale drawing here shows it as it would have appeared had it been completed.

armoured trains were more mobile than early armoured cars or tanks since they could be used in all but the deepest snow. They were far more reliable than the tank units which were plagued by constant mechanical breakdowns.

Tsarist Tanks

The Imperial Russian Army never managed to develop its own tank. Numerous proposals were put forward to the Central Technical Committee of the Army's Military Technical Administration, but only two projects were seriously funded. In December 1914, an engineer of the RBVZ, A. A. Porokovskikov, received permission to proceed with his suggestions for a track-laying vehicle with an armoured shell, which was to be built in cooperation with the Chief Engineer Officer of the North-western Front. The tiny vehicle was called the Vezdekhod (Go anywhere) and a test chassis without armour was completed in March 1915. Unlike tanks being developed by France and Britain at the time, the Vezdekhod used only a single track and was steered by two small wheels, one on each side of the vehicle, which acted like rudders. An armoured body was never fitted to the chassis, and in December 1915, the Central Technical Committee cancelled the project after determining that the Imperial Russian Army had no use for such a vehicle. In October 1916, the project was reopened in the wake of considerable public criticism after the first news had arrived of the new British tanks. The later programme was no more successful than the earlier effort, and even if a completed tank had been available, it is doubtful whether it could have been

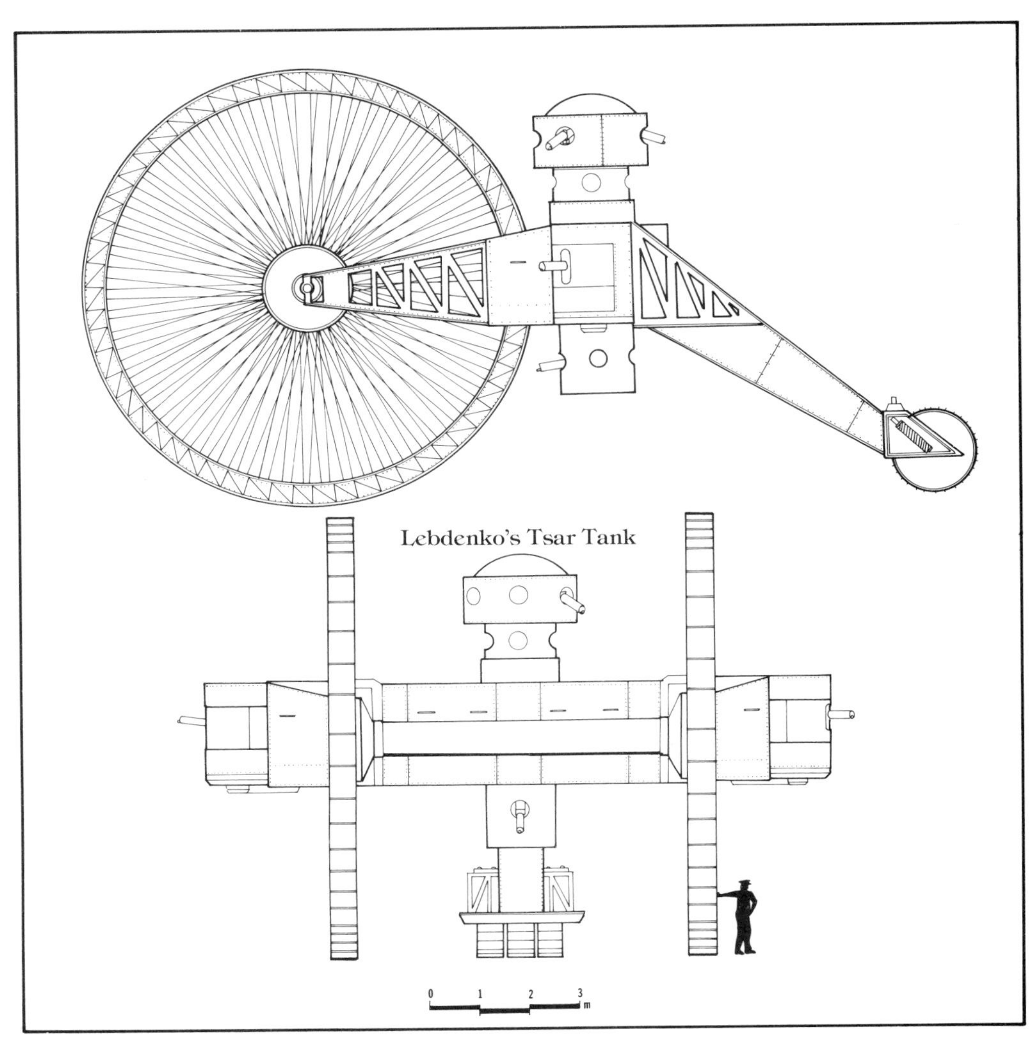

30. Certainly among the most bizarre armoured vehicles was Lebdenko's Tsar Tank, an enormous tricycle vehicle with gun tubs located in balconies off the main wheels. The vehicle was grossly impracticable and was never completed.

manufactured by Russian industry. More to the point, such a vehicle would have offered far poorer mobility, firepower or armour than contemporary British or French tanks.

Far more grotesque was the 'Tsar' Tank sponsored by the Central Technical Committee. In 1915, M. Lebdenko, head of the Experimental Laboratory of the War Ministry, persuaded the Tsar to lend support to the development of an enormous tricycle vehicle, the main wheels of which were 10 metres high. The engineering development of Lebdenko's tank was entrusted to the young Alexsi Mikulin who would later gain fame as one of the leading Soviet aircraft engine designers. A 40-ton vehicle was completed in the summer of 1915. Each of the two main wheels was powered by a Sunbeam 250hp engine and there were plans for machine-gun positions on the balconies near the wheel outriggers and in central turrets. It was soon evident that the vehicle was grossly impracticable and very vulnerable to hostile artillery fire because it was not heavily armoured. It was abandoned and the prototype was scrapped in 1923 after nearly 250,000 roubles had been squandered. The War Department attempted to purchase tanks from France and Britain, but these did not arrive before the collapse of the Tsarist régime in 1917. There was also a scheme to begin licensed production of tanks at the Ryabushinskiy-Kuznetsov Plant in Moscow, but this failed to materialize.

Armoured Vehicles in the Civil War

With the Bolshevik seizure of power from Kerenskiy's Provisional Government in October 1917, Russia abandoned the war with Germany, but gradually slipped into a brutal civil war which pitted the new RKKA (Rabochiy Krestyanskaya Krasnaya Armiya: The Workers and Peasants Red Army) against a host of counter-revolutionary and foreign armies. The bulk of the armoured units of the Imperial Russian Army defected to the Bolsheviks as neither the praetorian traditions of the Cossacks nor the aristocratic leanings of the other forces making up the White Russian cause held much appeal for them. The first to defect was the Petrograd Armoured Car Detachment which went over to the Red side on the night of 24 October 1917 and played an important role in preventing the march of General Krasnov's forces on the city. By the end of 1918, the

31. Among the first units to join the Bolsheviks was this armoured car detachment in Petrograd in October 1917. It had a considerable variety of equipment: from left to right Mgebrov-Renault, Fiat, Austin and Putilov-Garford armoured cars. (Sovfoto)

△32 ▽33

32. Many unidentified armoured cars have turned up in photographs from the period, such as this rather distinctive vehicle captured by the Czech Legion in 1919. (Ivan Bajtos)
33. This Bolshevik armoured car detachment in Moscow in 1919 was equipped with a Putilov-Garford heavy armoured car and two Putilov-Austins. The Putilov-Austin to the extreme right appears to have been the same vehicle shown here in another photograph that was later captured by the Poles in the 1920 war.
34. This Mk V was captured by the Bolsheviks from Wrangel's forces in 1920 in southern Russia.

RKKA possessed 23 armoured trains, 150 armoured cars and about 30 half-tracked armoured cars. On 20 December 1917, the Second Greater Russian Armoured Car Congress was held (the first having been held earlier in 1917) with an aim towards forming a central command for armoured units. As a result, the Armoured Unit Congress (Tsentrobron) was formed on 31 January 1918, and in August was renamed the Armoured Directorate (Bronievoye Upravleniye). It was initially headed by L. Zemmering and subsequently by G. Kotovskiy with an aim towards forming new armoured units and consolidating the armoured material left over from the Tsarist forces.

The White forces had very little armour except for a few improvised armoured trains, and were largely dependent on French and British supplies once these countries began to intervene militarily in 1919. In January 1919, the 3ème Compagnie, AS 301, with fifteen Renault FT tanks, supported the French drive on Odessa in cooperation with General Wrangel's forces. In March, one of these was left behind to the Bolsheviks and this single burned-out vehicle would later play an important role in the birth of the Soviet tank force. In April 1919, reinforcements for Wrangel's forces arrived when the British sent the South Russia Tank Detachment. This eventually numbered 57 Mk V and 17 Whippet tanks, and included a few FT tanks which were turned over to the Wrangel forces. The Detachment's intention was the training of General Deniken's Volunteer Army, but the lack of aptitude of their pupils meant that British crews on more than one occasion became involved in the fighting in the Kuban and the Crimea. The participation of tanks was the main cause of the victory at Tsaritsyn on 1 July 1919, but the Detachment was soon obliged to serve as a rearguard when the Volunteer Army retreated into the Crimea. By this stage, the tanks were gradually turned over to the White Russians, forming a Tank Battalion with two heavy and two light companies. Now sufficient British and Russian armoured cars had become available to form the 1st and 2nd Armoured Car Units each with three detachments. The Crimean forces also possessed four armoured

34▽

△35 ▽36

trains at this time. The tanks under Deniken and Wrangel never played a critical role in the fighting because of the inexperience of their crews, and indeed tanks captured from these units were the main source of the RKKA's burgeoning tank inventory. By the end of 1919, the Bolsheviks claimed to have 80 tanks though a number of these were probably armoured halftracks and many of the genuine tanks were in poor mechanical condition. There were two other White forces with armour. Yudenich's army in northern Russia had two Renault FTs borrowed from the Finns, and six Mk Vs of a small British detachment which had landed in Estonia in July 1919. In August 1919 the British landed six Mk Vs and Medium Bs at Archangel to protect the withdrawal of troops there, and one of these was lost.

In October 1919, the Revolutionary War Council (RVS) of the RKKA laid down its first formal instructions to cover the expanding armoured train force. Besides a few Tsarist armoured trains which had fallen into

35. A Whippet tank of the Deniken forces in the Crimea in 1919.
36. The Deniken Army in southern Russia received the largest number of tanks from the Allies, including this Medium Mk V, two FT-17s and a Whippet sitting in the Batum railway yard in 1919.
37. Although the tanks supplied to Deniken and Wrangel in southern Russia proved effective with British crews, the White Russian forces showed little affinity with the strange machines, like this Medium Mk V tank with Wrangel's forces in 1920. Most fell into Bolshevik hands.
38. This White Russian armoured train was assembled by naval crews in the naval yards in Vladivostok using parts from ships; the main gun came directly from a destroyer.

37△ 38▽

Bolshevik hands, many local soviets had built improvised armoured trains. The new orders distinguished three main types of trains: Type A, Type B and Type V as well as the naval coastal defence gun battery trains, the Type Ms which fell under naval jurisdiction. The Type A heavy assault train consisted of two armoured artillery cars armed with two turreted 76.2mm Model 02 guns and five to eight Maxim machine-guns. These trains had armoured locomotives and were usually followed by support trains for their 162-man crews. In combat, they were usually accompanied by an Armoured Train Landing Detachment which consisted of a rifle company with two machine-guns and a cavalry detachment with 35 horses, 265 troops in all. The Type B light armoured train generally consisted of only a single artillery car with two guns of less than 152mm and a partially armoured locomotive. The Type V was even smaller, having only a single howitzer on its artillery car. Despite these attempts to impose some order on its

△39 ▽40

39. Many of the armoured trains used in the civil war were improvised types like this one which is little more than a coal-hopper car with additional reinforcement and a 76.2mm divisional gun at the front.

40. Some of the armoured trains were mammoth designs created by the Putilov and Izhorskiy Works before the outbreak of the Revolution, like this train of the Bolshevik 6th Armoured Train Detachment. The artillery cars in these trains usually had two turreted 76.2mm guns plus many machine-guns.

armoured trains, the Red Army's inventory was incredibly motley, ranging from trains with little more than a sandbagged flatcar carrying a roped-down field gun, to large, fully armoured monsters built by the skilled naval engineers at the Putilov and Izhorskiy Factories. Of the armoured equipment used in the Civil War, the Field Armoured Trains were undoubtedly the most successful. Troops on both sides were ill-equipped, usually disheartened, and the sudden appearance of an armoured train often provoked panic and proved a decisive factor in many skirmishes. By the end of 1919 the Soviets had 59 such trains, increasing to 103 by the war's end. In contrast, they had only 38 armoured car detachments by 1919, each having about three armoured cars, and no tank units.

In May 1920, the RVS formed the first tank detachments, consisting for the most part of three Mk Vs, each with six lorries, three motorcycles and 81 men. In Russian service, the Mk V was known as the Rikardo (after its Ricardo engine), the Whippet as the Tyeilor (after its Taylor engine) and the Renault FT as the Reno. The first tank action involving the new Soviet tank units took place on 4 July 1920 when the 2nd Tank Detachment supported an RKKA attack on the Zyabki railway station. In August 1920, as a result of the variety of tank types entering Red Army service, the RVS ordered the reorganization of the tank detachments into three main types: Type B (bolshoi: large) with four Rikardos and 113 men; the Type S (sredniy: medium) with four Tyeilors and 109 men, and finally the Type M (maliy: small) with four Renos and 89 men. The unit name referred to the size of the tank type rather than the size of the unit. In contrast, most Western armies at the time referred to them by their weight. In spite of the effort devoted to them, Soviet tanks played a minor role in the Civil War. Their mechanical unreliability, slow speed and the lack of spare parts and fuel were all decided handicaps. They were hardly ever seen in action during the war with Poland in 1920, but were used on a small scale against Wrangel in the Crimea, against the Japanese in Siberia and against the remnants of the White resistance in 1921–22.

41▽

41. An interior view of an artillery car on a Russian armoured train, currently preserved at the Finnish armour museum at Parola. The child is looking up into the cupola between the two turrets where the commander directed the guns. Down the passage can be seen the machinery of one of the gun turrets. Each side of the passage is filled with ammunition racks for the guns. Lack of space meant that infantry were carried in separate armoured railcars. (James Cochran)

Armoured Vehicles in the Early 1920s

As a tense peace began to settle over the new Soviet Union in 1921, the RKKA gradually began to demobilize. The armoured train troops who made up the bulk of the forces under the Armoured Directorate were the most heavily affected. Many of the armoured trains were little more than ordinary freight trains with hastily-fitted armour, and were desperately needed in the rebuilding of the wartorn empire. From its peak strength of 103, the force fell to 51 armoured trains by 1926. The small tank detachments were the subject of constant fiddling. In August 1921, they reverted to their original form: a composite of one Rikardo, one Tyeilor, and one Reno with a reduced peacetime establishment of 68 men. The numerous armoured car units were consolidated from their peak strength of 51 units by weeding out the more hopelessly worn-out cars and by increasing the number of cars in each unit. Detachments assigned to rifle divisions had a nominal strength of four armoured cars plus a reserve car, and those attached to cavalry divisions had twelve armoured cars, four of which being the heavy, gun-armed car. A significant portion of the Army's armoured car inventory was appropriated by the OGPU (Internal Security Police) for use in suppressing the many uprisings and riots which continued to plague the infant Soviet régime. The OGPU detachments usually numbered about eight cars each, and some of those in European Russia were disbanded in 1923. In the outlands, however, they were retained or even strengthened.

The armoured units of the RKKA began to atrophy in the 1920s not only because of the demobilization, but also because of the lack of an industrial base to provide fresh equipment or spare parts. Nearly all the armoured vehicles were powered by imported engines, and the Western nations had broken off relations with the USSR because of its Messianic crusade to spread Soviet communism. The few surviving plants were at a standstill from shortage of spares and as a result of the anarchic confusion which followed in the wake of the workers' attempts to control the factories.

The first Soviet experiment in tank production began in 1919 after a French Renault FT had been captured outside Odessa. This was

▽42

later joined by other captured FTs and one was presented as a gift to V. I. Lenin to take part in the first May Day celebration in Moscow in 1919. The RVS decided to attempt to manufacture this type in the Soviet Union because it was smaller and simpler than the other types of tanks that had been captured, and it was by far the most modern in basic configuration. A team of engineers headed by N. Khrulev was recruited from the Putilov Works and the Izhorskiy Factory and set about reverse engineering the Renault tank. The only automotive factory functioning was the Ryabushinskiy-Kuznetsov Company in Moscow which was nationalized as the AMO Factory (Avtomobilnoye Moskovskoye Obshchestvo). Ryabushinskiy had arranged a trading monopoly with Fiat in Italy and was able to provide Fiat engines in small numbers before the embargoes took effect. The armoured plate came from the Izhorskiy Factory, the Hotchkiss gun and machine-guns from the Obukhov Works (SOOZ) in Petrograd (soon to be renamed Leningrad), and assembly of the new vehicle took place at the naval Sormovo Plant, renamed Krasnoye Sormovo (Red Sormovo) in Nizhni Novgorod. The first tank had been assembled by 31 August 1920 and underwent three months of testing and corrections. On 1 December 1920 its armament was added and it was christened 'Freedom Fighter Lenin'. Its official name was somewhat less sentimental, it being variously referred to as the Russkiy Reno, legkiy tank M (Light Tank M: maliy-small) or the Legkiy tank KS (KS: Krasnoye Sormovo). Soviet histories have claimed that a further fourteen tanks of this type were manufactured, but in fact it would appear that these Russkiy Renos were remanufactured French Renault FT light tanks.

The original Russkiy Reno was distinctive in that it had an additional machine-gun in the right turret rear. These fifteen tanks were used to form the 7th Tank Unit in Moscow which was used for all the parades in Red Square. They were also occasionally used on summer manoeuvres.

There were numerous attempts to develop an indigenous tank design, most of which never passed beyond the paper stage. In November 1919, the RVS sponsored a competition for aspiring designers to submit tank designs based around available automobile

42. The Medium Mk V, usually known as the Rikardo in Soviet service, became the staple of the Soviet tank force after the war.

43. A photograph from summer exercises in the late 1920s shows a full range of Soviet tank equipment including at least three Rikardos, a Russkiy-Reno in the foreground and two of the new T-18 light tanks. The T-18 behind the Russkiy-Reno appears to be fitted with a prominent radio mast.

43▽

44. A formation of Russkiy-Renos on parade in Moscow in 1927. The vehicle to the right is the original Russkiy-Reno named 'Freedom Fighter Lenin' and can be distinguished by the additional machine-gun in the right side of the turret. The other Russkiy-Renos appear to be modernized rebuilds of burnt-out Renault FT-17 tanks captured from White Russian forces. Soviet sources claim that they were built from scratch.

45. The first new armoured equipment began entering Soviet service in 1929 and 1930. Here on summer exercises are a T-18 with its turret pointed away from the camera, two new BA-27 armoured cars, and an old Izhorskiy-Fiat armoured car of 1916 vintage. Production of these new vehicles prompted the Red Army to begin experimenting with armoured formations.

engines. A rather unegalitarian prize of 250,000 roubles was offered and was won by a team of engineers at the Izhorskiy Factory headed by G. Kondratieyev. Their tank, the Tyeplokhod Tipa AM (Motor Vessel Type AM) was a three-man light (10 tons) amphibious tank with a turreted 76.2mm gun and three propellers. Work began on two prototypes at the Izhorskiy Factory, but was suspended in 1923 because of insurmountable technical problems. In the meantime, designers at the Obukhov Factory had won approval for their own wheeled/tracked tank, the K-14, which was an obvious copy of the American Christie M1919. This tank was one of Christie's original convertibles which could be run on tracks, or have its tracks removed and run on wheels. The attraction of this system was that it allowed the tank to ride on wheels during long road transits which would be impossible with tracks because of the very short track-life of the period. Two prototypes were completed and the factory received an order for 64 tanks on the condition that its designers, Fadeyev and Rosen, introduce needed improvements. Apparently, the Armoured Directorate came to its senses when it was realized that the prototypes were barely capable of 12km/hr even before the hull-mounted 76.2mm gun was added. As a result, no series production is believed to have taken place.

In the wake of these unhappy experiences, the Central Directorate of Military Industries set up a special Tank Bureau under Professor V. Zaslavskiy. A commission was organized to examine the equipment needs of the RKKA and proposed a small 3-ton tank armed with a 37mm gun instead of the large AM or K-14 which were beyond the engineering experience of Soviet industry at that time. In the spring of 1925, the requirement was changed to permit the design to weigh as much as five tons because it was realized that a 3-ton tank would be poorly armoured. Zaslavskiy focused his attention on modernizing the Renault FT, clearly the most modern tank of which the RKKA had had experience. It is interesting to note that many other armies took the identical step, and modernized versions of the FT flourished around the world in the 1920s. In 1924, Ryabushinskiy's old ties with Fiat were re-established and the AMO Factory in Moscow began producing the AMO-F-15 lorry, a copy of the Italian Fiat 15 ter. This provided the 35hp engine for the new tank. The gun was a modestly improved copy of the French Hotchkiss SA 18 37mm. The most serious attention was paid to redesigning the suspension with a new vertical spring system which considerably improved cross-country performance. A prototype of this tank, the T-16, was completed in May 1927. It was put through trials in June which proved satisfactory to the head of the RKKA's quartermaster, P. Dybienko and to the Commissar for Heavy Industry, G. Ordzhonikidze.

On 6 July 1927, the RVS formally decided to accept the T-16 in a slightly improved form to be known as the T-18. Ordzhonikidze assigned production responsibility to the old Obukhov Factory in Leningrad, which was subsequently renamed the Bolshevik Factory. This, under various names, would come to be the largest single tank production facility in the Soviet Union until the outbreak of the Second World War. Trials of the T-16 were not completed until November 1927, and production of the T-18 did not begin until 1928. The first batch of 30 T-18s were

44△ 45▽

△46 ▽47

46. The original version of the T-18 (also called MS-1) was plagued by manufacturing problems. Unlike the standard production model, it had no rear turret bustle.
47. The standard production model of the T-18 (also called MS-1A) incorporated many changes resulting from problems encountered in the original vehicles. Most prominent of these was the addition of a large bustle at the turret rear for stowage. This particular tank does not seem to have had its armament fitted. A company of these tanks was dispatched to the Far East in 1929 to resist Manchurian incursions.

turned over to the Army in May 1929, but were plagued with technical problems. Production at the Bolshevik Factory had been very difficult because of the lack of facilities to produce electrical equipment, ball-bearings or carburettors, which had to be imported. Production was halted on a number of occasions to correct serious flaws in the design. Before production was re-initiated in 1929, the T-18 was significantly redesigned with a more powerful engine (40hp), an added bustle to enlarge the cramped turret, and other technical improvements. When production ceased in 1931, about 960 T-18s had been built.

The T-18 was the RKKA's first Soviet-designed tank. It was also called the MS-1 (Maliy Soprovozhdyeniya-Pierviy: First Small Support Vehicle). Another outcome of the renewed ties with Fiat was the work on the first new armoured car since the Civil War. In 1927, a design team at the Izhorskiy Factory developed a heavy armoured car on the AMO-F-15 chassis, called the BA-27. Of fairly conventional design, it was equipped with both forward and rearward driving controls, and had a turret nearly identical with that on the early production T-18 tank. Several prototypes underwent lengthy two-year trials, after which the BA-27 was finally accepted for RKKA service in 1929. The Izhorskiy Factory built about 100 from 1928 to 1931, the last of them being mounted on Ford AA lorry chassis instead of the AMO-F-15. A small number were later rebuilt on heavier, three-axle Ford Timken chassis by the Rembaz Nr.2 (Repair Base Nr.2) as the BA-27M, and these remained in service up to the outbreak of the Second World War.

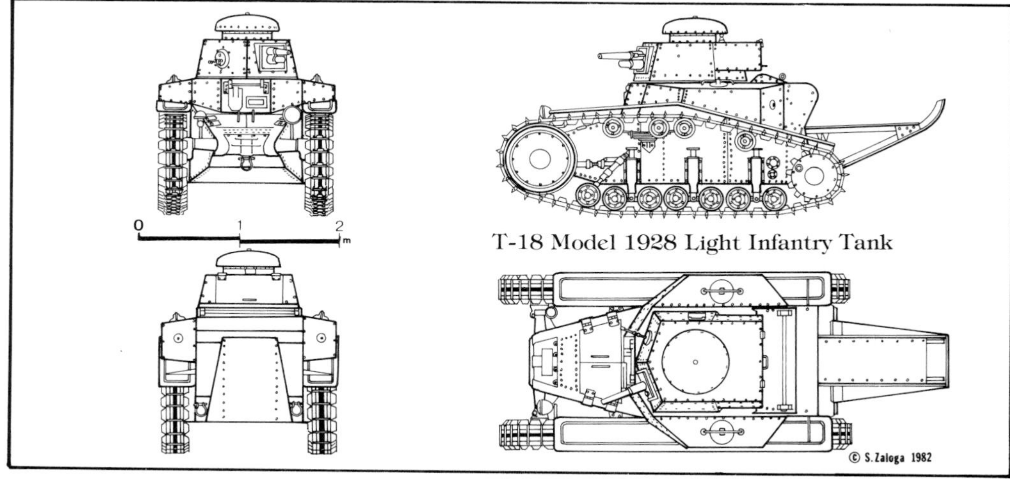

T-18 Model 1928 Light Infantry Tank

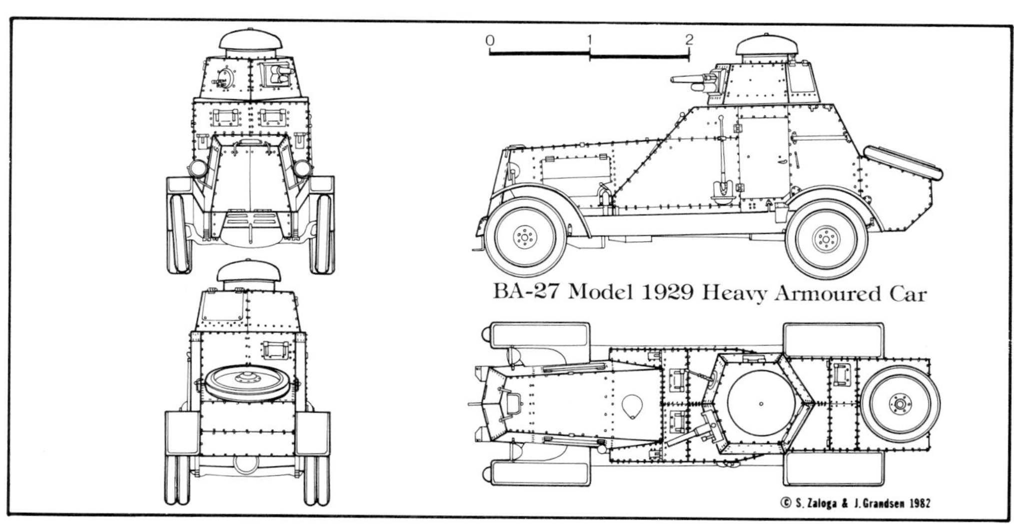

BA-27 Model 1929 Heavy Armoured Car

△48 ▽49

48. A pair of the new BA-27 armoured cars on patrol with the new T-27 tankette in 1932. The BA-27 was originally based on the AMO-F-15, but later batches were built on Ford AA chassis. It used a turret nearly identical with that employed on the MS-1 tank.

49. Some of the BA-27 were later rebuilt on Ford-Timken chassis because the shorter Ford AA and AMO-F-15 proved inadequate to withstand the weight of the armoured body. The variant was called BA-27M and this example was captured by Finnish forces in 1940. (Esa Muikku)

Mechanization of the Red Army during the 1920s

During the 1920s the armoured forces of the RKKA were scarcely larger than those of neighbouring Poland, and were stagnating because of lack of new equipment. The decline continued until 1929 when the first T-18 and BA-27 became available. This was an important period for the RKKA, however, marking the groundwork for the stupendous growth of their mechanized forces which was to begin in the 1930s. At the end of 1921 the Red Army had thirteen tank units: twelve detachments with three tanks each, plus the 7th Tank Unit with fifteen Russkiy-Renos. The initial post-war attempt to standardize the detachments by providing each with one example of the three major tank types proved a failure. It put a hopeless burden on unit repair facilities which had to deal with three different types of tank for which there were no spare parts. As a result, in the summer of 1922, the detachments were reorganized, yet again, into Type B units with four Rikardos, fifteen cars and lorries and 104 men, or Type M units with four Renos or Tyeilors, 12–14 cars and lorries and 77 men. This brought the number of units down to ten, with a total strength of 79 tanks. On 6 September 1922, the tank force was even further consolidated. An Auto-Tank Unit was formed, the first significant mechanized unit of the RKKA. It deployed a tank squadron with a heavy 'flotilla' of four Type B detachments, and a light flotilla consisting of a medium detachment with six Tyeilors, a 'destroyer' detachment with six Renos armed with 37mm guns, and a reinforced light detachment with six machine-gun armed Renos. Each of the flotillas was supported by an armoured car platoon, a tractor platoon and a repair detachment. This experiment was short-lived: during the general 1924 Army reform, the tank squadron became a tank regiment with a school and cadre battalion, and a number of the tanks were moth-balled because of persistent mechanical problems. In 1925, new regulations were published, the Current Combat Regulations for the RKKA Armoured Force. The two tank battalions were now redesignated light and heavy tank battalions, and each had three companies with about a total of 30 tanks per battalion. The new regulations devoted most of their attention to the more numerous armoured car and armoured train units. Tank doctrine was not fully elucidated until the arrival of the 1928 Current Combat Regulations for Tanks. In 1927, at the start of the first Five-Year Plan, the armoured force stood at one tank regiment with a light and heavy tank battalion, 45 Rikardos, 12 Tyeilors, 18 Renos and 15 Russkiy-Renos. There were six armoured car detachments with 54 armoured cars, not counting OGPU police units of which there were about seven.

The dominant and most active wing of the Armoured Force remained the armoured trains, and the June 1926 publication of the new Armoured Force regulations triggered a major reorganization of these. The new regulations were put to the test during the summer wargames of 1926, and the lessons learned were incorporated in an August revision of the regulations. The new regulations outlined two basic types of armoured train, the Light Field Armoured Train Type A and the Heavy Field Armoured Train Type B. The Type A consisted of an armoured locomotive, two artillery cars, each with a pair of fully turreted 76.2mm field guns and eight machine-guns, and four other support cars. This train was supported by a base train with 29 cars at war strength. The Type B was essentially similar, but had heavier field guns in the artillery cars. The Armoured Force was well aware of the growing vulnerability of armoured trains to aircraft attack, and gradually, many of the Type A trains had newly designed artillery cars added, with 76.2mm Model 14 anti-aircraft guns and heavier, 12.7mm, machine-guns added for air defence. A new category of train, the Type ON, was developed, which was equipped with heavy calibre artillery for coastal defence. Some of these, however, fell under Navy jurisdiction.

The basic tactical unit of armoured trains was the armoured train field detachment, consisting of two Type A armoured trains, one Type B and a section of armoured trolleys (bronedrezina). This section usually had two armoured trolleys for scouting and three others for liaison and repairs to the permanent way. The armoured trolleys were usually old armoured cars whose wheels had been replaced by flanged railway wheels. The Putilov-Garford was the most common type until the 1930s when the custom-built BD-39s came into service, and when the newer BA-20ZhD and BA-6ZhD were first deployed. In 1926, the first Territorial Armoured Train Regiment was raised at Karachev. This was structured like a detachment, but had a Type ON train added together with more sophisticated technical support units. In 1932, a minor reorganization took place and the detachments were renamed Independent Armoured Train Battalions. At peak strength in the 1930s, the armoured trains formed three regiments and nine battalions.

The armoured train troops were also the most seasoned arm of the Armoured Force. In 1926 when the Soviet Union began supporting Chiang-kai-Shek in the Chinese Civil War, numerous armoured train specialists and troops were sent to assist him. They supervised the construction of no fewer than 30 Chinese and Manchurian armoured trains, and many of these were manned in action by mixed Chinese/Soviet crews. Despite the important role played by armoured trains in the Russian and Chinese Civil Wars, their deployment was beginning to fade from the thoughts of tacticians by the end of the 1930s. The advent of air power raised serious questions about their viability on the modern battlefield, but their successes had opened the eyes of many Soviet military thinkers to the need for combat vehicles having the firepower and armoured protection of the armoured train, but of a far greater degree of mobility. The obvious solution was the tank, and it was in this direction that RKKA tacticians began to turn.

The Soviet Union was not the only pariah state of Europe. Germany had also been ostracized, and its army had been forcibly limited in size by the victorious Allies. This led to the curious marriage of the German Reichswehr and the Soviet RKKA initiated by the secret Treaty of Rapallo in 1922. The Reichswehr had been forbidden to develop any modern armoured vehicles by the Treaty of Versailles, but in light of the central role played by French, British and American tanks in their defeat in 1918, the Germans were desperately interested in experimenting with this crucial new weapon. The Russians, on the other hand, craved the engineering experience available to the Reichswehr which could be used to build up the decrepit Russian military factories. Many RKKA officers also looked forward to contact with the highly professional German military staff as an antidote to the overdose of military

50. This frontal view of the T-18 shows the peculiar armament configuration with a ball-socketed machine-gun on one side, and a 37mm gun in a swivelling mount on the other.

amateurism which had beset the Red Army since the Civil War. In 1926, they agreed to set up a special tank school at Kazan in the Urals where secretly-built German tanks could be tested and where tank tactics could be developed. The Germans agreed to assist in tank and tractor design and to help modernize Russian war industries.

During the formulation of the first Five-Year Plan in 1926, the priorities of the RKKA were envisaged as being: infantry with strong artillery support, strategic cavalry, and aircraft. This conservative view reflected the limited appreciation for mechanized units held by senior Red Army officials of the time. But it also recognized the poor state of Soviet heavy industry which could not support a mechanization effort without serious rebuilding. The initial plan called for the construction of 1,075 new tanks and the raising of three tank regiments and several independent tank battalions. Contact with the Germans as well as a profound reassessment of strategy by Red Army theorists seriously undermined these priorities and suggested instead that greater emphasis should be placed on the development of armoured units. In May 1929, the plan was reconsidered and the goal was raised to 3,500 tanks. The new military industrial priorities for the Red Army in the Five-Year Plan became aircraft, artillery and tanks in that order.

A critical ingredient in this about-face was the consolidation in power of Iosef Stalin. Stalin was not a profound military thinker. Indeed, he tended to be influenced in military matters by such cronies from the Civil War as Minister of Defence Klimenti Voroshilov and S. M. Budenny who were not only amateurs, but also the most narrow-minded of cavalry advocates. But Stalin himself was gripped by what his later detractors termed the 'machine cult' or, as some Western historians have described it, 'Fordism'. Stalin was obsessed with modernizing Russia at any cost and was deeply convinced that the route to the future lay in heavy machine industry. To lift the Russian peasantry from its feudal backwardness, Stalin chose the agricultural tractor as the key. Likewise, the new machines of war would lift the Russian Army from its backward state and even surpass the armies of Continental rivals. Stalin and many other Soviet leaders liked to envisage the USSR as the vanguard of a new European age, and these emotional roots further reinforced the drive for industrial mechanization. These factors overrode Stalin's loyalties to his conservative chums, and led him to support the efforts of the reformers, even men he detested such as Mikhail Tukhachevskiy. Stalin made two other decisions which laid the groundwork for the crash mechanization drive that was about to begin. With the support of the RVS, he decided to spend large portions of Russia's gold reserves to import American and German machine tools and technical experts to seed the new industrial programme. Next, he brutally suppressed the ineffectual management of factories by workers' councils and began to apply a malign discipline in the plants. Several of the new military plants were run by slave labourers as part of the Gulag system.

Factories that were exclusively concerned with military goods were modernized with German assistance under the terms of the Rapallo treaty. In the case of armoured vehicle production, this meant the Bolshevik Factory in Leningrad and the Kharkov Locomotive Factory (KhPZ). Other factories which produced civilian goods as well as military hardware were built or reconstructed with American aid. The US government did not officially recognize the Soviet government at the time, but neither did it hinder the development of commercial ties with Russia. Beginning in 1929, the Soviets began massive purchases of American metal-working machinery, industrial goods, electrical equipment, automotive and tractor parts and commercial licensing rights. This spree lasted until 1932. At its peak in 1932, the Soviets spent $79 million on industrial goods from the US which amounted to 64 per cent of all American metal-working machinery exported that year. The first and most influential of these deals was with the Ford Motor Company in 1929 which designed and helped build the Gorki Automobile Factory Nr. 1 (GAZ Zavod Nr. 1) to produce licence-built copies of the Ford A and Ford AA as the GAZ-A and GAZ-AA. This enormous plant was completed in 1931 and was based on the River Rouge and Highland plants. It was furnished entirely with American equipment and was vital not only to the rebirth of the Russian automotive industry, but would later prove of crucial importance to the mechanization and motorization of the Red Army.

51. The T-17 was an attempt by the Zaslavskiy design bureau to develop a cheap tankette on the basis of the T-18 tank. It proved too much for a single man to handle, and its development was abandoned in favour of the T-23 with a two-man crew. This is the T-17 in its later configuration with a new improved track.
52. A larger medium tank version of the T-18 was attempted as the T-19, but the project was terminated in favour of the improved T-12.
53. A two-man derivative of the T-17 was built, the T-23, but it was viewed unfavourably compared to the imported Carden-Loyd tankette and its development was abandoned before series production had been authorized.

Besides the Ford factory at Gorki, there were several other key factories built or revamped with American aid. An American consortium designed and built the Stalingrad Tractor Factory (STZ) which turned out Caterpillar-60 tractors for agricultural and military use, and would later become involved in tank construction. The STZ formed the model for two other factories, the Kharkov Tractor Factory (KhTZ) which was equipped by the Soviets with American and German machine tools, and the similar Chelyabinsk Tractor Factory (ChTZ) which was also equipped with American and German machinery. The AMO Factory in Moscow was re-equipped and expanded by the A. J. Brandt Co and became Automotive Factory Nr. 2 (ZiS Nr. 2) producing copies of the American Autocar 2 10-cwt lorry as the ZiS-5 and ZiS-6 for both military and civilian applications. The Yaroslav Automobile Factory Nr. 3 (YaZ Nr. 3) was similarly rebuilt by the Hercules Motor Company. The famous Putilov Factory was rebuilt with the help of the Ford Motor Company for the production of agricultural tractors, though it remained heavily involved with military production as well. It was renamed the Krasniy Putilov Factory (Red Putilov). Besides these obvious examples, scores of smaller facilities forming the basis for the new tank industry were modernized with foreign machine tools during this period.

The initiation of the rebuilding of the Soviet automotive industry in 1929 was accompanied by two other milestones, the release of the 1929 Field Service Regulations (PU-29) and the formation of the RKKA's first real mechanized unit. PU-29 outlined the projected deployment of tank units in combat, but provided little real guidance for the mechanization drive about to begin. It envisaged tank units no greater than of company strength, and progressed little from 1918 tactics, stressing close tank support of cavalry and infantry units. This left responsibility for drawing up requirements for the new tanks to the VTU (Voenno-tekhnicheskoye upravleniye: Military Technical Directorate) and the UMM (Upravlenie Mechanizatsiyi i motorizatsiyi RKKA: Directorate of the Mechanization and Motorization of the Red Army), because the PU-29 provided so little evidence of the type of armoured vehicle required. Further experimentation with actual mechanized units

▽51

52△ 53▽

54. The T-12 offered a larger turret than the T-19 and could mount a larger gun. Although production was authorized, the design was so plagued by problems that only prototypes were built.
55. An improved version of the T-12 was designed, and a small production batch was actually manufactured. It had so many mechanical deficiencies however, that it was relegated to parade and training duty.

would be required before a clear grasp of the material needs of the Red Army could be formulated.

In the summer of 1929, an experimental Mechanized Brigade was formed at Naro Fominsk near Moscow under the command of K. Kalinovskiy. Unlike the Auto-Tank Unit of 1923, this was a true mechanized formation combining a tank regiment, motor rifle regiment, artillery battalion and support units in, what today would be called, a combined arms team. At the time it contained a sizeable fraction of the RKKA's armoured resources including 60 tanks, 32 tankettes, 17 armoured cars, twelve tractors and 264 lorries. It took part in the 1930 Byelorussian and Moscow Military District manoeuvres and in the 1931 Ukrainian MD manoeuvres.

In the absence of clearly stated requirements as to the desirable characteristics of new tanks for adoption by the RKKA, a two-pronged programme was launched to examine alternatives. The Tank Bureau under Prof Zaslavskiy began the development of a full range of tanks, including a tankette, light tank and medium tank, along the lines being developed in the West. At the same time, the UMM under I. A. Khalepskiy began to examine suitable foreign designs available through commercial channels.

Although the PU-29 did not seriously examine the role of tankettes, these small vehicles held a great deal of appeal for armies such as the RKKA; on the verge of mechanization, with immature heavy industries and a lack of trained mechanics and drivers. Tankettes were cheap to produce, were within the limited capabilities of small factories to manufacture, and even if their combat capabilities were quite limited, they were excellent training vehicles for unit commanders, drivers, crews and mechanics. While designing the T-18, the Tank Bureau and the engineers at the Bolshevik Factory in Leningrad began considering the use of the T-16 chassis for a small self-propelled vehicle mounting a 37mm regimental gun. The project was named Lilliput, from the small size of the vehicle, and eventually became an examination of possible tankette designs for use by infantry units to knock out machine-gun nests and for scouting. Four versions were contemplated and were given the factory designations L-1, L-2, L-3 and L-4. The first two did not progress beyond the paper stage and the L-3 became the T-17 tankette. This was a small derivative of the T-18 using a related suspension and band track of the initial prototype. It was armed with only a single machine-gun. It was not deemed suitable for service use, and attention turned to the L-4 which was designated the T-21. Work on T-21 began in 1929, but was halted since it was felt that a single crewman could not drive and operate the vehicle's guns at the same time. Instead, work commenced on a two-man version, the T-23.

While the Zaslavskiy team had been working on the Lilliput projects, a team under S. Prakhie at the Bolshevik Factory had been developing an improved T-18 with suspension modifications and a more powerful engine. This rather paralleled the French NC-1 tank programme of stretching out a proven design by adding modest improvements. The T-19 was completed in 1931 and was powered by a 90hp engine which considerably improved its speed and mobility. Another direct derivative of the T-18 was built with a 60hp engine, the T-20.

The RKKA had recognized the need of a more heavily armed tank than the T-18 or its immediate derivatives, but was wary of embarking on such a project until more experience had been gained. In 1928, a new design team was organized at the Kharkov Locomotive Factory (KhPZ) headed by I. Aleksienko and working in cooperation with the Zaslavskiy Tank Bureau. Among the new team was a young engineer, A. Morozov, who would subsequently head the design bureau for nearly all Soviet medium tanks from 1940 until the 1970s. Their first tank, the T-12 (also called T-1-12) was essentially a scaled-up T-18, with a more powerful engine and capable of mounting a more potent main gun. It was well armoured, had a 200hp engine and a novel planetary transmission. The 1930 budget contained funds for 30 T-12s, but trials revealed the design to be irredeemably flawed. It was decided to cancel the programme in favour of an improved version, the T-24. This resembled the T-12 externally, except in the turret area. While T-12 first used a small turret, the T-24 took better advantage of the larger hull and made use of a larger turret. The prototype was completed in 1931 and permission was granted by the VTU to build 24 vehicles. The new 45mm gun was not yet available, however, so the vehicles were initially accepted into service with only machine-gun

54△ 55▽

56. The Vickers Medium Mk IA was one of the less successful acquisitions of Khalepskiy's purchasing commissions which went abroad in the late 1920s to obtain foreign tanks for the Red Army. They were not accepted for quantity production, but sent for training duties to the joint Russo-German tank training grounds near Kazan. This vehicle, without armament or engines, together with half a dozen others was captured by Finnish forces near Vitele in the autumn of 1941. (Esa Muikku)

armament. They were finally armed in 1932, but the T-24 proved so troublesome in use that it was relegated to training duties and a few parades.

The efforts of the Tank Bureau and its associated design teams in the late 1920s were a string of failures, leaving the RKKA without a single suitable Soviet design upon which to base the new armoured formations. Fortunately, the UMM had in the meantime succeeded in obtaining several foreign designs suitable for mass production in the Soviet Union.

Foreign Influences in Soviet Tank Design of the 1930s

In the late 1920s, the UMM under the direction of I. A. Khalepskiy began examining foreign designs for possible production in the USSR. Several Fiat 3000 light tanks were purchased as gifts for the RKKA by Polish communists, but these offered no significant advance over the T-18 design. Soviet representatives began discussions with European armament firms and from 1928 Khalepskiy himself visited the US under false pretences, to examine suitable American vehicles. In Czechoslovakia, the Soviets purchased the KH-50 convertible tank, and in England they purchased eight Vickers Carden Loyd (VCL) Amphibious Tanks, Model 1931, fifteen Vickers-Armstrong 6-ton E Tanks, 26 Mk VI Tankettes and fifteen Mk II Medium Tanks. Approval of the British sale came from the government in March 1930. Efforts to buy American T1 Light Tanks in quantity failed, but the Soviets managed to acquire two Christie M1930 convertible tanks with the connivance of the manufacturer, who listed them as agricultural tractors on the bill of lading. There are unconfirmed reports that the Soviets also bought a number of French light tanks during this period, presumably UE tractors and AMR light tanks. It is worth noting that the Soviets' great expectations about their German connections at Kazan were never fulfilled. Although in the next decade Germany would come to world prominence for its revolutionary tactics pioneered at Kazan, its tank technology at this point was considerably behind that of Britain, France, the USA or Sweden.

On arrival in the USSR, the foreign designs were put through gruelling trials and then the Soviets sought licence production rights for the more promising types. This was necessary because as yet they had not the engineering skills to back manufacture and copy such complicated systems. Licence rights also gave the Soviets the opportunity to send a crop of young engineers overseas to study the latest in design technology. For example, during 1930, about 60 Soviet designers and engineers spent time at the Christie factory to facilitate production of a Russian Christie tank. Of all the major purchases, only the Medium Mk II proved a total disappointment and was relegated to the training station at Kazan with the Germans. Surprisingly, these dinosaurs later turned up on the Finnish front in 1941.

The beginning of the RKKA's headlong dash for mechanization can be traced to the RVS decision on 13 February 1931 to begin production of the VCL Mk VI tankette and the Vickers-Armstrong 6-ton tank. This was followed by a decision on 13 May 1931 to begin production of the Christie convertible tank. These vehicles would form the basis of the new Soviet armoured units: the tankette for direct infantry support and scouting, the Vickers 6-ton as the infantry armoured battalion support tank to replace the T-18, and the Christie as the cavalry support tank for deep penetration. It is worth noting that in the decade from 1930–40, 97 per cent of Soviet tank production was of vehicles that were either identical copies of foreign designs, or closely related, improved derivatives. Still it is curious that the designs which the Soviets so wisely chose, for their excellent capabilities and ease of manufacture, were in most cases not procured in any numbers by the armies of the countries in which they originated.

The T-27 Tankette

The VCL Mk VI tankettes were subjected to extensive testing and several were sent to Zavod Nr. 37 in Moscow. There, a design bureau headed by N. Kozyrev began frantic work to prepare the factory for mass production. The tankettes were given the factory designation K-25, but before production started several improvements were introduced. The headcovers were redesigned with extensions to permit the two crewmen to talk to each other. There were a number of other less noticeable changes such as the use of larger drive sprockets, clutch improvements and a more powerful engine. Production of this vehicle began in the final quarter of 1931, and 348 vehicles were produced as the Tankietka T-27. As production got under way, Kozyrev's team examined the possibility of arming the tankette with a 37mm gun in place of the machine-gun. The vehicle also had a more powerful Ford AA (GAZ AA) engine, and two added road wheels for greater flotation on soft ground. Although the plan to adopt the 37mm gun was dropped, the improvements in the automotive features of the vehicle were subsequently standardized in production vehicles, the new version being called the T-27A. The 1932 plan called for an incredible number of 5,000 T-27 to be manufactured. In that year, in fact, only 1,693 were built, and in 1933 production amounted to a further 500. This brought production to a total of 2,540 T-27 of both models. The decrease in production was due not only to the absurd production plan, but also because the RKKA was coming to recognize the limited utility of tankettes. Although handy as training vehicles, they had poor mobility because of their small size

57. The first Soviet tank of the 1930s generation was the T-27 which was based on the Carden-Loyd tankette. Several improvements were incorporated including a new headcover design, and this vehicle, a T-27A, had an extra set of wheel bogies to improve mobility. Although serving a useful training function, the Red Army soon appreciated that the tactical utility of these tiny vehicles was negligible, and severely cut back on production plans for these tankettes.

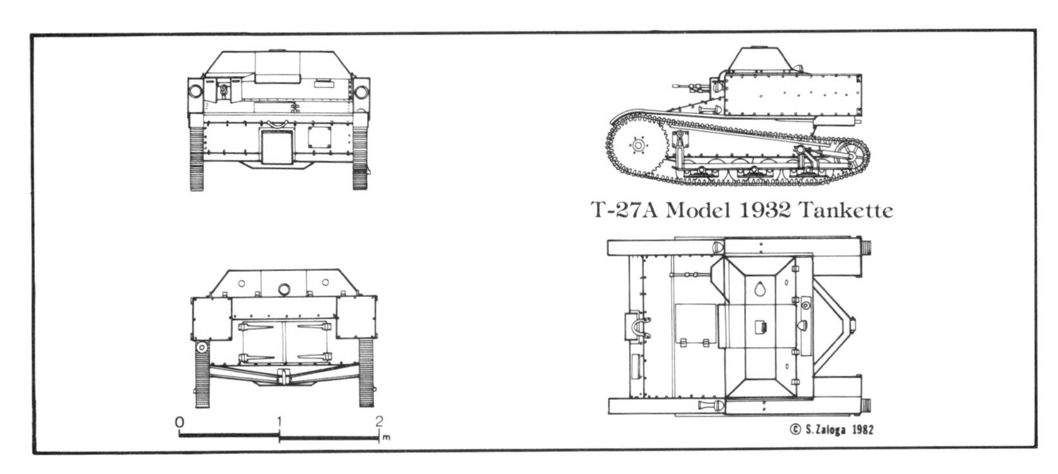

△58 ▽59

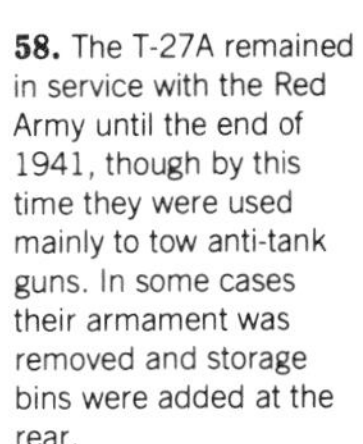

58. The T-27A remained in service with the Red Army until the end of 1941, though by this time they were used mainly to tow anti-tank guns. In some cases their armament was removed and storage bins were added at the rear.

59. Before direct licence production of the Vickers 6-ton E tank was permitted, a Soviet design team from Moscow was allowed to develop its own derivative, the TMM-1.

60. Neither the TMM-1 nor the similar TMM-2 were accepted for production, and instead the Red Army proceeded with a licensed copy of the Vickers E tank as the T-26.

61. The original T-26 Model 1931 had twin machine-gun turrets armed with DT 7.62mm machine-guns. The white dashes painted around the turret sides are unit markings.

62. A small percentage of the T-26 Model 1931 tanks were armed with 37mm guns in the left turret. These were sometimes called the T-26TU and were generally assigned to platoon and company commanders. In this view, the vehicle to the right is fitted with both the gun and external gun shield, while the one on the left has the 37mm gun without the external shield. This shield was used to prevent bullet splash through the gun mounting.

60△

61△ 62▽

and small engine, poor firepower and wretchedly thin armour. In their place, the RKKA began to acquire the T-37 amphibious tank, based on the VCL Model 1931 Amphibious tank. Besides its widespread employment throughout the RKKA's infantry and cavalry formations, the T-27 was the first armoured vehicle adopted by the new Aviamotodesantniy otryad, an airborne mechanized platoon formed in the Leningrad MD in 1930 by M. N. Tukhachevskiy as a part of his ambitious scheme to develop airborne units in the RKKA. In 1930, the designer, V. I. Bekauri, designed a cradle to permit the TB-1 bomber to carry a tankette under its fuselage. The first flights took place in 1930, using VCL Mk VI tankettes. In 1935, this technique was displayed to Western observers during the famous 1935 Kiev MD manoeuvres. The T-27 was used by security detachments during the early 1930s against the *Basmachi* bandits of the Karak desert on the Afghan border. By the late 1930s, most had been relegated to reserve or training units. Many were subsequently refurbished and used as tractors for 37mm and 45mm anti-tank guns, and small frame containers were added at the rear for this purpose. Some of these were still in service at the time of the Great Patriotic War.

The T-26 Light Infantry Tank

The first Vickers-Armstrong 6-ton E light tanks arrived in Russia in 1930 and were examined by the staff of the Mechanization and Motorization Faculty of the Dzherzhinskiy Artillery Academy in Leningrad. Prior to authorization to begin construction of the Vickers E, the staff was permitted to begin work on improved derivatives of the British designs. These were called TMM tanks, and the Russian-built Vickers were designated T-26. There were two types of TMM, the TMM-1 and the TMM-2, both having numerous detail differences with the Vickers. About twenty were built, but comparative trials led the RVS to select the Vickers for production. Production was assigned to the Bolshevik Factory in Leningrad where a new design team called OKMO (Opytniy konstruktorsko mekhanicheskiy otdel: Experimental Design Mechanical Section) under N. Barykov and S. Ginzburg was formed to take care of needed design changes before construction commenced. OKMO would become the leading Soviet tank design staff of the pre-purge period. A few small design changes were incorporated in the new T-26 Model 1931, mainly the configuration of the turret. In 1931, 120 of the twin-turreted T-26 Model 1931s were completed. There were two basic models, the standard T-26 with a DT 7.62mm machine-gun in each turret, and a command tank version, the T-26TU (Tank Upravleniya) which had a 37mm gun in the right turret and a DT machine-gun in the left. A small number of command tanks were fitted with the improved 37mm gun PS-2 Model 1930 which had a longer barrel. There were plans to equip some with 45mm guns, but this idea was dropped, it being decided to proceed instead with a single-turreted version of the T-26. There were two other versions of the T-26 Model 1931 built in modest numbers, the OT-26 flame-thrower tank and the ST-26 (Saperskiy Tank: Engineer Tank) which was fitted with a 7 meter bridge. The ST-26 was built in very small numbers and was used in tank units from 1934 to 1938 to bridge small dry gaps or obstacles. The OT-26 originally had a flame projector

63. The T-26TU Model 1931 was the first Soviet tank to carry a standardized vehicular radio transmitter. The larger external clothes-line attenna is very evident.
64. Plans were under way to fit T-26 command vehicles with a longer 37mm gun to improve anti-tank performance, but instead a new version of the T-26 with a single larger turret was adopted.
65. A small number of ST-26 engineer tanks were built, fitted with a bridging device to cross small gaps or obstacles.

△63 ▽64

mounted in the right turret, but because of the need to fit larger fuel tanks in the hull, the left turret was omitted from later models. The OT-26 was used by chemical tank battalions and the 1935 mechanized corps each had 52 OT-26. Production probably totalled a few hundred tanks. Production of the T-26 Model 1931 and its derivatives in 1932 amounted to 1,032 tanks and production was halted in 1933. The last batches had welded instead of riveted turrets.

In 1930, the RKKA purchased licence rights for the German Rheinmetall 37mm anti-tank gun which they planned to adopt as their standard infantry gun/anti-tank gun. This was produced as the 37mm anti-tank gun Model 1930, and small numbers of a tank gun derivative, the PS-2 were also built. However, the gun did not fire an effective high explosive round, which seriously undercut its utility as an infantry gun. Soviet engineers found that by a modest redesign, the bore could be increased to 45mm and would accept the more useful high explosive round. This became the 45mm anti-tank gun Model 1931, which remained in production in various forms until 1943. It was also decided that this would become the standard tank weapon, and it was first mounted on the unsuccessful T-24 medium tank. In 1932, the UMM instructed the design bureau at the Bolshevik Factory in Leningrad and KhPZ in Kharkov to coordinate their efforts in adapting the new 45mm gun into a standard turret which could be used on the T-26, BT and T-35 heavy tank. The first turret to mount the 45mm tank gun Model 32 was of simple cylindrical shape with a small square bustle at the rear. It was used in very small numbers on the T-26 Model 1933 and on the early BT-5 Model 1933. A modified version without the bustle was used on the T-35, but a better designed turret quickly replaced it. This had a larger rear bustle and two roof hatches in place of the single hatch of the earlier type. This turret became the standard style used on the T-26 Model 1933. In order to accommodate expanded tank requirements, production of the T-26 was extended to Zavod Nr. 174 (K. E. Voroshilov). Several other factories in the Leningrad area, notably the Red Putilov Works, also became involved in the manufacture of T-26 components. It is worth pointing out here that in the wake of the assassination of the popular party boss of Leningrad, S. M. Kirov, many of the Leningrad tank factories were renamed in his honour. Kirov had played an important role in building up the tank industry in Leningrad and had attracted many young engineers to these factories. The similarity of the new names, has caused a great deal of confusion in histories of Soviet tank production. The Red Putilov Works became the Kirovskiy Works (Kirovskiy Zavod Nr. 100) while the former Obukhov Works, later renamed the Bolshevik Factory Nr. 232, in 1935 became the Zavod Nr. 185 (S. M. Kirov) although it was still called the Bolshevik Works by many of the inhabitants of Leningrad. The T-26

65▽

△66 ▽67

66. One of the most common Soviet flame-thrower tanks, the OT-26 was based on the T-26 Model 1931 with one of its turrets removed. This tank carried a prominent flame-gun in the turret and large fuel cells in place of the deleted turret.

67. With the Red Army's decision to adopt the 45mm gun as its standard anti-tank and infantry gun, the tank force was instructed to adopt it as well. Both KhPZ and OKMO were instructed to design turrets to mount the new gun on the T-26 and BT because the earlier turrets were too small to accommodate the new gun. A rare example of a pre-production T-26 Model 1933 can be seen in this view. It is easily distinguishable from the standard production type on the right by its single hatch and smaller rear turret bustle.

68. Although there were plans to equip all T-26 Model 1933 tanks with radio, this was never possible. As a result, radio-equipped tanks, sometimes called T-26TU Model 1933, were used mainly by unit commanders. Here, an infantry tank battalion parades during a May Day celebration in Kharkov. The horseshoe antenna gave this version of the T-26 a very distinctive appearance. (Sovfoto)

69. (overleaf) This impressive overhead photograph of a formation of T-26 tanks during the 1935 May Day Parade in Leningrad shows the full range of T-26 tanks up to this time, including both the double turreted T-26 Model 1931, and single turreted T-26 Model 1933. To the extreme left in the last row can be seen two OT-26 flame-thrower tanks. (Sovfoto)

68△

Model 1933 was the most widely produced tank in the Soviet Union prior to 1941 with some 5,500 completed when production ceased in 1936. There were about 12,000 T-26 of all models produced from 1931 to 1941, and to place this in some perspective, total French production during the same period was only 4,000 tanks and German production, 3,400.

During the course of T-26 Model 1933 production, several modifications were incorporated. There were two types of mantlets, one drop-forged and the other made up of welded parts. In 1934–35, fighting broke out in the borderlands between Manchuria and Mongolia with Japanese forces, and Soviet tank units took part. Some T-26s were involved in the fighting and alarming reports were sent back to the UMM and RVS critical of the use of rivets in tanks. It was found that rivets came free when struck on the outside by bullets, causing the inner face of the rivet to careen about the inside of the tank, often with lethal results. The problem was so serious that Tukhachevskiy ordered the production lines closed down temporarily until the problem could be resolved. As a result, Soviet tank designs began to drop the use of riveting in favour of welding and the later production batches of the T-26 Model 1933 gradually showed more and more welding. The final batches of T-26 Model 1933 manufactured in 1935 and 1936 had two additional DT machine-guns added, one on a new circular roof hatch for anti-aircraft protection, and one in a ball-socket in the turret rear

△70 ▽71

70. The T-26 Model 1933, shown here during a parade in Turkey, was the most widely exported Soviet tank type of the pre-war years. The Turkish vehicles were from a later production batch, with fully welded turrets and hulls at the insistence of Tukhachevskiy who was concerned that exported tanks give the best possible impression to foreign observers.

71. The final production batches of the T-26 Model 1933 were of all welded construction and had a redesigned turret with an additional rear-ward firing machine-gun and a new fully travers-able hatch with DT machine-gun for use against aircraft. These alterations were the result of encounters between Soviet T-26s and Japanese troops in the Far East in 1934 and 1935 which uncovered technical shortcomings in the T-26. This particular T-26 Model 1933 served with Franco's forces in Spain after having been captured from the Republicans. In Spain, the Russian tanks completely dominated Italian and German types, and a captured T-26 was a prized possession. (National Archives)

72. In an attempt to provide fire support to infantry tank battalions, prototypes were built mounting a T-28 medium tank turret on a T-26 hull as the T-26A artillery tank. A small series of these was built, but the turret overloaded the chassis and large-scale production was thereby ruled out.

for use against infantry. One of the most distinctive features of the T-26 Model 1933 was the use of a prominent horse-shoe antenna fitted to vehicles with radios. All T-26 Model 1933 were supposed to be fitted with radios, but in fact only a fraction had them. These were reserved for platoon and company commanders and were sometimes referred to as T-26TU Model 1933.

Besides the standard version of the single-turret T-26, there were a number of specialized types. The T-26A was an artillery support tank fitted with a large turret derived from that on the T-28 medium tank and equipped with a 76.2mm Model 27/32 howitzer. Only a small number were produced because the turret proved too heavy for the chassis. From 1938, some single-turret T-26 were rebuilt as the OT-130 flame-thrower tanks. The original batch had a long flame projector without an armoured sleeve and used the same Model 1933 flame-thrower system as the earlier OT-26 flame-thrower tank. The later batch of OT-130 used the Model 1938 flame-thrower and had a shorter, armoured projector fitted into a new mantlet. The type with the Model 1938 flame-thrower carried 360 litres of fuel in internal tanks for 40 6-second bursts at ranges of 45-50 metres. With the aid of a special compressor, a 10-25 second burst to 100 metres could be made. There were also attempts to develop a T-26 capable of crossing water obstacles. In 1934, K. Sirken developed a method using rubber sealing and a telescopic 280cm air tube. These successfully completed trials in 1935, crossing several rivers by driving underwater. In 1937, the prototypes took part in the Leningrad MD manoeuvres, and a small production batch was built called the T-26PKh (PKh-Podvodnogo Khoda: Mobile Underwater). In 1935, an attempt was made to develop an amphibious type that could swim with the aid of pontoons attached to the side. The prototype was capable of swimming in the water at 3.5km/hr, but the pontoons were very large and cumbersome, and would have been very vulnerable to hostile fire. No series

72▽

73. The OT-130 flame-thrower tank version of the T-26 Model 1933 was built in two types. The early version as shown here used the same flame projector as the OT-26 in a largely unmodified turret.
74. In 1937, the T-26 was heavily redesigned. The most obvious change was the use of a new turret with sloping armour to offer better protection. This version was called the T-26S Model 1937. This particular vehicle, its turret traversed to the rear, was abandoned in a bog during the summer of 1941. The vents on the rear deck over the radiator were added after experiences in Finland showed the problem of allowing snow to accumulate over the cooling grilles. (National Archives)

△73 ▽74

75. The OT-130 was first used in action in Finland in 1940 against the Mannerheim line. Their main problem was that they had to approach very close to the target, and were very vulnerable to even the simplest weapons such as the anti-tank rifle. (Sovfoto)
76. In 1939, further improvements were made on the T-26, including a new drop-forged front for the turret and a redesigned hull superstructure with sloping armour. This T-26S Model 1939 was part of the force that occupied Persia in 1941 in unison with the British Army. (IWM)

75△ **76**▽

△77

production was undertaken. Two anti-mine versions of the T-26 were tested, one using a roller system and the other using chain flails, but problems prevented any series production. Besides these basic tank variants, there were a number of self-propelled gun derivatives and artillery tractor versions of the T-26 which are covered below.

In service the T-26 proved less mobile in cross-country use than the BT series. This should not have been altogether surprising because the BT had been selected as the cavalry tank specifically because of its better speed and mobility. Nevertheless, in 1935 S. Ginzburg of the OKMO team at Zavod Nr. 185 began adapting the T-26 to accept a Christie suspension. The new vehicle was called the T-46, and a small production batch of about 70 vehicles was planned. It was soon found that the vehicle was too complicated and expensive to mass produce, and in any case was redundant. At least one brigade fighting in Finland in 1940 used a T-46 prototype.

In the wake of the T-46 failure, Ginzburg's design team at OKMO was redirected to modernize the T-26. The result was the T-26S Model 1937. The original version of the T-26S differed from the T-26 Model 1933 in the turret design which was sleeker and better armoured. This increased the effective armour thickness of the turret without resorting to a major increase in weight. Several other improvements were introduced, including stabilization of the gun on one axis. In 1939, the T-26S was further improved. A new turret, closely related to the original type, was produced which had a new cast or drop-forged forward section which made for easier assembly. In addition, the hull was redesigned with a new upper superstructure which was wider, better armoured and had angled sides for better protection. This also permitted increased fuel and ammunition stowage. This version remained in production until 1940, though specialized versions of the T-26 remained in production until 1941. During the course of the war in

77. The later version of the OT-130 had a redesigned turret front with a special armoured flame projector. Note that on this version the turret was moved to the right side of the hull from its usual position on the left.
78. A small number of flame-tanks were built on the T-26S as the OT-133. These used the same flame projector as on the later OT-130, and also had the turret moved to the right side. This OT-133 lies abandoned next to a T-34 Model 1941 during the summer disaster in western Russia in 1941. (National Archives)
79. As an outcome of the Finnish fighting in 1940, some T-26 had armour added to the turret and hull as the T-26E. This particular vehicle was captured by the Finns in Karelia in 1941 and used by their own troops. (Esa Muikku)

78△ 79▽

Finland, it quickly became apparent that the T-26S was too thinly armoured to resist contemporary anti-tank guns, or even modern anti-tank rifles. As a result, a small number of T-26S were rebuilt with added turret and hull armour bringing the thickness to 50mm. These were called the T-26E (E-s ekranami: with appliqué). In 1939, Zavod Nr. 185 began production of a flame-thrower version of the T-26S called the OT-133. Because of the size of the fuel tanks in the hull for the flame projector, the turret was moved to the right side of the hull. The OT-133 used the same Model 1938 flame-thrower system as the later model OT-130. The main drawback to these flame-thrower tanks was that they could not carry the usual turret gun, and so were defenceless once the flame fuel ran out. In 1940, the Kompressor Factory in Moscow developed a new flame-thrower which was more compact and could be fired from a projector in the hull instead of in the turret. This was fitted to a new T-26S variant with a new turret reminiscent of the type later used on the T-50. A small series of these vehicles, designated T-134, were produced in 1941. These flame-thrower tanks retained the 45mm main gun.

Besides the OKMO programme to modernize the T-26, a design team at the Stalingrad Tractor Factory (STZ) was also assigned a similar task to improve the tractive qualities of the tank. In 1938, they built a prototype for the T-25 which used a Christie suspension on a T-26, but did not incorporate extensive hull modifications like the OKMO T-46. The suspension proved too complicated for mass production, and a simplified version, the ST-25 was also tested. By this time, however, a wholly new infantry tank was being developed by OKMO that would result in the T-50 light tank.

80. An improved version of the T-26 with Christie suspension was built as the T-46. It was too complex and expensive and production ceased after only 70 had been built. These saw action against Finland in 1940.

LIGHT INFANTRY TANKS, 1920–41

Designation	Russkiy-Reno	AM	T-18	T-19	T-20	T-26TU Model 31	T-26 Model 33	T-26S Model 37	T-50
Crew	2	3	2	3	2	3	3	3	4
Weight (tonnes)	7	10	5.9	8	5.6	8.6	9.4	10.5	14
Length (cm)	500		438	450	450	488	488	488	520
Width (cm)	175		176	216	216	341	341	341	247
Height (cm)	225		210	210	210	208	241	241	216
Main armament	SA-18		Model 28	Model 28	Model 28	Model 28	Model 32	Model 38	Model 38
Gun calibre (mm)	37	76.2	37	37	37	37	45	45	45
Main rounds stowed	250		104	84	84	180	100	165	150
Secondary armament	—		Fiodorov	DT	DT	DT	DT	DT	DT
Engine type	Fiat		T-18	T-19	AMO-2	Arm.Sid.	T-26	T-26	V-4
Horsepower	33	90	35	100	60	91	91	91	300
Fuel (litres)			90			182	258	292	350
Max road speed (km/h)	8		17	30	22	32	28	30	60
Max road range (km)	60		50			140	175	225	220
Max terrain range (km)						100	120	150	145
Armour (mm)	8-16		6-16	4-16	7-15	6-15	6-25	6-25	12-37

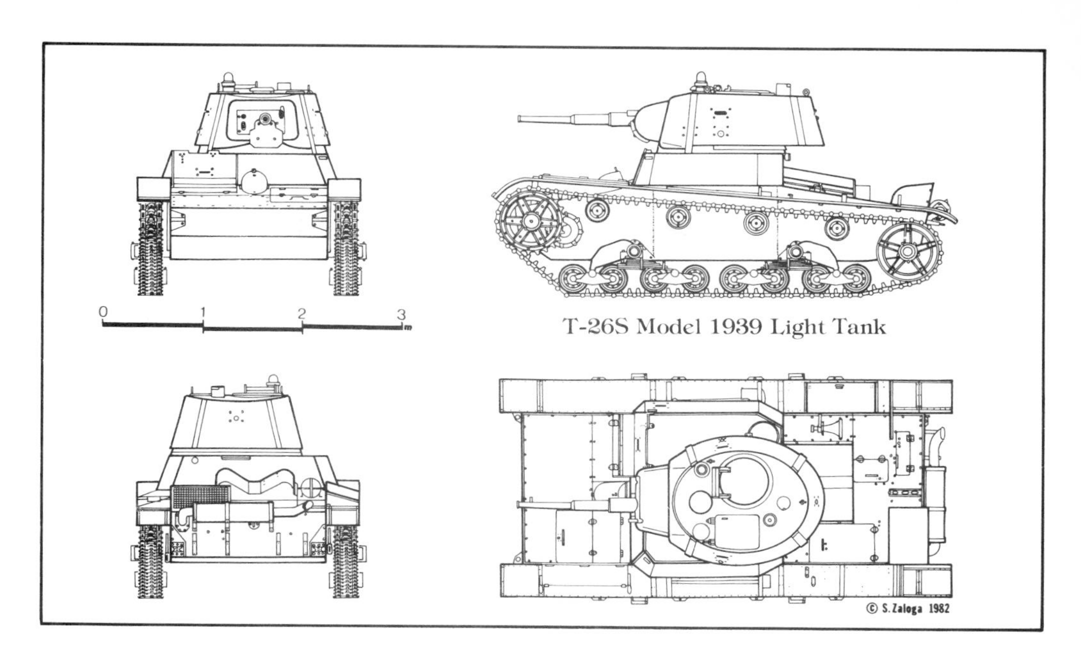

81. One of the main problems with flame-tanks was that they could not defend themselves when their fuel was exhausted. This lesson became apparent in Finland, leading to the development of the T-134 which retained the main gun. Notice that this vehicle also had the added armour of the T-26E.
82. The T-25 was a late attempt by the design team at STZ to develop a faster version of the T-26. By this time, however, the Red Army was interested in a more heavily armoured vehicle which would eventually result in the T-50 infantry tank.

81△ 82▽

The BT Fast Tanks

The companion of the T-26 was the BT series of 'fast' tanks. The T-26 was employed primarily by tank units assigned to the support of infantry, while the BT was assigned to independent tank brigades and in support of cavalry formations. The BT series was based on the American Christie M1930 convertible tank. Convertible tanks were a fad of the 1930s prompted by the lack of reliable tank tracks. Tracks had a short running-life, and were a primary source of the mechanical breakdowns which afflicted early tank units. The convertible tank skirted the problem by making it possible to remove the tracks and run the tank on its road wheels. This was accomplished by providing a special chain drive to power the rear road wheels while in the wheeled mode. In this fashion, the tanks could be moved at high speed over roads with no wear on their tracks, and the tank converted to provide cross-country mobility once the battlefield was reached; it took about 30 minutes to change a Christie from track to wheel mode.

83. The initial production version of the BT, the BT-2 Model 1932, was armed with only three DT machine-guns, which was considered adequate against infantry and cavalry.
84. The more numerous version of the BT-2 Model 1932 was armed with a 37mm tank gun, and was the preferred type in Red Army service. This vehicle was knocked out in Finland in 1941. (Esa Muikku)

△83 ▽84

The two M1930 prototypes arrived in the USSR early in 1931, having been shipped from the USA under the guise of agricultural tractors. They were turned over to a new design team at the Kharkov Locomotive Works (Komintern), (KhPZ Nr. 183) which was already preparing for production on the basis of engineering drawings already sent by Christie. On 23 May 1931, the RVS accepted the new tank for RKKA use as the BT-2 although not even a single prototype had been completed. The BT-1 designation was applied to the American prototypes. The Christie prototypes had arrived without turrets, so the main design change involved the development of turrets and armament combinations. The first three BT-2 prototypes were completed without armament in October and took part in the Moscow parade on 7 November 1931. After trials, KhPZ began quantity production of the BT-2 in 1932, manufacturing 396 tanks that year. There were two variants of the BT-2 Model 1932, one armed with a 37mm Model 1930 gun and the other armed with machine-guns. Both vehicles had a DT machine-gun mounted in a ball socket to the right of the mantlet, so the machine-gun armed variant had a total of three DT machine-guns. The machine-gun variant was not popularly received and subsequent production turned entirely to gun-armed types. As mentioned before, in 1932, the UMM instructed the design teams in Leningrad (T-26) and Kharkov (BT) to adapt the new 45mm Model 1932 tank gun for their tanks, using a common turret. The KhPZ team brought out the BT-5 Model 1933 as a result of these instructions. The main change on the BT-5 was the larger cylindrical turret and the new gun, but the wheels were also changed to a simpler convex style. The new turret dispensed with the ball-mounted machine-gun and used a more practical co-axial machine-gun alongside the main gun instead. Both the BT-5 Model 1933 and the early version of the T-26 Model 1933 with the new turret were short-lived, because in the meantime, the OKMO team had developed a better designed turret for the 45mm gun. The original turret developed at KhPZ had only a single, awkwardly placed roof hatch and had inadequate stowage. The new turret had twin hatches and a larger bustle. This became the standard production turret on the BT until 1937, and production of the BT-5 lasted until 1935.

As in the case of the T-26, numerous experimental versions of the BT were manufactured. The BT-5PKh was a direct counterpart of the T-26PKh and was fitted with snorkel and rubber sealing to enable it to cross rivers under water. They were first employed by the 4th Mechanized Regiment of the 4th Don Cossack Division in the 1936 summer Byelorussian MD manoeuvres near Slutsk. This unit was commanded by the then unknown Georgi Zhukov. A somewhat less harrowing method for crossing rivers was investigated by a special OKMO team

85. The final production batches of the BT-2 Model 1932 had several minor changes introduced, such as new concave wheels and a simplified gun mantlet.

△86 ▽87

86. About 50 BT-5s were sent to Spain to serve with the Russo-Spanish Republican tank units. This tank was captured by the Condor Legion in Ebro in July 1938. (National Archives)
87. The BT-5 was essentially similar to the BT-2, except that it had a new turret with a 45mm tank gun. The original production batch had a turret with a very small rear bustle, while the standard production model had a more ample turret bustle. The first two tanks seen here are the BT-5 Model 1933 standard production types, while the third and fourth are of the initial series production.
88. A pair of BT-5 knocked out in Karelia in the autumn of 1941. The tank to the right is from the initial production batch with the early turret, while the vehicle to the left has the larger standard production turret. (Esa Muikku)

88△

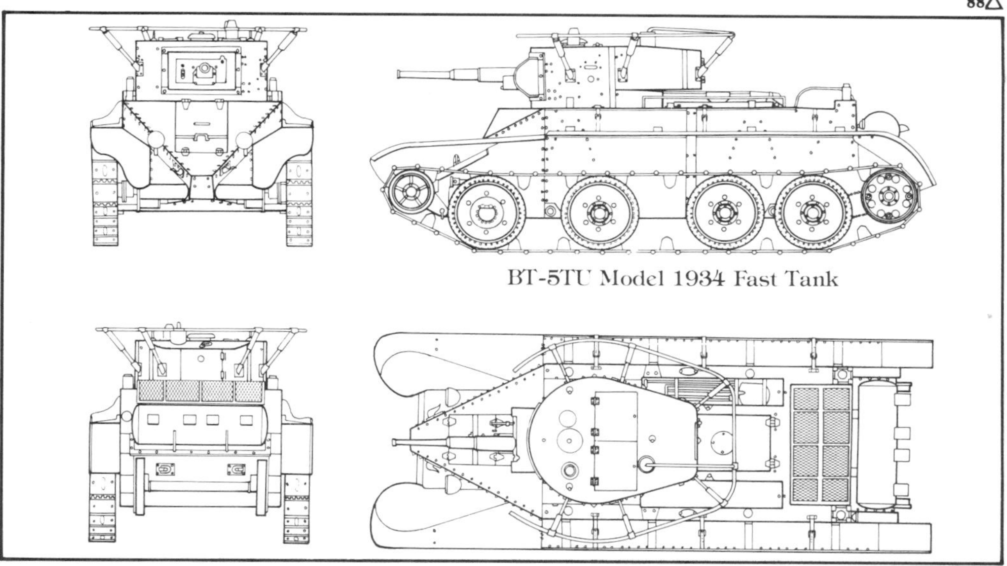

BT-5TU Model 1934 Fast Tank

headed by N. Astrov and N. Tsiets. In 1932, they completed the prototype of the PT-1 (Plavayushchiy Tank-1: Amphibious Tank-1) which used many BT components, but had a larger hull to provide enough buoyancy to permit the tank to float. Propulsion came from a propeller under the hull, and a rudder was provided for steering. Trials took two years and there were so many problems that it was decided to develop an improved type, the PT-1A based on the lessons learned. The PT-1A had many small technical refinements and this version can be distinguished from the earlier model by the lack of side turret machine-guns and a shorter pitched track. Both prototypes were unarmed during trials, and in any event the UMM and the RVS both agreed that the vehicle was too complicated for mass production. However, a small production run of the PT-1A was completed to permit tactical trials of amphibious tanks.

An artillery tank counterpart of the T-26A, the BT-5A was built on the BT-5 chassis. It used a large turret derived from that on the T-28 with a 76.2mm regimental howitzer, but was more successful than the T-26A and a small production run ensued. Likewise, flame-thrower versions of the BT were also built. Unlike the T-26 versions, the flame-projector on the BT-5 flame-throwers was carried in the hull, allowing retention of the main gun. This left the turret so crowded, however, that servicing the gun was nearly impossible. As a result, no quantity production of BT-5 flame-thrower tanks was undertaken. Other combat support derivatives of the BT included fascine carriers for bridging gaps and anti-tank ditches; bridging tanks. and tanks with 'supplementary track' (a primitive form of grouser) for use in poor terrain. None of these were built in anything but small trial batches.

△89 ▽90

89. In 1935, concern over the vulnerability of riveted tanks led to the redesign of the BT-5 as the BT-7. The BT-7 Model 1935 used a turret nearly identical in appearance with that of the BT-5 except that it was nearly all-welded. The main difference was the new hull design which had a new front configuration that was more noticeably rounded than the BT-5. At the rear, the muffler was completely enclosed.

90. In 1937, the BT-7 was modernized in parallel with a similar programme on the T-26 in which the older, vertically configured turret was replaced with a new turret using sloping armour to improve the effective armour thickness without increasing weight. The new BT-7 Model 1937 was essentially similar to the earlier model except for the new turret. Here, a BT-7 Model 1937 tows a disabled lorry during the hectic fighting in European Russia in the summer of 1941.

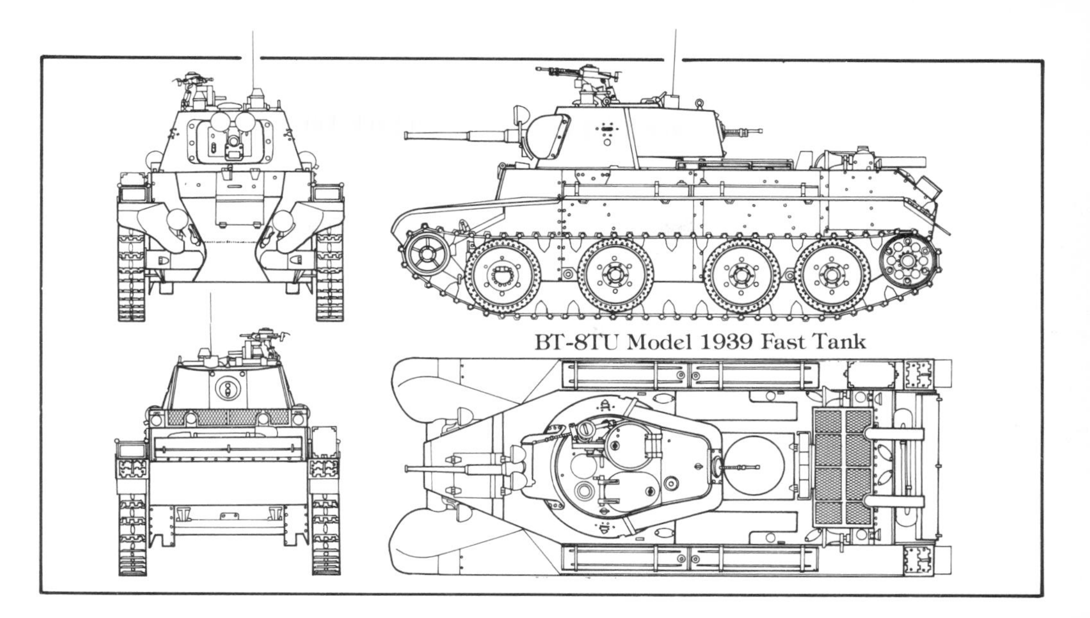

91. The V-2 powered BT-8 was virtually identical externally with the earlier BT-7 Model 1937 except in some minor details. The BT-8 to the left differs from the BT-7 on the right in having a circular hatch with AA machine-gun. Another external difference was the use of a machine-gun in the turret rear of the BT-8.

92. The combat début of the BT-7 and BT-8 came at Khalkin Gol in 1939. Here, a BT-7 of the 11th Tank Brigade is supported by infantry during the Mongolian fighting.

91△ 92▽

93. The PT-1 was a large amphibious tank based on BT-5 components. Its larger hull gave it greater buoyancy.
94. A small number of the improved PT-1A were manufactured for tactical trials, but the type never entered Red Army use in any sizeable numbers. This rear view shows the vehicle without the flotation pontoons fitted, and the steering rudder is very evident.

△93 ▽94

The concern over the vulnerability of riveted tank construction highlighted by the 1934 and 1935 fighting in the Far East led to the decision to redesign the BT-5 with welded construction throughout. The BT-5 had been continually plagued with power-train problems as well. It was powered by the M-5 engine which was a Soviet copy of the American Liberty engine, manufactured for both tanks and aircraft at Zavod Nr. 24 (Frunze). In 1935, A. Morozov in Kharkov and Prof V. Zaslavskiy, now on the faculty of the new Academy of Motorization and Mechanization (VAMM-RKKA I. V. Stalin) in Moscow, completed work on a new clutch and braking system respectively. These were mated to the new M-17T engine, a copy of the German BMW engine used in the T-28 medium tank. The resulting vehicle with a redesigned hull was called the BT-7 Model 1935. It closely resembled the BT-5 Model 1934 as it used the same turret, but the hull front had been completely redesigned and was more rounded, and the muffler at the rear had been entirely enclosed. Also, a new short-pitch track was used. Not only was the new hull completely welded, but it also offered the advantage of greater fuel capacity; additional exterior fuel panniers could be fitted if needed. The BT-7 Model 1935 remained in production until 1937 when it was superseded by the BT-7 Model 1937. The new version had a modernized turret with sloping armour to provide better ballistic protection. Otherwise, the vehicles were nearly identical. The command versions of these later BT-7s, the BT-7TU, usually used whip antennae instead of the archaic horseshoe antenna seen on the BT-5TU or BT-7TU Model 1935. The final derivative of the BT-7 was developed in 1938. It featured the new V-2 diesel engine based on the Hispano-Suiza 12Y aero engine. The new version, designated BT-7M and eventually BT-8, also had several other changes. Like late production BT-7 Model 1937, it had a ball-mounted machine-gun in

95△

96△

95. The BT-IS was one of the first experiments in the use of heavily sloped armour to improve ballistic protection from modern anti-tank guns.

96. The experimental BT-IS was followed by Tarshinov's BT-SW-2. Although not accepted for production, the BT-SW-2 laid the ground work for the revolutionary armour layout of the T-34.

97. Although not produced in such large numbers as the T-26 flame-tanks, the OP-7 was the BT-7 derived counterpart. Like the T-134, it retained its main gun. The flame projector on this vehicle was mounted in a fixed position on the hull, with a fuel pannier on the right fender.

98. To support cavalry tank formations, small numbers of BT-7A were built, mounting a 76.2mm howitzer in a new larger turret.

97△ 98▽

△99
△100
△101 ▽102

the turret rear, but redesigned hatches on the roof permitted use of a P-40 (DT machine-gun derivative) for anti-aircraft protection.

Two major support versions of the BT-7 were built, the BT-7A and the OP-7. The BT-7A was the artillery support version armed with a 76.2mm regimental howitzer in a larger turret. It was the only artillery support tank version of the BT series manufactured in any quantity. The OP-7 was a flame-thrower version of the BT-7 Model 1937, which skirted the internal space problem of the earlier BT-5 flame-thrower tank by mounting the fuel cell for the flame-gun externally in an armoured pannier on the right hull side. However, this type was not produced in large numbers like the T-26 flame-thrower tanks. A total of about 7,000 BT tanks were built. BT-8 production began in 1939, and 706 were built in 1940. Production was terminated in 1941 after a small number had been completed. In Russian service it was known as the Betka or Betushka which was slang for its acronym, and its diminutive form.

The Light Amphibious Tanks

As mentioned earlier, operational experience with the T-27 convinced the RKKA that tankettes were not entirely practical or useful as scouting vehicles. When the VCL Mk VI tankettes had been purchased, the Russians also bought VCL Amphibian tanks which were light, 3-ton tanks with machine-gun armament capable of crossing small waterways. These arrived in Russia in 1931 and were sent to Zavod Nr. 37 in Moscow together with technical documentation provided as part of a licence production scheme. A design team headed by N. Kozyrev undertook production design of the type as the MT-33 (Maliy Tank-33: Small Tank-33). It was later renamed T-33 and a prototype was built. At the same time, the Kozyrev team designed a somewhat similar vehicle, the T-41 which had a larger hull for greater buoyancy, and also undertook design of a derivative light tank that was not amphibious, the T-34, so that the tactical utility of both amphibious and non-amphibious light scout tanks could be examined. None of these vehicles proved entirely satisfactory during trials, which led the team to develop a third light amphibious

99. An artillery tank version of the BT-8 was also proposed, the BT-8A, shown here in model form; no production is known to have ensued.
100. The T-33 was the first attempt at developing a satisfactory derivative of the VCL amphibious tank, and most closely shows its British parentage.
101. The T-41 was a rival design to the T-33 and had a larger hull for greater buoyancy.
102. The T-34 light tank was an attempt to develop a non-amphibious scout tank which would also be suitable for use by airborne troops.
103. The eventual winner in the scout tank sweepstakes was the T-37. The prototype shown here was put through gruelling water trials which uncovered a number of design problems which were corrected in the series production vehicle. The suspension on the T-37 was derived from that developed on the French AMR 33.
104. The T-36 was another of the contenders in the Red Army's trials for a new scout tank to replace the T-27, but few details about it are known, and it may in fact have been designated T-39.
105. The T-34 light tank prototype was later rebuilt with a 20mm gun, but was no more successful than in its original version.

103△

104△ 105▽

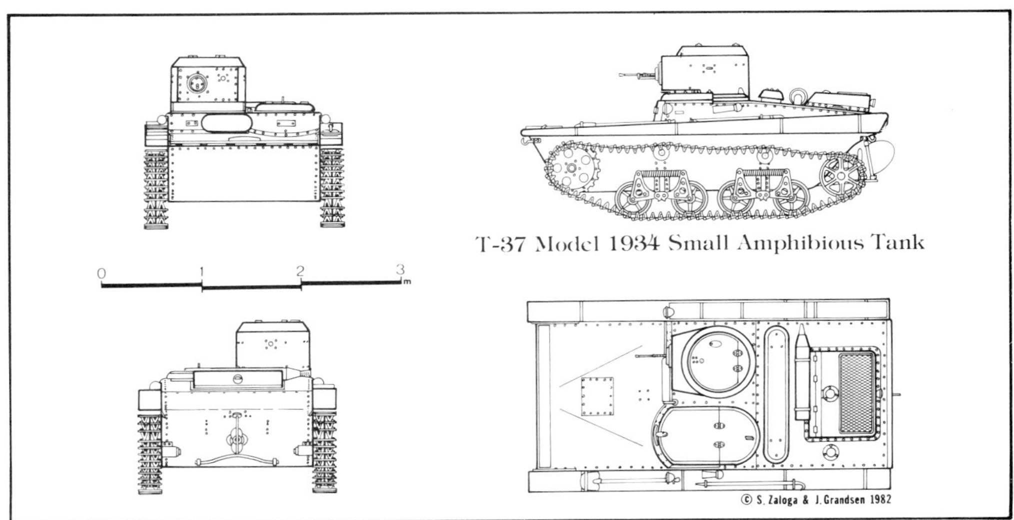

▽106

type, the T-37. The T-37 used a GAZ AA engine and an improved suspension derived from that of the French AMR light tank. On 11 August 1933, the RVS accepted the T-37 for use in the RKKA as a replacement for the T-27. That month, a special unit was organized in the Leningrad MD under A. Zhukov to push seven T-37s through a gruelling trial. In eleven days, the tanks travelled 700 kilometres, 600 of them in water. Although the trials reinforced the RKKA's commitment to amphibious tanks for the scouting role, serious technical deficiencies had to be corrected before quantity production ensued.

The improved series-production type was initially called the T-37A, but after a short time, this was dropped officially in favour of the simpler T-37. In addition to the standard production type, there were three major

106. A production model T-37 in its swimming role; it was supported by small pontoons on each side.
107. A number of the later production T-37s had the simpler turret taken from the T-28 or T-35 tank, and a modified driving position.
108. In 1936, the T-37 was redesigned with a new more powerful engine. At the same time, the hull was modified, and this resulted in the new T-38 light amphibious scout tank.

107△ 108▽

variants. The T-37TU was a command variant with a 'clothes-line' antenna running around the hull. Some T-37s had an all-welded turret like that used on the T-35 or T-28 instead of the usual type. Finally, towards the end of the production run in 1936, some vehicles had a slightly redesigned hull, most noticeably in the driver's area, and dispensed with the flotation pontoons on the side of the hull. A total of approximately 1,200 T-37s were manufactured between 1933 and 1936.

In 1934, with the T-37 only just beginning to come off the assembly lines, design studies of more advanced amphibious tanks were begun. The emphasis in the new designs was the incorporation of convertible track features, as it was felt that a scout tank could be expected to spend a great deal of its time on roads. Two projects were undertaken,

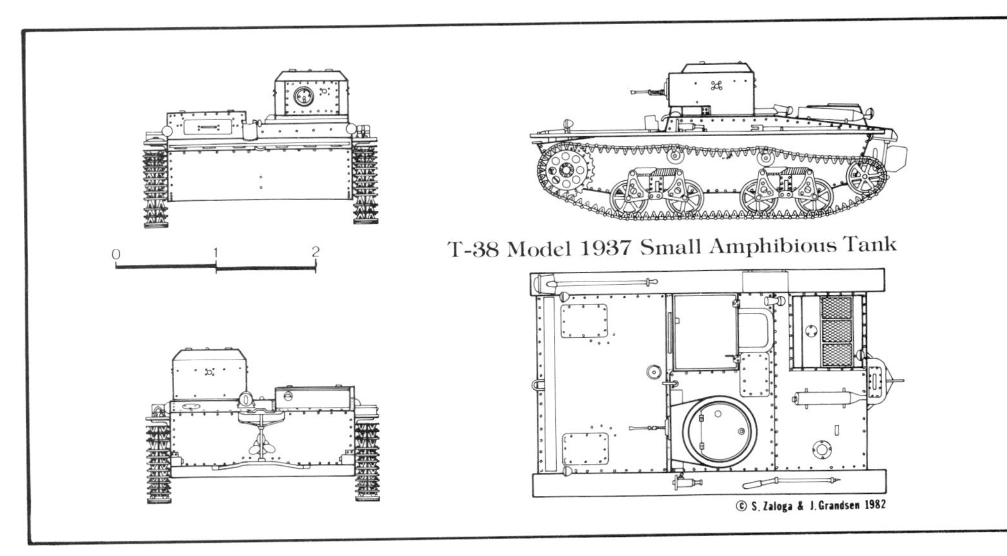

109. A company of T-38 amphibious scout tanks during summer manoeuvres.

the T-43-1 at Zavod Nr. 37 in Moscow and the T-43-2 by the OKMO in Leningrad. The T-43-1 was amphibious while the T-43-2 was not. Both vehicles were competitively tested at the NIIBT (Nauchno Ispytatielny Institut Bronietankovoy Tekhniki: Scientific Test Institute of Tank Technology in Kubinka, but these were unsatisfactory and led to th decision to proceed instead with the T-37.

The task of modernizing the T-37 fell agai to the design bureau of Zavod Nr. 37 i Moscow directed by N. Astrov with N Kozyrev as the chief engineer. The redesig of the T-37 was so extensive that it was desig nated T-38, and a prototype was complete in 1936. Like the T-37, the T-38 was base on the power-train and engine of the GAZ AA lorry, but was wider and lower than th T-37 and had better swimming abilities Series production began in 1937 in place o the T-37. Later that year, the T-38-M1 wa developed which used a superior planetar transmission. This proved too complicate for mass production and was not accepted fo service use. In 1938, however, productio switched to the improved T-38-M2 whic used the power-train and engine of the ne GAZ-M1. Production of the T-38 continue until 1939 by which time some 1,300 ha been built. In some units, some T-38 tank were improved by the addition of a 20mm ShVAK cannon in place of the usual D machine-gun. In 1940 one of the mor interesting experiments with the T-38 wa conducted by the Scientific Experiment Institute (NII). Several T-38, Komsomolyet and T-26 were modified to permit radi

110. The T-43-1 was an attempt to develop a convertible light scout tank which could run on wheels or tracks.
111. The T-43-2 was a rival design of the T-43-1 which examined the convertible mode on an amphibious scout tank. Neither type was accepted for production.
112. The TM was one of the final Red Army attempts to develop an amphibious scout tank with only light armour and a light machine-gun. Action in Finland highlighted the vulnerability of the T-37 and T-38 which fell prey even to heavy machine-guns.

110△

111△ 112▽

control. The T-26 was fitted with explosives so that it could be radio-directed towards bunkers, bridges or other vital targets and then detonated. The T-38 used in the trials was called the NII-20 and had radio equipment in the hull, and an antenna in the driver's position. Some of the T-26 and T-38 types were used in Finland in 1940. In 1939, efforts were begun to modernize the T-37/T-38 series and to examine possible successors. While the Astrov bureau at Zavod Nr. 37 concentrated on a wholly new design, the T-30, the GAZ team in Gorki developed the TM amphibious tank based partly on T-38 components; this project offered few advantages over the T-38 and was terminated.

△113

113. The TG-1 was one of the most futuristic-looking tanks of its day, but proved too complex and expensive and lost out to the more conventional T-28 medium tank.

114. The prototype of the T-28 contrasts sharply with the elegant lines of its rival, the TG-1, but the T-28 was more acceptable to the still immature Soviet tank industry of the time.

Indigenous Tank Designs of the Early 1930s

Although the RKKA was heavily dependent on foreign designs for the majority of its mass produced tanks in the early 1930s, in two categories, medium and heavy, it was largely self-sufficient. Following the failure of the KhPZ T-24 design, the OKMO bureau in Leningrad was assigned the task of developing both a new medium and a new heavy tank. The bureau under N. Barykov's direction was divided into two working groups, a team headed by the German engineer Grotte working on a vehicle given the bureau designation TG-1 (Tank Grotte-1) and the Army designation T-22, and a team under N. Tsiets, working on a design known as the T-28. In 1932, the Grotte TG-1 was built in prototype form. There were three variants, one armed with a 37mm gun and four machine-guns, one armed with a 76mm gun and four machine-guns, and a third armed with a 76mm gun, a 37mm gun and one machine-gun. The TG-1 was remarkably sophisticated for the period and indeed is one of the most modern-appearing tanks to have emerged from the 1930s, a period better known for its archaic engineering horrors so far as tank design is concerned. For example, it used pneumatic steering and a pneumatic suspension. Grotte also proposed the TG-3, a somewhat heavier design, also known as the T-29. The TG-1 was not accepted for production because of its complexity and the difficulties it would have presented to the nascent Russian tank industry.

While Grotte and his team were developing the TG-1, the Tsiets team designed a more conventional tank, the T-28, which was influenced by both the Vickers A-6 and the German Grosstraktor. Several Grosstraktor had arrived at the Kazan tank school in 1929, and their employment in field exercises had prompted the Soviets to interest themselves in medium and heavy tanks. The first prototype of the T-28 was completed in 1932 and was put through trials. The main objection to the design was that its 45mm gun was inadequate as primary armament because by this time even light tanks were beginning to carry such a weapon. In October 1932, the RVS decided to authorize production of the T-28 in an improved form. Design responsibility was transferred to the Red Putilov Factory in Leningrad, the Bolshevik Factory by this time being heavily committed to production work on the T-26 light tank. The first production batch of ten T-28 was turned over to the Army in February 1933 and took part in the May Day parade in Moscow. After further trials, the T-28 was officially accepted by the RKKA on 11 August 1933. With official acceptance granted, and production approved, a small design team under O. Ivanov was established at the Red Putilov Factory, but remaining under the supervision of the OKMO. The standard production model of the T-28 shared the same main turret and machine-gun subturrets with the T-35 heavy tank. This version remained in production, at a slow rate, from 1934 until 1938 when it was modernized by the substitution of the new L-10 76.2mm gun in place

114△

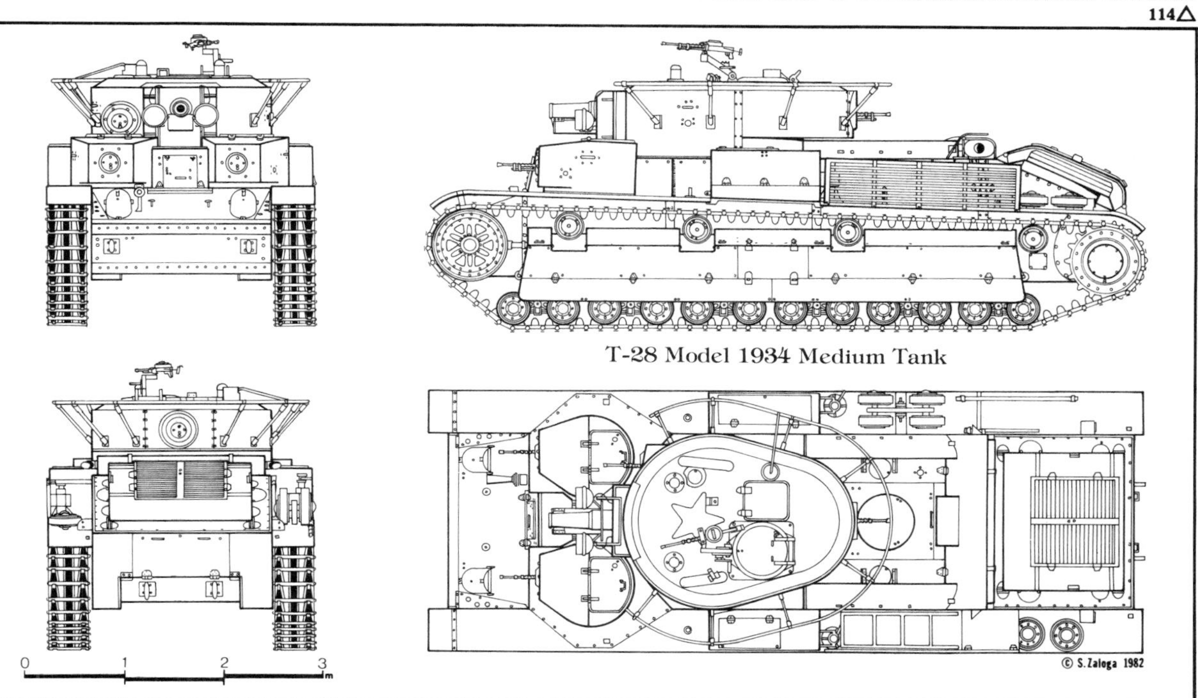

of the earlier Model 27/32 tank gun. At the same time, other improvements were made such as a stabilization system for the main gun, and engine improvements. The T-28 Model 1938 remained in production until 1940. During the fighting in Finland in 1940, there were at least two T-28 brigades, the 10th and 20th Heavy Tank Brigades. These units suffered heavy losses from Finnish anti-tank gunners, who quickly dubbed the clumsy tanks 'The Mail Train'. The main problem was its thin armour, and a crash programme was initiated to add appliqué armour. This version, based on rebuilt T-28 Model 1938s, was called the T-28E. The final production batch of about twelve T-28 Model 1940 had the conical turret used on the late production T-35 heavy tank. There were several experimental self-propelled guns built on the T-28 chassis (see below). An experimental bridging tank version was also tested but not produced. The same fate befell the IT-28 engineering tank which was fitted with a mine roller system as an outcome of

△115 ▽116

115. The production version of the T-28 differed markedly from the prototype, most notably in the turret designs. These new turrets were shared with the T-35 heavy tank. (National Archives)

116. The T-28 Model 1938 used the new L-10 76.2mm gun which had better anti-tank performance than the shorter and earlier type used on the T-28 Model 1934.

117. The standard means of air defence for Soviet tank columns was the vehicle-mounted machine-gun. This particular mount is the P-40 which consisted of a standard DT 7.62mm on a traversable ring mount, in this case, fitted on the roof of a T-28.

118. The T-28E was a T-28 Model 1938 with armour added to the turret and hull in the wake of the 1940 Finnish *débâcle*; the modification was not entirely successful. This T-28E was captured by Finnish forces in the spring of 1942 at Saamajarvi. (Esa Muikku)

117△ **118**▽

△119

△120 ▽121

119. Among the earliest projects with which the designer Koshkin was connected was the T-29, an effort to modernize the T-28 by substituting a Christie suspension.
120. This view of the T-29-4 prototype shows the track stowed so that the vehicle can be driven in the wheeled mode.
121. The IT-28 was a bridge-laying version of the T-28 tank but was not accepted for quantity production.
122. After encounters with Finnish mines in 1940, a mine roller version of the T-28 was developed. The system was unsuccessful, however, and the Red Army would have to wait for the development of the Mugalev mine roller system in 1942 before an effective mine clearing technique was available for tanks.
123. The T-35 Model 1932 was the first in this peculiar family of behemoths equipped with five turrets. On this version, the main turret had a 76mm gun and two of the turrets had 37mm guns. The remaining turrets were armed with machine-guns.

Soviet problems with anti-tank minefields during the Finnish campaign. Total production of the T-28 from 1933 until 1940 was about 600. They equipped four heavy tank brigades, three of which used the T-28 exclusively. The 5th Heavy Tank Brigade was a mixed formation of T-35 heavies and T-28 medium tanks.

One of the experimental offshoots of the T-28 was the T-29 (not to be confused with the identically designated, but aborted project of the Grotte team). Work on the T-29 was undertaken by Barykov and Tsiets at OKMO using graduate students from the Technical Institute in Leningrad working on their engineering theses. Among this group of students in 1934 was M. Koshkin who would later win fame as head of the KhPZ design bureau responsible for the T-34. The first version, the T-29-5, was a standard T-28 re-designed with running gear from a BT, using a complicated gearing system to power the rear wheels when in the wheeled mode. The vehicle was put through trials at NIIBT which led to an improved type, the T-29-4 being built in 1935. The new T-29-1 was built in 1935, but tests indicated that more work on it was needed. In the late 1930s work resumed on the T-29-1, with thicker armour added and a new gun as a result of experiences in Spain. This vehicle was considered in the A-20/T-32 competition, but by then it was outdated.

The T-35 Heavy Tank

In 1930, the OKMO in Leningrad began design studies of a heavy tank. Barykov divided the staff into two teams, one headed by the German engineer Grotte, and the other by N. Tsiets. The Grotte design, called TG-5 or T-42, was reputedly a 100-ton tank armed with a 107mm gun and having four subturrets, using pneumatic servo-mechanisms for engine control, and a pneumatic suspension, but it is doubtful whether the prototype was completed.

A far less ambitious project was the Tsiets T-35 heavy tank. This was obviously influenced by the Vickers Independent, and had a main turret with a 76.2mm Model 27/32 howitzer, flanked by four subturrets, two with 37mm guns and the other two with machine-guns. The first prototype of this land battleship was completed in July 1932 at the Bolshevik Factory and was put on trial at NIIBT in April 1933 before performing at

122△ 123▽

the May Day parade of 1933. On 11 August 1933, the STO (Soviet Truda i Oborony-Work Defence Council) authorized acceptance of the T-35 for Red Army use after improvements had been effected. Production engineering was shifted to the Kharkov Locomotive Works because of the overflow of T-26 work at the Bolshevik Factory. The first production batch of ten vehicles was completed in 1933 after Syachenko had developed a tank mounting for the 76.2mm Model 1927 regimental gun (PS-3 76.2mm tank gun Model 1927/32). A second production batch of ten followed, using the new turret which was also being adopted by the T-28. The standard production type did not enter production until 1935. It had a lengthened hull with an extra set of bogie wheels on each side, a redesigned bow and improved subturret armament (two 45mm in place of the earlier

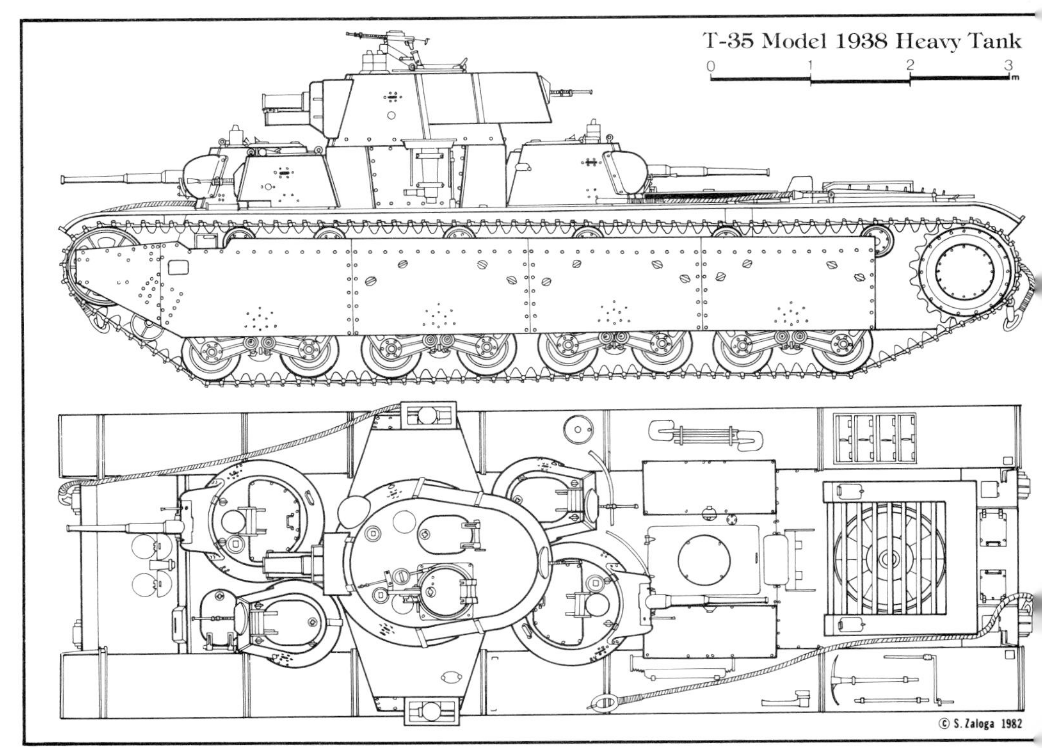

▽124

124. The T-35 Model 1933 used the same turrets as the T-28, but retained the rounded headcovers for the driver and bow machine-gunner; only ten were built.
125. The T-35 Model 1938 was essentially similar to the earlier Model 1935 but had new turrets with sloped armour which were *de rigueur* on new Soviet tanks from 1937 onwards. Only about ten were built. (National Archives)
126. The standard production model of the T-35 was the T-35 Model 1935. This version had a lengthened hull, and new sub-turrets with 45mm guns derived from those on the T-26 and BT-5 minus the rear bustle. About 35 were built and they proved a popular attraction at the annual military parades in Moscow.

37mm guns). About 35 were built in Kharkov from 1935 to 1938. A final batch of six modernized vehicles was completed in 1938 and 1939, using new turrets with angled side armour. This brought total T-35 production to 61 tanks. The T-35 equipped the 5th Independent Heavy Tank Brigade which participated in the annual Moscow parades. In service it proved a disappointment; its enormous length made it difficult to steer and the multiple guns were difficult to fire accurately unless the tank was stationary. It would seem that production was maintained as much to keep the annual parades amply supplied with an awe-inspiring, albeit thinly armoured behemoth, rather than for any tactical requirement. Only one battalion of T-35s actually became operational because so many of the tanks were permanently stationed in Moscow.

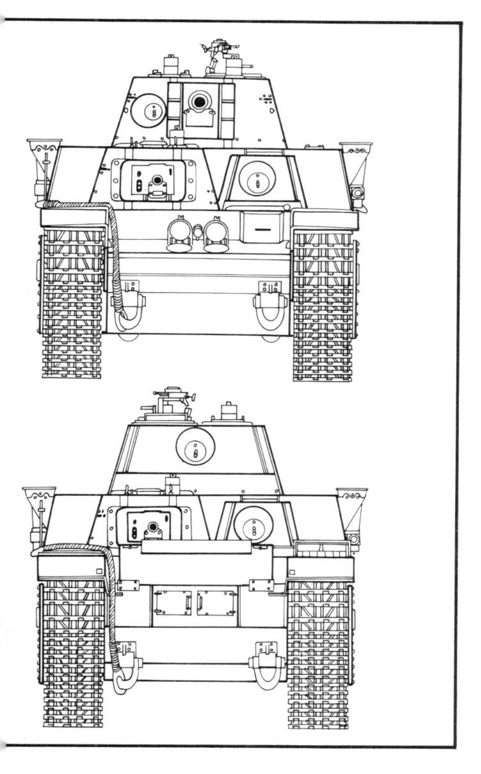

125△ 126▽

Armoured Cars of the 1930s

As a result of their extensive experience with armoured cars during the Civil War, the Soviets showed a great deal of interest in developing more modern ones during the 1930s, though initial efforts had to await the rejuvenation of the Russian automobile industry which began in the late 1920s. Like the Imperial Russian Army before them, the RKKA saw the armoured car as falling into two main classes, light and heavy. Light cars were armed with machine-guns, heavies with guns in the 37mm–45mm range. Following the BA-27 project covered earlier, the next projects were undertaken at the Izhorskiy Factory in Kolpino on the basis of newly imported Ford A automobiles, and their Soviet copies, the GAZ-A. The first of these was the D-8, in its original form a very simple open-topped design. The D-8 had a two-man crew sitting back to back so that the rear man could fire a rear-mounted machine-gun. A small number was produced from 1932 until 1934, and the later production batches were fully armoured.

Concurrently, the D-12 was manufactured which had a longer wheel base and a small turret. Both types were intended for use as scout vehicles, but they were roadbound because of the weight of their armour. Far less primitive was the FAI light armoured car developed at Izhorskiy later in 1932. This too was based on the GAZ-A, but had a larger turret with a full field of fire. It replaced the D-12 on the assembly lines at the end of 1932. In 1933, a special rail scout version was built, the FAI-ZhD, which had steel wheels for travelling on railway lines in support of armoured trains. In 1936, when the improved GAZ-M1 chassis became available, the FAI was modified to use it, becoming the new FAI-M light armoured car. The FAI was the standard light armoured car of RKKA scout units throughout the 1930s. It was superseded in 1936 by the modestly improved BA-20, which was also based on the GAZ-M1, but with thicker armour and angled turret panels instead of perpendicular panels as on the FAI. The initial command versions had a clothes-line aerial, but on the improved BA-20M version, the command vehicles had whip antennae. Production of the BA-20 was undertaken by the Vykunskiy Factory instead of the Izhorskiy Factory because of Izhorskiy's growing commitment to supply armour plate to the other tank factories. Like the FAI, the BA-20 also had a rail scout version, the BA-20ZhD, a small number of which were built.

Besides these standard production cars, at least four other light armoured cars reached

▽127

▽128

127. The prototypes of the D-8 armoured car were completely open, but on the production version like this one they were fully enclosed.
128. The clumsy D-8 and D-13 were replaced by the FAI armoured car which placed the main armament in a conventional turret.
129. The FAI was followed by the very similar BA-20. The BA-20 can be distinguished by the sloped turret armour. This particular version has the prominent clothes-line antenna running around the hull. (National Archives)
130. The BA-20M was an improved version of the BA-20. The clothes-line gave way to a more conventional whip antenna, and other internal improvements were incorporated. These BA-20M are on their way to the fighting in 1941.

129△ **130**▽

the prototype stage. In 1935, Zavod Nr. 38 mounted a lengthened FAI armoured hull on a 6×4 GAZ-TK, but no production of this vehicle was undertaken. In 1939, the Vykunskiy Factory designed a variant of the BA-20, mounted on the new GAZ-21 6×4 lorry, designated the BA-21, but the project was terminated when the RKKA decided to drop the GAZ-21 in favour of the GAZ-11 and GAZ-61 jeep. Zavod Nr. 38 also developed a version of the BA-20 on a GAZ-22 6×4 chassis, known as the LB-23, but this proceeded no further than the prototype stage. In 1940, in the wake of these half-hearted efforts, both Vykunskiy and Zavod Nr. 38 were instructed to begin development of a more sophisticated light armoured car on a 4×4 chassis using the T-40 light tank turret. The Vykunskiy entry was the LB-NATI which was mounted on a GAZ-AA lorry chassis with a more powerful ZiS-5 engine. The Zavod Nr. 38 entry was the LB-62, which was mounted on the new GAZ-62 chassis. Several prototypes of each were built and were undergoing trials when the war broke out and halted any further development.

Work on heavy armoured cars to replace the BA-27 started in 1932 at the Izhorskiy Factory. The first type was called the BA-1 and was based on imported Ford-Timken lorry chassis. A small experimental series was built, but it was not particularly well armed. Before production in quantity began, the new GAZ-AAA lorry chassis became available and this formed the basis for the new BA-3 armoured car, which used the turret from the T-26 Model 1933 light tank. Production began in 1934, but was short-lived because initial service use showed that the chassis was grossly overloaded. An improved version, the BA-6 was designed using a strengthened rear

△131 133▽

△132

LIGHT ARMOURED CARS, 1920–40

Designation	D-8	D-12	FAI	BA-20	GAZ-TK	BA-21	LB-23	LB-NATI	LB-62
Crew	2	2-3	2	3	3	3	3	3	3
Weight (tonnes)	1.5	1.65	2	2.5	2.6	3.2	3.5	4.6	5.2
Length (cm)	354	354	375	431	425	448		420	335
Width (cm)	170	170	170	175	170	175		180	170
Height (cm)	168	202	195	213	210	210		215	192
Main armament	2 × DT	2 × DT	DT	DT	DT	2 × DT	2 × DT	DShK	DShK
Engine type	GAZ-A	GAZ-A	GAZ-A	M1	GAZ-A	M1		ZiS-5	GAZ-11
Horsepower	40	40	40	50	40	50		90	85
Max road speed (km/h)	80	75	80	85	63	53	70	57	70
Max road range (km)	600		200	450	230	400	200	290	500
Max terrain range (km)			160	335	190	340	140	100	360
Armour (mm)	5-7	3-7	8	10	6	11	11	10	10-13

suspension, a new transmission and a lighter armoured body. The BA-3 and BA-6 are very difficult to tell apart, though it would seem that one of the few apparent differences was the omission of a right rear access door on the BA-6. At least three variants of the BA-6 were built. The BA-6ZhD was a rail scout version with steel railway wheels substituted for the usual tyres. The BA-6M was a modernized version produced in small numbers with a new lighter conical turret. The BA-9 was a derivative of the BA-6M, armed with a

135▽

131. These armoured cars in action during the Spanish Civil War bear more than a passing resemblance to Soviet armoured cars of the period like the BA-6 and BA-20. They were designed in Spain by a Soviet technician, N. Alymov, and built on imported Soviet ZiS-5 lorries at the Union Naval de Levante in Barcelona in 1937. (National Archives)
132. The LB-NATI was an attempt to develop a modern armoured car using a lorry chassis and the turret from the T-40 light tank as is shown in this artist's conception.
133. The BA-21 was an attempt to improve the BA-20 by mounting it on a heavier chassis as is shown in this artist's conception.
134. The LB-62 was a rival design to the LB-NATI and used the GAZ-62 jeep chassis in place of a lorry chassis. Prototypes of both were completed just before the war's outbreak in 1941 but in the chaos of the time neither entered production. This artist's conception shows the general appearance of the vehicle.
135. This view of a parade in the early 1930s shows the new BA-1 armoured cars in the foreground, FAI armoured cars in front of them and a number of Kommunar artillery tractors in the background. The BA-1 enjoyed only a short production run because it was underarmed and overweight.

136. A Japanese soldier examines a BA-3 armoured car disabled during fighting in the Far East in 1938. The BA-3 used the same turret as the T-26 or BT tank. The later BA-6 armoured car was virtually identical but did not have the rear door seen here, and had internal improvements. The tracks stowed on the rear were fitted over the rear wheels to provide better traction in snow or mud and made the BA-3 into a half-track when needed. (IWM)

137. The BA-10 was the most common of the medium armoured cars developed in the Soviet Union in the 1930s. It had a smaller, lighter turret than its predecessors. The vehicle to the right is from the later production batches, with a fender stowage bin for the track, while the vehicle to the left has the track stowed externally. (National Archives)

△136 ▽137

138. The BA-11D was the final version of the BA-3/BA-10 family. It used a longer chassis and was diesel powered, but very few were produced prior to the war's outbreak.
139. The BA-6ZhD was a rail trolley version of the BA-6 used to scout for armoured trains. It had steel flanged wheels substituted for the usual tyres, but could be converted if necessary.

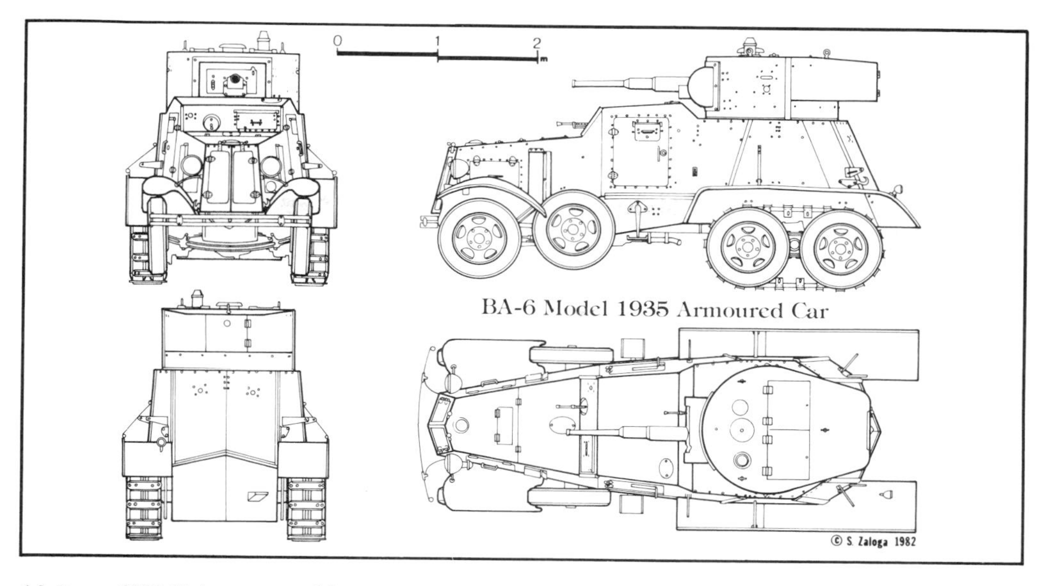

12.7mm DShK heavy machine-gun in place of the usual 45mm gun. The BA-6M was thoroughly modernized in 1938, resulting in the BA-10. This used the conical turret of the BA-6M, but the body design was lightened and improved. It was produced at the Izhorskiy Factory until the outbreak of the war and was the standard heavy armoured car of the RKKA even throughout the Great Patriotic War. A rail scout version, the BA-10ZhD was built in small numbers. In 1939, the design bureau at the Izhorskiy Factory tried to develop a BA-10 derivative on the ZiS-6 lorry chassis which had greater horsepower. A small series was built in 1940 in both a petrol engine version, the BA-11, and in a further modernized type with diesel engine, the BA-11D. However, this type did not supersede the BA-10.

The Soviet Army was one of the few to experiment with amphibious armoured cars during the 1930s. The first of these was the BAD, built on an AMO-F-15 chassis in very small numbers. In 1932, the Bolshevik Factory developed a more advanced derivative with a unibody welded hull on a GAZ-AAA lorry, called the BAD-2. A small experimental series was manufactured, including a few of the rail scout version, the BAD-2ZhD. The Izhorskiy Factory design bureau tried their luck with the PB-4 on the GAZ-AAA chassis, but this was no more promising than the BAD-2. One last attempt, the PB-7 was produced in a small batch for tactical trials before the whole programme was terminated. One of the problems was that the armoured cars found it difficult to climb river banks as their wheels tended to stick in the mud, and they did not have sufficient horsepower to overcome this. The same problem frustrated attempts to resurrect the old half-tracked armoured car concept: the BA-30 was built in prototype form by combining a BA-20 body with a GAZ-60 half-tracked lorry chassis.

138▽

139▽

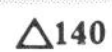140

△141

△142

△143

△144

△145

HEAVY ARMOURED CARS, 1920–40

Designation	BA-27	D-13	BA-1	BA-3	BA-6	BA-6M	BA-10	BA-30	BA-11
Crew	4	3	4	4	4	4	4	3	4
Weight (tonnes)	4.4	4.1	5.2	6	5.1	4.8	5.1	4.6	8.1
Length (cm)	462	520	465	465	465	465	465	470	545
Width (cm)	181	210	210	210	210	210	207		220
Height (cm)	252	265	220	220	220	220	221	225	240
Main armament	37mm	37mm	37mm	45mm	45mm	45mm	45mm	DT	45mm
Engine type	AMO		Ford A	GAZ-A	GAZ-A	M1	M1	M1	ZiS-150
Horsepower	35		40	40	40	50	50	50	90
Max road speed (km/h)	48	55	50	63	55	55	55	37	64
Max road range (km)	350	130	150	260	200	290	300	153	316
Max terrain range (km)		95	100	140	130	170	200	165	178
Armour (mm)	4-7	8	8	6-15	10	10	6-15	6	13

140. The BA-21 was an attempt to develop an armoured ambulance or troop carrier on the basis of the BA-10 armoured car.
141. The D-13 was the unsuccessful rival of the BA-1 built on a Ford-Timken chassis at the Izhorskiy Works in 1931.
142. The B-3 was an attempt by the ZiS auto factory to develop a half-tracked armoured transporter using T-40 tank components, but none was accepted for service use.
143. The BA-30 mated a BA-20 body on a half-track chassis. It proved unsuccessful in trials because it was too slow, and by using supplementary track the BA-6 could be given the same degree of mobility.
144. The BAD-2 was the culmination of work on the BAD, but vehicles like these proved too weakly powered to extricate themselves from river beds, and their intended role was already satisfied by the superior amphibious tanks such as the T-37 or T-38.
145. The BAD was the first Soviet attempt at developing an amphibious scout armoured car, and was built in small numbers for trials.

Trials in 1937 proved the vehicle too heavy and offering no advantages over light scout tanks already in production.

The important role played by armoured cars in the RKKA can be gathered from the large numbers produced. Although precise figures for individual types are not available, the list below of RKKA armoured car strength provides a rough idea of the scale of production:

ARMOURED CAR STRENGTH OF THE RKKA, 1933–41

1933	244	1936	1,033	1939	2,594
1934	326	1937	1,428	1940	4,034
1935	464	1938	1,801	1941	4,819

Self-propelled Artillery of the 1930s

The Russians have traditionally called artillery 'the God of War' and it has always retained a favoured position in Russian armies, Imperial or Soviet. The artillery branch, however, has usually been very conservative; the Imperial Central Artillery Directorate (GAU) favouring fortress artillery and the Soviet Central Artillery Directorate favouring horse- and tractor-drawn rather than mechanized guns. There was little serious development of self-propelled artillery during the 1920s because of the lack of technical resources. In 1922 the Bureau for Self-propelled Artillery was organized at the Krasniy Arsenal in Kiev, and similar organizations were formed in Leningrad (Bolshevik and GAROZ (K. Voroshilov)), and at Mastyazhart and Zavod Nr. 8. The first actual design effort was undertaken in 1922–23 by P. Korotieyev at Krasniy Arsenal where he built a small tracked vehicle to carry a 45mm battalion gun. Several examples were built in 1925–27 and plans were laid for a version mounting a 60mm howitzer. The vehicle offered no armoured protection, however, was slower than a horse-drawn gun and was not terribly reliable. There was no rationale to build such weapons. Other projects included the 76.2mm AR gun, which consisted of a tracked portee with a dismountable 76.2mm gun firing over the rear, and a self-propelled 76.2mm Model 1915 anti-aircraft gun. The Red Putilov Factory briefly studied a Tank Fighter (Istriebitiel Tankov) which, had it been built, would have mated a 76.2mm gun to a T-18 chassis.

The first Five-Year Plan in 1929 led the RVS to issue a policy statement called 'A System for Artillery Armament for the RKKA in the Five-Year Plan' which paid lip-service to the SP gun notion. Some of the new mechanized formations of the time listed SP guns on their table of equipment, but it was another matter to get the UMM and GAU to agree on this issue. The first true self-propelled guns to enter RKKA service were the SU-12. These were simply Ford-Timken or GAZ-AAA lorries with 76.2mm Model 1927 regimental guns mounted on a rear flatbed with a thin armoured shield. They were produced in modest numbers from 1932 to 1935 and issued to cavalry and mechanized formations in place of towed regimental guns. Other units simply received portee guns which consisted of various lorry types, with special skid rails to permit them to carry and unload 76.2mm guns on the rear flatbed. This was an interim solution until an improved motor-drawn version of the regimental gun was adopted, and these guns had to be dismounted before firing. In 1932, the design bureau at the Red Putilov Factory in Leningrad developed a mounting for the 76.2mm Model 1928 anti-aircraft gun on a Kommunar 3-90 tractor, and a small experimental series of twelve were built for use with the new mechanized formations. Further production was inhibited by the indifferent performance of the Kommunar tractor and the development of the improved Model 1931 anti-aircraft gun.

The inhibiting factor in early Soviet self-propelled gun development was the lack of a pressing requirement or a clear appreciation of the characteristics that would justify the high cost of such weapons in favour of conventional artillery. The growth of mechanized formations after 1933 provided a catalyst since a need developed to provide fast-moving formations with guns that could keep apace. In 1935, three T-27s were experimentally fitted with 76.2mm regimental guns, but this proved excessive for so small a chassis. Tests were also conducted with a T-37 armed with a Model 1931 37mm anti-tank gun, which could be used as a tank destroyer to accompany scout units to defend them against enemy armour. Probably the most radical approach was taken by the Soviet rocket designer, Kurchevskiy, who developed a family of recoilless rifle guns. In 1935–36, the RKKA experimentally fitted

△146

△147 ▽148

146. The Korotieyev 45mm mechanized gun was a 1923 attempt at self-propelled artillery. The tiny chassis was bulky, and only a small trials batch was built.
147. The SU-12 was the first mechanized gun adopted in any numbers by the RKKA. It consisted of a lorry, in this case an imported Ford-Timken, with a shielded 76.2mm regimental gun on a traversable rear mounting. SU-12s were also built on the GAZ-AAA lorry and were used in the early mechanized formations to examine the tactical utility of mechanized guns.
148. The SU-2 was a 76.2mm Model 28 anti-aircraft gun mounted on a Kommunar 3-90 tractor. A dozen were built in 1932 for trials with the new mechanized formations. They were despised by the artillery because they were unsteady when firing and suffered continual mechanical breakdowns.

149. The AT-1 was the rival of the T-26A artillery tank. While more successful than its rival if for no other reason than its lighter weight, it found little favour because of the limited traverse of its gun. The programme was resurrected in 1938, but it was not until the war that the Red Army appreciated the tactical utility of close support assault guns for infantry.
150. The SU-5-2 mounted a 122mm howitzer in a fitting similar to that on the SU-5-1. The Small Triad programme highlighted one of the main problems of the mechanized gun programmes of the 1930s: mere motorization of artillery did not justify the cost and complexity of weapons like these compared to conventional artillery.
151. The SU-5-1 was the first of the experimental Small Triad series which examined various guns fitted to a modified T-26 tank chassis. This particular version tested the mounting for a 76.2mm Model 02/30 divisional gun.

149△

150△ 151▽

△152

△153 ▽154

the 76.2mm K recoilless rifle on the GAZ-TK car and re-configured a T-37 tank with a K gun, known as the SU-76K. Kurchevskiy also contemplated building a self-propelled 305mm recoilless field howitzer called the SPGK, but he was killed in one of the purges before it could be completed.

In 1935, the OKMO teams at Zavod Nr. 185 began design of the first comprehensive family of self-propelled guns, called the Small Triad (Maliy Tripleks) and the Large Triad (Bolshoi Tripleks), based respectively on the T-26 and T-35 tank chassis. The Small Triad programme envisaged modifying the T-26 to carry 76mm guns, 122mm howitzers or heavy mortars. The SU-5-1 was built in two versions, one with the 76.2mm Model 1927 regimental gun and the other with a 76.2mm Model 02/30 divisional gun. The SU-5-2 was armed with a 122mm divisional howitzer Model 1919/30 and the SU-5-3 was armed with a 152mm Model 1931 mortar. All of these designs had the weapons mounted on a rotating platform at the rear of the vehicle, with limited armour coverage towards the front, and had the engine moved towards the centre of the vehicle. An experimental series of fifteen vehicles was built, five of each sub-type, between 1935 and 1937. None was accepted for service use because it was felt that the heavier weapons over-extended the chassis and the role of the lighter vehicles could be better satisfied by conventional artillery or by artillery support tanks like the BT-7A.

The Large Triad envisaged mounting a 254mm gun, 305mm howitzer and 400mm mortar on a modified T-35 heavy tank chassis, called the SU-7. This would have resulted in a 106-tonne monstrosity, so the programme was trimmed back to a vehicle armed with a 203mm gun-howitzer or a 305mm howitzer. In 1935 the programme was renamed the Mechanized Duplex (Samokhodnoi Dupleks) or SU-14. The new chassis was modified from that of the T-35 and used the power-train of the T-28 medium tank. The first prototype was built in 1935 with a 203mm howitzer, followed by trials in which the SU-14 was refitted with a 152mm B-10 naval gun Model 1935. This version was called both SU-14 and SU-BU-10. These vehicles were put through trials in 1936, but the programme stagnated from a lack of support. In 1939, the programme was resuscitated with work on the SU-14-2, also known

152. This tank hunter was an experiment using a 37mm anti-tank gun on a T-37 chassis to develop a vehicle to protect scout or airborne tank units from enemy tanks. Only a single vehicle was built and it is believed that its failure stemmed from problems with its amphibious capability.
153. The SU-14-1 mounted a 152mm B-10 naval gun on a modified T-35 chassis as part of the Mechanized Duplex programme to develop heavy mechanized guns.
154. The SU-14 mounted a 203mm B-4 Model 1931 howitzer on a chassis related to that of the SU-14-1.
155. In 1939, the SU-14 programme was dusted off and the SU-14-2 was built. This differed from the earlier versions in that the rear compartment was fully armoured. The prototype took part in the defence of Moscow in 1941.
156. The SU-6 was an Artillery Academy project to mount the new 76.2mm Model 1931 anti-aircraft gun on a T-26 chassis. It was better thought-out than the SU-2 to accommodate gun recoil, and the side panels folded down for convenience of the gun crew. It proved underpowered, however, and the suspension was still too weak for the gun. No production ensued.

155△ 156▽

as the SU-14-Br-2, which mounted a 152mm gun Br-2 Model 1935 on a heavily modified chassis with more extensive armour protection. Trials were still underway in 1941 when the war broke out, and it is believed that the prototype was used during the defence of Moscow.

Aside from these co-ordinated projects, several other mechanized gun programmes were studied by the OKMO. In 1932, S. Ginzburg designed a simple mounting for the PS-3 76.2mm gun in a partially armoured superstructure of a modified T-26, to compete with the T-26A artillery tank. The vehicle was known as the AT-1 and a single prototype was built in 1935. Problems during the trials led to its rebuilding in 1938, but by this time, there was no further interest in the design because the requirements had changed. The design team of the Artillery Academy (F. Dzhierzhinskiy) under F. L. Khlystov designed two anti-aircraft mechanized guns, the SU-6, mounting a 76.2mm gun Model 1931 on a T-26 chassis, and the SU-8, mounting the same anti-aircraft gun on a T-28 chassis. The SU-6 was built in a small trials batch, but only one SU-8 was built. Rather than these complicated and expensive vehicles, for air defence, the RKKA decided to adopt the 4M system for defence of mechanized columns. The 4M consisted of a quad mounting of the 7.62mm Maxim heavy machine-gun pedestal mounted on a GAZ-AA lorry. Production of these began in 1931 and they became the standard air defence vehicle of the RKKA until 1942. In 1940,

157. Despite the lack of success with tank mounted guns, the Red Army did adopt a number of lorry-based mechanized guns in the late 1930s, the largest of which was this YaG-10 heavy lorry, fitted with a 76.2mm Model 1931 anti-aircraft gun. It had large outriggers to stabilize the mounting while firing and was sometimes used in fire support roles despite its design as a mobile anti-aircraft system.

158. The 4M was the most common form of mobile anti-aircraft defence in the RKKA during the early years of the war. It was a quad mounting of four Maxim 7.62mm machine-guns on the back of a GAZ lorry. Each air defence section had four of these vehicles, usually with one such section per regiment. They were built on GAZ-AA and ZiS-5 lorries. Besides this type, smaller numbers of air defence vehicles mounting a 25mm auto-cannon on a GAZ-AA were built immediately before the outbreak of the war.

△157 ▽158

they were supplemented by a small number of YaG-10 heavy lorries modified at YaZ to carry the 76.2mm Model 1931 anti-aircraft gun. Also, some ZiS-5 lorries were converted to the ZiS-42 which mounted a 25mm Model 1940 AA gun on the rear of the chassis.

The GAU's resistance to the adoption of self-propelled guns by the RKKA was due in no small measure to the mechanical unreliability of tank chassis of the period. In the case of many of the proposed vehicles, the chassis was badly overtaxed by the heavy gun, and the repeated firings of the weapons at high elevations severely strained the chassis. There was great anxiety among artillery officers that in battle, the vehicle would break down, leaving the artillery piece stranded and immobile. More importantly, the mechanized guns developed during the 1930s offered no real advantages over towed weapons with regard to armoured protection because few had full armoured coverage. The RKKA preferred artillery tanks, that is conventional tanks fitted with short-barrelled howitzers, to provide close fire support for tank units, and preferred motorized or mechanized traction for towed artillery pieces for the indirect fire role.

Mechanization of Artillery during the 1930s

The development of Caterpillar-type tractors in the Soviet Union was prompted as much by military as by civilian needs. In 1918, the People's Commissariat for Supplies ordered 2,000 Bolshevik tractors from the Bolshevik Factory in Leningrad, which were copies of the American Holt Caterpillar purchased by the Tsarist government. In fact only eight were finished by 1922 when an improved type, the Nr. 75 entered production, also based on a Holt model. Production continued throughout the 1920s and it was used mainly by anti-aircraft units. In 1922, the Agricultural Tractor Commission of Gosplan purchased rights for the German Hanomag WD-50. Production was supposed to be undertaken at the RBVZ in Taganrog, but in fact production started at KhPZ in 1922. In 1924, the improved Kommunar entered production which was a direct derivative of this type. The Kommunar 9G used a 60hp engine and 850 were built. The Kommunar 9GU had a 75hp engine and 1,100 were built. The Kommunar 9EU and Kommunar 3-90 both used a 90hp engine and about 1,750 were built. Total production until 1930, of all Hanomag WD derivatives amounted to about 3,500 tractors. An American engineer who visited the factory in the late 1920s was aghast by the poor quality of workmanship on the Kommunar and commented: 'If they run at all, their life is limited to a few hours.' The RKKA used mainly the 9EU and 3-90 types. In 1932, ChTZ began production of the American Caterpillar 60 as the S-60, and 68,977 were completed up to March 1937 when production shifted to the diesel version, the S-65, of which 37,626 were built before the outbreak of the war. In 1937, the Stalingrad Tractor Factory began production of the first Soviet-designed tractor, the STZ-3 (STZ-NATI-1TA) designed by NATI. It was also produced in a militarized form, the STZ-5, which had the cab moved forward to permit the use of a lorry bed at the rear for

159▽

159. The Kommunar tractor was the first modern tractor adopted by the RKKA and was a license produced version of the German Hanomag WD-50. Here it is seen towing a disabled BT-2.

160▽

160. The STZ-3 was the first indigenously designed Soviet tractor and was extensively used by the Army for artillery towing. The tractor shown was captured by the Finns in 1940. (Esa Muikku)

161▽

161. The STZ-5 was a militarized version of the STZ-3 with the cab moved over the engine so that a rear bed could be fitted for carrying supplies or artillery crews. (Esa Muikku)

162. The heavy Voroshilovyets tractor used the same V-2 diesel engine as the T-34 tank and was used to tow heavy artillery.
163. The Voroshilovyets tractor was developed on the basis of the failed T-12 and T-24 medium tanks and used the same suspension. (National Archives)
164. The only fully armoured transporter version of the T-26 tank to enter service was the T-26T which was used by 76.2mm divisional gun units.
165. The Komsomolyets artillery transporter was a small, fully armoured tractor which was used to tow the 45mm anti-tank gun, and could carry six troops and a two-man crew. A DT machine-gun was provided for the commander. The troops in the rear were unprotected except for a canvas tilt. These Komsomolyets took part in the Soviet occupation of Persia in 1941.

△**162** ▽**163**

carrying supplies. Approximately 4,000 STZ-3 and 7,000 STZ-5 were manufactured for the Army prior to the outbreak of the war. The STZ-3 and its derivatives were the most widely produced tractors of this period, with some 210,744 completed by 1952 when production ceased. Although the RKKA absorbed only a small quantity of these vehicles before the war, initial war losses caused the large inventory of agricultural tractors to be quickly scooped up for use in artillery units, tank repair sections and for a host of other military functions.

The first tractor designed exclusively for military use was the Komintern, which was designed by Zhubarev's engineer team at KhPZ in 1930, using the suspension of the T-12 medium tank. About 50 were built until 1935 when an improved type was introduced using T-24 suspension. About 2,000 of these were produced by 1941. This was the standard military tractor used in medium motorized artillery units towing such weapons as the 152mm gun-howitzer. In 1937, KhPZ began work on a heavy artillery tractor, the Voroshilovyets. About 230 of these were built from 1939 up to the outbreak of war in 1941. Production was shifted to STZ where they were manufactured until August 1942. The Voroshilovyets used the new V2 diesel first employed on the BT-8 tank. In 1938, two separate development efforts were initiated to develop a light artillery tractor. GAZ in Gorki developed the

164△

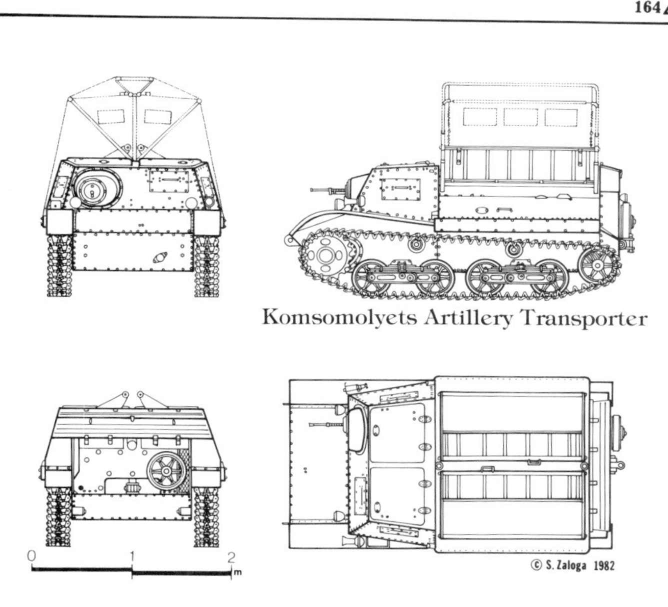

GAZ-20, which was basically a T-38M1 light tank chassis with a 60hp GAZ-MM engine and a GAZ-AA cab. A second type, the GAZ-22 or GAZ-23, was later built on the T-40 tank chassis with a GAZ-AA cab and a GAZ-11 engine. The RKKA decided to adopt instead an armoured artillery transporter, the Komsomolyets, developed and manufactured at Zavod Nr. 37. The Komsomolyets was the only Soviet artillery tractor to be partially armoured. It was developed primarily to tow infantry 45mm anti-tank guns and their limbers, but in a pinch it could be used like a tankette because it was fitted with a DT machine-gun in the hull front. Total production from 1937 to 1941 was 4,401 vehicles, and there were two production models. The later Komsomolyets Model 1938 differed from the standard production Komsomolyets Model 1937 in having an uprated engine and a redesigned station for the hull machine-gunner. It was manufactured in very small numbers compared to the earlier type. Several derivatives were built, including the Pioneer, which was a smaller version without armour, and the LT-1 which used the GAZ-AAA lorry cab and either a GAZ-M1 or GAZ-11 engine. Neither type was manufactured in any significant quantity.

Besides tractors developed for use for artillery units, from the early 1930s a number of efforts were made to develop tractors and transporters on the basis of tank chassis. The most prevalent types were based on the T-26 hull. The TR-26 was an infantry transporter developed in 1932, and it could carry eight riflemen in addition to its 2-man crew; only a prototype was built. In 1933, OKMO

165▽

△166 ▽167

designed the TR-4, which could carry its driver and fifteen riflemen. It had a hull-mounted machine-gun as well, but was not accepted for production. A direct derivative, the TR-4-1 was also designed for carrying ammunition, and experimental quantities were manufactured for trials with mechanized units. No mass production ensued. Another design team developed the TP-26 infantry transporter, and the related TB-26 armoured transporter, but no production was sanctioned. Two of the most bizarre of these transporters were the T-26-Ts and TTs-26. These were a competitive effort in 1935 between Zavod Nr. 185 and Zavod Nr. 174 in Leningrad, to develop a vehicle to carry fuel and lubricants for tank units in the field. The T-26-Ts was completed at Zavod Nr. 185 in 1935 and the TTs-26 at Zavod Nr. 174 in 1936, but neither was accepted for service use. The only T-26 variant produced in any quantity as a transporter was the T-26-T developed by OKMO. The initial type had an unarmoured cab and was designed to haul heavy artillery. It was designated T-26-T2. A later type was built using an armoured cab, designated simply T-26-T. Small numbers of both types were manufactured in 1933 for motorized artillery batteries, and some remained in service even as late as the 1945 drive into Manchuria. An observation version of the T-26-T was built

166. The TN was an attempt to develop a command tank version of the T-26 with more extensive radio equipment.
167. Small numbers of the T-26T2 were built for towing medium field artillery. It differed from the T-26T in that it did not have an armoured superstructure.
168. The TR-4 was a 1933 experiment to develop a fully-tracked armoured infantry carrier. The Red Army did not adopt a fully tracked transporter until the 1950s.
169. The ungainly TTs-26 was an armoured fuel-carrying vehicle designed to support tank units on the battlefield.
170. The TB-26 was an experimental ammunition-carrying vehicle for supplying Soviet artillery or tank units on the battlefield.
171. The TR-4-1 was an ammunition transporter version of the TR-4 infantry carrier.

168△ 169▽

170▽

171▽

△172 ▽173

172. The T-26Ts was a rival fuel transporter design to the TTs-26. Neither was accepted for production.
173. The TR-26 was an early Soviet armoured infantry carrier resembling the later French Chenillette Lorraine. It was not accepted for service use.

called the TN (tank nabludatiel: observation tank) with a 5-man crew and a UNAF radio station. Small numbers were built for tactical experiments.

The last vehicle of this class designed before the war was the AT-42, designed by Koshkin's team at KhPZ on the basis of the new T-34. It was a multipurpose transporter or towing tractor, but only one was built before war halted any further development. Besides fully tracked transporters, two wheeled transporters were designed before 1941. The BA-22, designed by the Izhorskiy Factory, was a modified BA-6 armoured car with an enlarged superstructure to enable it to be used as an armoured ambulance. Only small trials batches were built. The B-3 was a half-tracked transporter developed by ZiS in Moscow using ZiS-6 components with the tracked suspension of a T-40 light tank for the rear suspension. Only a small number were built. Despite its massive production of tanks in the 1930s, the RKKA seemed entirely indifferent to the need to mechanize infantry so that they could keep up with tank units moving across country. Motor rifle units were transported entirely by lorries which had very limited cross-country capabilities and which had no armoured protection whatsoever. This short-sightedness was a reflection of the basic immaturity of Soviet mechanized doctrine during the pre-war period.

Organization of Mechanized Units during the 1930s

By 1931, annual Soviet tank production was approaching 1,000 vehicles. In the summer of 1931, the Kalinovskiy Mechanized Regiment was reorganized and expanded with a Scout Group with two tankette battalions, an armoured car detachment, a machine-gun battalion (on lorries) and an artillery battery; an Attack Group with two tank battalions and two batteries of SU-12 SP guns; a Support Group of a motor rifle battalion; and an Artillery Group with three 76mm and 122mm gun batteries plus an anti-aircraft battery. This unit totalled some 4,700 men, 119 tanks, 100 tankettes and fifteen armoured cars. The expansion in tank production permitted the formation of three more tank regiments in 1932, the 1st Tank Regiment in Smolensk, the 2nd Tank Regiment in Leningrad and the 4th Tank Regiment in Kharkov, in addition to the 3rd Tank Regiment in the Moscow MD. Three independent tank battalions were also formed in 1932, which were used as territorial units in other military districts. In March 1932, a special commission of the STO issued a report calling for the formation of large mechanized units to support corps and to perform independent missions; for independent tank battalions and regiments for STAVKA Reserve; and for organic tank units such as tank battalions for attachment to rifle divisions and mechanized regiments for attachment to cavalry divisions. In response, the RVS on 11 March decided to form the first divisional-sized mechanized formations in the RKKA: the 11th Mechanized Corps in Leningrad and the 45th Volynian Mechanized Corps in Kiev. These each had a T-26 tank brigade, a BT tank brigade, an infantry brigade and support units. Each mechanized corps had 430 tanks and 215 armoured cars. Besides the new corps, in 1934, the RVS organized five more mechanized brigades: the 2nd Mechanized Brigade in the Ukrainian MD, the 3rd, 4th and 5th Mechanized Brigades in the Byelorussian MD and the 6th Mechanized Brigade with the Independent Far Eastern Army. Each cavalry division was to receive a mechanized regiment with 60 BT tanks, and 12 of these were formed in 1932. These actions brought total RKKA mechanized strength in 1934 to two mechanized corps, 6 independent mechanized brigades, 6 independent tank regiments, 14 (cavalry) mechanized regiments, 23 (infantry) tankette battalions and 37 tank companies. Later in 1934, two more mechanized corps were raised: the 5th Kalinovskiy Mechanized Corps at Naro Fominsk, on the basis of the experimental mechanized brigade, and the 7th Mechanized Corps near Leningrad. The December 1935 table of equipment for these units totalled 463 tanks and tankettes, twenty artillery pieces, 1,444 lorries and 8,965 troops. At the same time, the first eight independent tank brigades were also formed.

The flurry of activity in the organization of these units was matched in the Russian professional military press which began to examine the tactical and strategic use of mechanized formations. Among the most influential of the studies published was S. Ammosov's 'Tactics of Motor-Mechanized Units' which was released in 1932. The summer manoeuvres triggered publication of dozens of articles on the employment of the new units. The manoeuvres were climaxed in 1935 by the enormous Kiev Military District wargames which were opened to Western observers. Participation of the 45th Volynian Mechanized Corps and other armoured formations had a shocking effect on foreign observers who had previously denigrated the RKKA as being hopelessly backward. More experienced observers wondered if the grand show were not intended to deflect attention from other problems besetting the country at the time. In fact by this time, the RKKA possessed more armoured vehicles, and more tank units than the rest of the world combined. The modernization of the RKKA, led by Mikhail Tukhachevskiy, culminated in 1936 by two grimly opposite events: the appearance of the 1936 Field Service Regulations (PU-36), and the beginning of the purges. The PU-36 stood in stark contrast to the earlier, PU-29, paying a great deal of attention to mechanized formations and other novel concepts such as airborne units. Unfortunately, its effects were to be completely distorted by the madness that was about to engulf the RKKA.

The purges which tortured Soviet Russia from 1936 to 1941 are among the most grotesque passages in modern European history. In 1936, Stalin began to stifle any possible political opposition by attacking the Old Guard of the Bolshevik Party in a series of show trials and executions. In June 1937, he turned his malignant attention to the Army. Stalin had borne a personal grudge against Tukhachevskiy since the 1920 Russo-Polish War, and he feared the popular and brilliant leader of the Army as a possible Bonaparte. To remove any threat of a *coup* from the military, he began having the Army leadership slaughtered. Tukhachevskiy was among the first to go, and during the next few years, the RKKA lost 3 of 5 Marshals, 14 of 16 Army commanders, 60 of 67 corps commanders, 136 of 199 divisional commanders, 221 of 397 brigade commanders, apart from thousands of lower-ranking officers. Particularly hard-hit were the new mechanized formations which were viewed as hotbeds of pro-Tukhachevskiy sedition by Stalin's cavalry cronies such as Voroshilov and Budenny. The RKKA's leading armour expert, I. A. Khalepskiy, who had guided and pushed for increased tank production, was shot in 1938. The purges not only wiped out much of the finest Army leadership, but were extended to embrace the leadership of the defence industry and even weapons designers. The heads of both ZiS and GAZ were killed, and the same fate probably befell the heads of many of the tank factories, though details are lacking. Professor Zaslavskiy, designer of the original Soviet tank, was killed as was Kurchevskiy, the pioneer of Soviet recoilless rifles. The full extent of the purges on the tank industry is hard to gauge, given the sensitive nature of the subject even today in the Soviet Union. However, the main design bureaux such as OKMO appear to have been gutted and broken up by 1940, and most design bureaux after this date were headed by younger engineers. The purges were probably a major factor in the decided drop in armoured vehicle production after 1936; any further maturation of Soviet tactical thinking was frozen, and issues of critical importance such as infantry mechanization were never fully addressed.

In the midst of the purges, the armoured units of the RKKA underwent another reorganization in 1938. The four mechanized

SOVIET ARMOURED VEHICLE PRODUCTION, 1928–41

	1928	1929	1930	1931	1932	1933	1934	1935	1936	1937	1938	1939	1940	1941
Tanks	92	26	170	740	3,121	3,509	3,565	3,055	4,803	1,559	2,271	3,110	2,666	2,413
Armoured Cars	20	25	35	30	30	50	85	140	570	400	375	800	1,450	800

Armoured car production figures are estimates based on inventory change. Figures for 1941 refer only to first half of year.

corps were renamed and renumbered, becoming the 10th, 15th, 20th and 25th Tank Corps. The new formations were somewhat larger, having a total of 600 tanks, 118 artillery pieces and 12,710 troops. The 1938 plan reorganized armoured vehicles into 25 independent tank brigades (four heavy, and the rest light tank brigades), three independent armoured car brigades, eleven tank training regiments and a large number of organic units such as T-26 battalions for the rifle divisions, and a BT mechanized regiment for the cavalry divisions. One of the major aims of the 1938 plan was to increase platoon strength from the traditional three tanks to five tanks. Independent tank brigades of the period had 145 tanks, 56 artillery and flame-thrower tanks, 28 armoured cars, 482 lorries, 39 tractors and 2,745 troops. The light tank brigades of the tank corps had four tank battalions with 278 BT or 267 T-26 tanks. The heavy tank brigades had three tank battalions with 136 T-28s, 37 BTs and ten flame-thrower tanks. One of these brigades, the 5th Independent Heavy Tank Brigade, was equipped with T-35s in two battalions and T-28s in the third. There were three independent armoured car brigades, the 7th, 8th and 9th Armoured Brigades, all stationed in the Far East, with about 80 BA-6 or BA-10 armoured cars and 38 BA-20 light armoured cars. Three independent armoured chemical tank brigades were formed, equipped with flame-thrower tanks. Prior to the 1938 plan, each rifle division was supposed to be supported by a company of seventeen T-26 tanks. Under the new plan, this was increased to a battalion with 22 T-26 and 16 T-37 tanks. The 1938 plan renamed the cavalry's mechanized regiments as tank regiments and these had 64 BT fast tanks. At the time, the Soviet Army had about 110 first-line infantry divisions and 32 cavalry divisions.

Foreign Involvement of the RKKA Armoured Force

As mentioned earlier, Soviet armoured train troops took an active part in the Chinese Civil War of the 1920s. The Soviets kept a wary eye on the region, fearing Japanese expansion towards Siberia and the allied state of Mongolia. Small numbers of refurbished Renault FTs were sent to Mongolia as part of the Soviet attempt to build up its army. The first action of Soviet tank troops since the 1920 Civil War came in 1929 when an experimental tank company, equipped with the new T-18 light tanks, took part in the warding off of attacks by Manchurian forces against the Far Eastern Railway. Soviet tank forces in the Far East were constantly expanded during the 1930s in the wake of the turmoil in China, and Japanese activity there. In 1934–35 there were a series of border clashes between the RKKA and the Japanese. In 1936, the Soviets signed a mutual aid pact with Mongolia and in the following year, moved the 7th, 8th and 9th Armoured Brigades into Mongolia. In addition, the new 8th Mongolian Armoured Battalion was equipped with BT-7 tanks and BA-10 armoured cars. Aid was also extended to Chiang-kai Shek's forces in China to assist in combatting the Imperial Japanese Army. Soviet advisers were sent to China to help form the 200th Army Mechanized Corps, equipped with 88 T-26 Model 1933s purchased from the Soviet Union, as well as a number of BA-10 and BA-20 armoured cars, and various British, Italian and German tanks already in Chinese service. The first serious fighting directly involving Soviet and Japanese forces since 1935 took place in 1938 in the Lake Khasan region. The escalation in tension prompted the Soviets to send further reinforcements into Mongolia, including the 6th and 11th Tank Brigades, equipped with BT-7 fast tanks. Fighting broke out in earnest in the summer of 1939 at Khalkin Gol. Soviet armoured units played a central role in the rout of the Japanese Kwangtung Army. The Japanese Type 89 and Type 97 medium tanks proved no match for the BT-7 fast tank.

The first Soviet export of armoured equipment to Europe and the Middle East came in 1935 when the USSR sold to Turkey 60 T-26 Model 1933, five T-27 tankettes, two T-28 medium tanks and about 60 BA-6 armoured cars. These were used to form the 1st Tank Regiment of the 2nd Cavalry Division at Luleburgaz. A small number of armoured vehicles including T-26 tanks were also sold to Afghanistan at this time. The most substantial commitment of Soviet troops and material began in 1936 when the USSR decided to aid Republican forces in Spain during the civil war. The first shipment of fifteen T-26 Model 1933 arrived in Spain in September 1936. Soviet aid eventually totalled 362 tanks, 120 armoured cars and 351 'volunteer' tank crews. The majority of the tanks were T-26 Model 1933, but about 50 BT-5s and a single T-28 were eventually shipped. The armoured cars were primarily FAI and BA-6. Under Soviet supervision, the first Batallon de Carros was formed in 1937, followed by the Primera Brigada Blindada commanded by D. G. Pavlov. Pavlov remained in command of the Soviet tank troops in Spain and in 1937 helped to organize the Division de Ingenios Blindados, made up of two mixed T-26/BA-6 brigades and the Regimento de Carros Pesados, formed with the newly arrived BT-5 fast tanks. The Soviet tanks proved totally superior to the Italian and German tanks occasionally encountered, though it was also painfully clear that the thin armour of the T-26 and BT-5 was not at all adequate against the 37mm anti-tank guns of the period. In the wake of the purges, D. G. Pavlov was put in charge of the new Directorate of Armoured Forces (ABTU, which replaced the earlier UMM). The lessons of the Spanish Civil War proved largely irrelevant to RKKA tactical and strategic doctrine as the purges had terrorized most thoughtful observers into silence, and the conservative cronies of Stalin were happy to distort the Spanish experiences to fit their own murky preconceptions of the utility of horse cavalry for the strategic manoeuvre role. Nevertheless, the technical lessons of the fighting in Spain were eagerly digested by the young survivors in the tank design teams, and would become manifest in the superb tank designs that entered production before the outbreak of the war.

On 17 September 1939, the Soviet Union invaded eastern Poland in keeping with a secret pact made with Nazi Germany. Among the invading units were the 15th and 25th Tank Corps as well as scores of tank battalions and cavalry tank brigades. The Soviet thrusts were not met with any significant resistance since the Poles were already preoccupied with the Germans. In the wake of the Polish campaign, a meeting of the Main Military Council (GVS, formerly RVS) was held in November 1939. The performance of the tank corps was deemed unsatisfactory, presumably because of logistical problems and mechanical breakdowns, and the tank corps were ordered to be disbanded. In their place came four motorized divisions with about 275 tanks apiece, or half the strength in tanks of the previous corps. These were supposed to be used for manoeuvre operations as part of horse-mechanized groups! The independent tank brigades were ordered to become more closely integrated into rifle and cavalry division service, and plans were initiated to increase the armoured complement in a rifle division from a tank battalion to a tank brigade. This disheartening reversion to the foolish predilections of the cavalry clique of Voroshilov, Budenny and their boot-licking sycophants was only a weak prelude to the next embarrassment that would befall the Red Army.

In November 1939, the RKKA invaded Finland. In view of the overwhelming numerical superiority of the Soviets, the world awaited a quick Soviet victory. Instead, the Finns fought the Russians to a bloody standstill which lasted more than three months, and cost the RKKA more than 250,000 dead and at least 1,600 tanks. The Finnish campaign was humiliating evidence of the disarray of the RKKA; the consequence of the slaughter of the Army's professional officers, leaving incompetent leadership. At its peak strength, the RKKA fielded five independent tank brigades in Finland, plus many tank battalions attached to the rifle divisions. They performed no better than the rest of the army, and some of the brigades were wiped out to the last man. The last straw came in May and June of 1940 when the Germans swept through the Low Countries and France. This defeat as much as the Finland fiasco made it clear, even to Stalin and his clutch of ignoramuses, that the disbandment of the tank corps had been a foolish waste of time. In June 1940, the GVS ordered the formation of new mechanized corps. But in view of the chaotic state of the RKKA in the wake of Finland and the purges, these units were barely on their feet when the Germans struck one year later.

Soviet Armour of the Great Patriotic War 1941–45

Soviet Tank Design on the Eve of War

Although the vast inventory of tanks built under the two Five-Year Plans was almost entirely based on foreign designs, this was not the case with the new generation of vehicles developed in the years preceding the outbreak of the Second World War. The new tanks were the finest in the world, and were one of the few bright spots in the RKKA in 1941. The most immediate result of the experiences in Spain and the Far East was recognition of the need for thicker armour to resist contemporary 37mm anti-tank guns, and the need for diesel tank engines for better fuel economy and reduced fire risk. Both the BT and T-26 had proven vulnerable, even to anti-tank rifles, thus exposing the fallacy that armour sufficient to resist heavy machine-gun fire was adequate. The trend now turned from 'bullet-proof' armour to 'shell-proof' armour, or in other words, to armour that could resist a 37mm anti-tank gun at any range and a 76mm gun from ranges in excess of 1,000 metres. In both the Far East fighting and Spain, Soviet tankers had complained that the current Soviet tank engines were too capricious, bursting into flames at the slightest provocation. This led to intense interest in diesel engines because diesel fuel is less explosive than petrol. Experience in Finland also impressed upon Soviet designers the need to use lubricants capable of operation in very low temperatures.

The first of the new generation of tanks was the T-111 (originally called the T-46-5) which began development in 1936–37. The prototype, developed by OKMO at Zavod Nr. 185, was completed in 1938. The 60mm armour came from the Izhorskiy Factory and was the thickest ever employed on a Soviet tank. Its speed was inadequate, however, and it was soon realized that even if its armour couldn't be penetrated frontally by a 45mm gun, neither could its gun penetrate the armour of an enemy vehicle of comparable build. The project was terminated. In the meantime, one of the designers temporarily assigned to OKMO, M. Koshkin, was transferred back to KhPZ in Kharkov in 1937 to head a design bureau (the fate of the previous leadership being unknown). The new team consisted of A. Morozov (powertrain), N. Kucherenko and P. Vasiliev (suspension) and M. Tarshinov (armour layout). The team had important experience under its belt. Tarshinov had studied the advantages of

▽174

heavily sloped armour on the experimental BT-IS and BT-SW test tanks, Morozov was closely connected with the new V-2 diesel, first employed in the BT-8 and Voroshilovyets tractor, and the suspension team had worked on the T-29-4 test tank which examined the applicability of a Christie suspension on medium tanks. The design bureau was assigned the task of developing a replacement for the BT fast tank, and the new design was designated (internally) A-20.

In May 1938, a wooden model was presented before the Defence Committee of the SNK. The A-20 followed the requirements laid down by Pavlov of the ABTU, who desired a nimble vehicle with 20mm armour, a 45mm gun and convertible traction. The design team was unenthusiastic about the convertible feature, arguing that it added needless weight to the design and that fighting experience had shown the feature to be useless. Koshkin argued that the vehicle should have

FAST TANKS, 1931–41

Designation	BT-2	BT-5	PT-1	BT-7	BT-7A	BT-8	A-20
Crew	3	3	4	3	3	3	4
Weight (tonnes)	10.2	11.5	15.5	14	14.5	14.7	18
Length (cm)	558	558	670	566	566	566	570
Width (cm)	223	223	300	229	229	229	270
Height (cm)	220	225	230	242	252	242	240
Main armament	Model 30	Model 32	Model 32	Model 35	Model 27/32	Model 38	Model 38
Gun calibre (mm)	37	45	45	45	76.2	45	45
Main rounds stowed	96	115		146	50	146	152
Secondary armament	DT	DT	DT	DT	2 × DT	3 × DT	2 × DT
Engine type	Liberty	M-5	M-17	M-17T	M-17T	V-2	V-2
Horsepower	400	400	500	500	500	450	450
Fuel (litres)	400	360		620	620	620 + 170	
Max road speed (km/h)	100	72	80	86	86	86	65
Max road range (km)	300	200		250	250	700	
Max terrain range (km)	100	90		120	120	400	
Armour (mm)	6-13	6-13	10-13	6-13	6-13	6-22	10-20

174. The T-111 was the first of a new generation of more heavily armoured Soviet tanks developed in the wake of experiences in Spain and in the Far East. It was a poorly balanced design with a gun too small to penetrate the armour of enemy tanks as well protected as itself. No production was undertaken.
175. The A-20 was an attempt to update the BT-8 by using the advanced armour layouts investigated by Tarshinov on the BT-SV-2.

175▽

an armour basis of at least 30mm to withstand existing and future threats, and that a 76mm gun would be necessary to defeat enemy armour that was equally well protected. Stalin was personally taken by Koshkin's presentation and this led to GVS permission for the KhPZ to build both an A-20 prototype and a heavier prototype, first called A-30 and later, T-32, which incorporated Koshkin's suggestions.

Prototypes of both vehicles were completed in July 1939 and sent to NIIBT in Kubinka for trials. As predicted, the A-20 performed miserably in field trials if used without track, while its tracked performance was similar to that of the T-32. On 1 September 1939, a special display of all the new RKKA tanks was held for the GVS, including the A-20, T-32, KV, T-40 and T-50. There was still no consensus in the GVS over the A-20 or T-32. Koshkin argued that the T-32 should be considered a universal tank capable of satisfying the needs formerly fulfilled by the BT fast tank, the T-26 infantry tank and the T-28 medium tank. Some members of the GVS were bothered by the fact that the T-32 would cost at least as much as 3 T-26 light tanks, and Pavlov still supported the A-20. A

△176 ▽177

meeting to settle the matter was scheduled for the Defence Committee of the SNK on 19 December 1940. In the meantime, reports from Finland had stressed the vulnerability of Soviet tanks to Finnish anti-tank guns and the inability of Soviet 45mm guns to damage bunkers. In view of the anxiety of the committee members, Koshkin interjected that his staff had prepared estimates which indicated that the T-32 could be up-armoured even further without an unacceptable degradation in mobility. As a result, the Defence Committee of the SNK approved an up-armoured version of the T-32 medium tank for immediate production to replace the BT fast tank and T-28 medium tank.

The new version was designated the T-34 medium tank, and representatives of the Commissariat for Medium Industry were given an objective of 200 T-34s to be manufactured in 1940. The first two prototypes of the T-34 were completed in February 1940 and put through gruelling trials. In June, Koshkin and the director of KhPZ, Maksarev, were summoned before an anxious meeting of the Central Committee of the Communist Party who were worried about the defeat of France. The Soviet leadership

176. Koshkin's design team was unhappy with the thin armour, weak gun and convertible features of the A-20, and received permission from Stalin to develop a heavier vehicle, the T-32 which eventually became the renowned T-34 medium tank.
177. This interesting view shows the lineage of the T-34. From left to right is the BT-7, the A-20, the T-34 Model 1940 and the T-34 Model 1941.
178. The original version of the T-34, the T-34 Model 1940, had an inadequate L-11 main gun and a poor transmission. This T-34, which was abandoned in the summer of 1941, has a spare transmission unit tied to the rear deck in case the transmission fails. (National Archives).

178△

MEDIUM TANKS, 1930–41

Designation	T-12	T-24	T-22	T-28	T-28E	T-29-4	T-32	T-34
Crew	4	5	11	6	6	5	4	4
Weight (tonnes)	19.8	18.5	25	28	32	28.5	19	26
Length (cm)	750	650	750	744	744	682	592	592
Width (cm)	300	300	300	281	281	300	300	300
Height (cm)	280	281	284	282	282	280	245	245
Main armament	Model 32	Model 32		Model 27/32	L-10	L-10	L-11	L-11
Gun calibre (mm)	45	45	76.2	76.2	76.2	76.2	76.2	76.2
Main rounds stowed	100	100		70	70	70	72	76
Secondary armament	4 × DT	3 × DT	4 × DT	3 × DT	5 × DT	5 × DT	2 × DT	2 × DT
Engine type		M-6	M-5	M-17	M-17L	M-17	V-2	V-2
Horsepower	200	250	250	500	500	500	450	450
Fuel (litres)				650	650	650	460	460
Max road speed (km/h)		25	35	37	23	81	65	55
Max road range (km)				220	190	350	320	300
Max terrain range (km)				160	120	160	240	230
Armour (mm)	12-22	8-20	10-50	10-30	10-80	20-30	10-30	15-45

was gravely shocked by the rapidity of the French defeat, and in view of the RKKA's miserable showing in Finland, feared that the Wehrmacht would soon eye Russia as its next meal. Stalin insisted that T-34 production be increased from 200 to 600 tanks, with 500 coming from KhPZ and 100 from STZ. Mass production of the new design proved extremely difficult and the situation was not helped by continuing controversy over the selection of the T-34 and bitterness on the part of many army leaders who were unenthusiastic about it. The first production T-34 Model 1940 did not roll out of KhPZ Nr. 183 until September 1940. Later that month, its designer, M. Koshkin, died, reputedly of pneumonia. In 1940, only 115 T-34s were produced, and some had to be manufactured with M-17T engines and BT tank clutches because of continuing shortages of the new V-2 engine and the new transmission.

179. The T-34 Model 1940 was also built with a cast turret which cut down production time. The distinctive feature of the Model 1940 was the shorter, lower-slung L-11 gun.

Pavlov and the ABTU remained unconvinced about the universal tank notion and pushed for the development of the SP tank (Soprovzhdieniya Piekhoty: Infantry Support) to replace the obsolete T-26. The task was assigned to S. Ginzburg and L. Troyanov of OKMO at Zavod Nr. 185 in 1939. Despite the fact that the new T-126 and related T-127 offered no major improvement over the T-46-5 abandoned earlier that year, the programme continued. The two designs were nearly identical, with the T-127 being somewhat lighter. Trials of the prototypes led to the selection of the T-126 for further development and, because of shake-ups occurring in OKMO at the time, the project was shifted to Zavod Nr. 174 in May 1940. Troyanov remained in control of the programme, and an improved series prototype, redesignated T-50, was finally completed in January 1941. It was accepted for RKKA service, but no production took place before the war broke out.

Besides a light infantry tank, Soviet designers were also committed to the development of a light scout tank to replace the T-38 amphibious scout tank. In 1938, N. Astrov's team at Zavod Nr. 37 in Moscow was given the task. During the course of its design, the ABTU instructed Astrov to develop an amphibious and a non-amphibious version so that both could be compared in tactical trials. These were designated T-30A for the amphibious and T-30B for the non-amphibious type. A prototype of the T-30A was completed in 1939 and on 19 December 1939, it was accepted for RKKA use as the T-40 amphibious scout tank. There were several changes between the T-30A prototype and the production T-40, notably the use of a 12.7mm DShK machine gun in place of the 20mm ShVAK used on the prototype. In 1940, 41 were completed and prior to the war's outbreak in 1941, 18 more were manufactured. Some consideration was given to building a modified version with thicker armour and the 20mm ShVAK as an alternative to the T-30B. A prototype of

180. The new T-40 amphibious tank was intended to replace the T-38. Few were produced because of the war's outbreak, and its non-amphibious relative, the T-60, was adopted in its place.

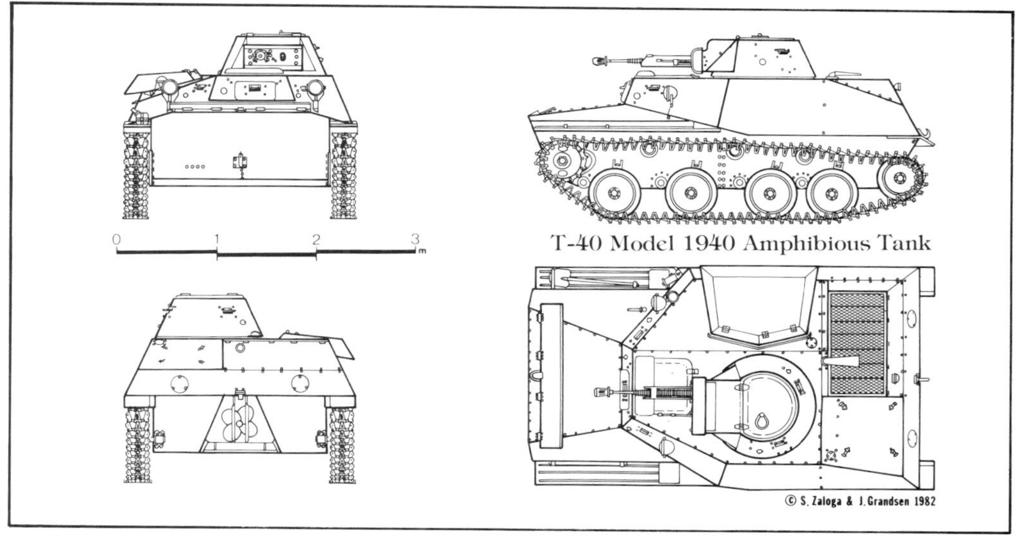

this vehicle, the T-40S (sukhoputniy: land version) was built which was not amphibious, but it was bulkier and more complicated to assemble than the T-30B and production was not authorized. The T-30B shared a common chassis with the T-40, but its superstructure was much smaller since it didn't require bulk for water buoyancy. It was decided to place it in production even though the T-40 scout tank had already been authorized, since it was cheaper to manufacture and could be used as a scout tank in units not rèquiring the amphibious characteristics of the T-40. Production work began at Zavod Nr. 37, but none of the production series of the T-30B, redesignated T-60 scout tank, were completed until July 1941 by which time the war had broken out.

The third tank of the new generation was a heavy tank, to replace the T-35. From 1938, the new tank was developed competitively between Barykov's OKMO team at Zavod Nr. 185 in Leningrad and a new team headed by Lieutenant-Colonel Zh. Kotin at the

SMALL AMPHIBIOUS TANKS AND SMALL SCOUT TANKS, 1930–41

Designation	T-33	T-41	T-34	T-37	T-43-2	T-38	T-38-M2	T-40	T-60
Crew	2	2	2	2	2	2	2	2	2
Weight (tonnes)	3	3.7	4.8	3.2	3	3.3	3.8	5.9	5.8
Length (cm)	396			375	443	378	378	411	410
Width (cm)	208			210	220	333	333	233	230
Height (cm)	183			182	183	163	163	195	174
Main armament	DT	DT	DT	DT	DT	DT	DT	DShK	TNSh
Gun calibre (mm)	7.62	7.62	7.62	7.62	7.62	7.62	7.62	12.7	20
Main rounds stowed	2,520	2,500	2,500	585		1,512	1,512	550	750
Secondary armament	—	—	—	—	—	—	—	DT	DT
Engine type	Meadows	Ford AA	Meadows	GAZ-AA		GAZ-AA	GAZ-MI	GAZ-202	GAZ-202
Horsepower	60	40	60	40	50	40	40	70	70
Fuel (litres)	120			100		100	100	206	320
Max road speed (km/h)	63	36	45	35		40	46	44	44
Max road range (km)	250			185		170	170	360	450
Max terrain range (km)	130			115		95	95	185	300
Armour (mm)	4-9	4-9	4-9	3-9	6-10	3-9	3-9	7-14	7-20

Kirovskiy Factory, also in Leningrad. Kotin had been one of Tukhachevskiy's protégés, but had survived the purges and was head of the design bureau of the Academy of Motorization and Mechanization (AMM) in Moscow before his Leningrad assignment. In his team was the veteran designer of the T-28 and T-35, N. Tsiets, as well as several talented younger engineers such as N. Dukhov, A. Yermolayev and N. Shashmurin. The heavy tank requirement called for an 'anti-tank gun destroyer' with five turrets and armour sufficient to resist the 37mm gun at any range and a 76.2mm gun at ranges over 1,200 metres. Both teams were opposed to the five-turret idea, and this was reduced to three before serious work began. In May 1938, models of the OKMO design, called the T-100 'Sotka', and the Kotin team design, the SMK (S. M. Kirov) were displayed at a special meeting of the Defence Council of the SNK. Kotin's presentation was critical of the three-turret concept, which provoked Stalin to go to one of the models, rip off a sub-turret and quip: 'Why make a tank into a department store?' With this both teams developed revised plans for a twin-turreted tank and these proposals were presented to a special

181. The Kotin design team entry in the heavy tanks sweepstakes of 1939 was the SMK shown here in an artist's conception. (J. Magnuski)

82. The OKMO entry in ne heavy tank ompetition was the -100 Sotka seen here uring combat trials in inland with the 20th leavy Tank Brigade.

meeting of the Central Committee of the Communist Party in August 1938 where they were approved.

Kotin and his team were still troubled by the archaic quality of twin-turreted design, and secured permission from Stalin to develop a single-turreted version of the SMK called the KV Tank (after Stalin's friend Klimenti Voroshilov who was Defence Commissar at the time). Basically the T-100 and SMK were similar in appearance. Each had a main turret on a long stalk with a 76.2mm gun and, in front of it, a small sub-turret equipped with a 45mm gun. The first T-100 prototype was rolled out in May 1939 while work continued on another. The first SMK prototype was finished in August together with a KV prototype. Both the SMK and KV were supposed to be powered by new V-2 diesels from the Kharkov Diesel Works (Zavod Nr. 75), but because of shortages, the SMK used an AM aircraft engine. The SMK was armed with the L-11 76.2mm gun developed at the Kirovskiy Works, and the KV was supposed to be armed with the more potent F-32 76.2mm gun developed by the Grabin team at Zavod Nr. 92 in Gorki. The F-32 wasn't ready in time, however, and the L-11 was used in its place.

In September 1939, the prototypes were sent to NIIBT in Kubinka for trials and for displays to leading party and army officials. Not surprisingly, the KV performed far better in the mobility trials than either the SMK or T-100. With the outbreak of the Finnish War, the prototypes were sent north for experimental combat trials with the 20th Heavy Tank Brigade, a T-28 unit. Even before the conclusion of the Finland trials, the Defence Council of the SNK accepted the KV as the RKKA's new heavy tank, and began planning its production. During the fighting in Finland, one KV prototype was damaged, and the SMK was knocked out when it rolled over a large mine. The disabled SMK was photographed by the Finns, and German Intelligence analysts mistakenly identified it as the T-35C. The Finland trials removed any doubt about the future of the SMK or T-100, though Kotin was granted permission to begin work on a heavily modified SMK, the SMK-2 which was never completed. One of the most strenuous requests from the commander of the Soviet 7th Army in Finland, K. Meretskov, was for a heavy tank with an even larger gun for destroying reinforced bunkers of the sort encountered in Finland.

Meretskov's request led to three projects. Before its disbandment, the OKMO team rebuilt one of the T-100 prototypes with a fixed superstructure and a B-13 130mm naval gun. It was designated SU-100Y, and though not accepted for production, was later used in the defence of Moscow in 1941. The Koti team began work on a lengthened KV arme with either a 152mm Br-2 gun or a 203m B-4 howitzer called SU-212 or Obiekt 21 but this was never completed. A mor practical solution for bunker-busting was th effort to mount a 152mm howitzer in a large turret on the KV hull as a heavy counterpa to the BT-7A artillery tank. This artiller tank version of the KV was accepted for pr duction. It was originally called 'Large-turre KV' to distinguish it from the 'Small-turre KV', but the tanks were eventually desig nated KV-1 heavy tank and KV-2 heav artillery tank. Production of the KV wa assigned to the Kirovskiy Works and th

△183 ▽184

183. Kotin's design team had the foresight to recognize the inadequacy of a multi-turreted heavy tank design, and pressed for permission to build a single turret version of the SMK which resulted in the KV. This is from the second production batch of the KV with the bow machine-gun which was not fitted on the initial production batch.
184. The initial KV-1 Model 1940 was armed with the L-11 gun because of delays in producing the superior F-32 gun as fitted to this KV-1 Model 1941.
185. Some idea of the enormous size of the KV-2 Model 1941 can be gathered from this view showing a KV-2 and a T-26 during the fighting in the summer of 1941. The KV-2 was popularly known as the 'Dreadnought' by its crews. (National Archives).

Chelyabinsk Tractor Factory (ChTZ). Up to the end of 1940, the Kirovskiy Works finished 141 KV-1, 102 KV-2 and one KV prototype (KV-3). The ChTZ did not produce any KVs up to this time.

In the wake of its success with the KV-1 and KV-2, the Kotin team turned its attention to an improved heavy tank version, the KV-3, and to two superheavy tanks, the 100-ton KV-4 and 150-ton KV-5. Neither of these two latter efforts progressed beyond paper studies. Two versions of the KV-3 were examined, the Obiekt 220, which was a heavily redesigned KV-1 with a lengthened hull, larger turret, heavier gun and more powerful engine, and the Obiekt 222, which was far less extensively modified from the KV-1. Apart from the introduction of the F-32 which finally became available, the main improvement offered by the Obiekt 222 was the re-configuration of the turret layout. Until this time, Soviet tanks had generally relied on two-man turret crews: a gunner who aimed the main gun, and a tank commander who was responsible for leading the tank as well as loading the main gun. The latter task seriously interfered with the former, but this did not become completely apparent in the summer wargames which tended to practise mechanized choreography rather than realistic tactics. In heavy tanks, a third crewman was provided to fire a rear-mounted machine-gun, but he was badly placed to assist the commander in loading. In the Obiekt 222, the crew duties were re-arranged so that the third crewman became the loader, freeing the commander of this burden so that he could concentrate on his principal task. He was also provided with a new cupola which offered better all-around vision. Unfortunately, this sensible modification was not introduced into Soviet tanks until 1942, by which time the short-sightedness of the previous layout had become bloodily apparent.

The up-gunning of the Obiekt 220 project with a new 85mm tank gun was hampered by another stupid imbroglio visited upon the RKKA by the nitwit head of the GAU, Marshal I. Kulik. Kulik insisted that Intelligence reports proved that the current

185▽

HEAVY TANKS, 1935–41

Designation	T-35	T-100	SMK	KV-1 Model 1940
Crew	11	7	7	5
Weight (tonnes)	45	58	55	43
Length (cm)	972	740	838	668
Width (cm)	320	320	330	332
Height (cm)	343	320	345	271
Main armament	Model 27/32	L-11	L-11	L-11
Gun calibre (mm)	76.2	76.2	76.2	76.2
Main rounds stowed	100			111
Secondary armament	2 × 45mm	45mm	45mm	2 × DT
Engine	M-17M		AM-34	V-2K
Horsepower	500	500	850	600
Fuel (litres)	910			600
Max road speed (km/h)	30	35	36	35
Max road range (km)	150		150	335
Max terrain range (km)	70		90	150
Armour (mm)	11-30	20-70	20-60	25-75

German tanks were so heavily armoured that the new Soviet 57mm anti-tank gun and 76.2mm tank guns would be ineffective. On the basis of this ludicrous belief, Kulik ordered a halt to 57mm and 76mm gun production in favour of an as yet undeveloped 107mm gun. Grabin's gun design team shifted their efforts from the 85mm gun to the new ZiS-6 107mm gun which was not finished when the war started. As a result, the Obiekt 220 was not completed until late in 1941, and Kulik's bungling needlessly delayed the production of excellent and desperately needed tank and anti-tank guns.

186. As an outcome of the Finnish fighting, and at the insistence of GAU chief I. Kulik, additional armour was added to the KV in the form of *appliqué* plates. This KV-1E rests at the Finnish Armour Museum in Parola; it was captured and used by Finnish tank troops in 1941.

187. A KV-2 Dreadnought lies abandoned by the wayside, having been knocked out by troops of the German 12.Panzer Division whose runic insignia is painted on the turret front as a road marker. (National Archives)

△186 ▽187

188. The KV-2 was also experimentally fitted with a longer 107mm gun for trials in the presence of Stalin.
189. Immediately before the outbreak of the war, the Kotin team designed a heavily modified version of the KV-1, the KV-3 Obiekt 220 which was to be armed with a 107mm gun. This would have replaced the undergunned KV-1 if the war had not broken out.
190. Following the loss of the T-100 to the KV, one of the prototypes was rebuilt as a bunker buster, the SU-100Y. No production of the type was authorized, but the prototype took part in the defence of Moscow in 1941.

188△

189△ 190▽

△191

△192 ▽193

191. The Obiekt 217 was a tiny armoured vehicle powered by a motorcycle engine intended for use by infantry commanders and by special squads to attack Finnish bunkers. About a hundred were built, but did not arrive in time to take part in the war with Finland.

192. Just before the war started, about 200 old T-18s were rebuilt as the T-18M and shipped to th western military districts.

193. The ZiS-30 was an improvised mounting for a ZiS-29 57mm anti-tank gun on a Komsomolyets artillery transporter. Intended as a tank hunte it was built in small numbers at the outbreak of war.

TANKETTES, 1928–41

Designation	T-17	T-23	T-27A	Obiekt 217
Crew	1	2	2	2
Weight (tonnes)	2.4	3.5	2.7	2.5
Length (cm)	368	430	260	
Width (cm)	116	150	183	
Height (cm)	137	140	144	
Main armament	2 × Fiodorov	DT	DT	2 × DT
Gun calibre (mm)	7.62	7.62	7.62	7.62
Main rounds stowed	1,500		2,520	
Engine type	Bolshevik	T-18	GAZ-AA	
Horsepower	20	60	40	25
Fuel (litres)	30	100	46	
Max road speed (km/h)	20	40	42	25
Max road range (km)		300	120	
Max terrain range (km)		150	60	
Armour (mm)	7-14	6-10	6-10	5-8

One of the strangest vehicles to be built as an outcome of the fighting in Finland was the Obiekt 217, a small tankette manufactured by the Kirovskiy Works in 1940 on a crash basis. Soviet infantry took frightful losses when engaging Finnish bunkers, and one field expedient was to tow special armoured sledges behind tanks to bring assault teams closer to Finnish strong-points with some degree of protection. The Obiekt 217 was an effort to develop a cheap, self-propelled sledge carrying two men in a prone position and two machine-guns, with some armoured cover. It was powered by a motorcycle engine, and about 100 were built. They arrived in Finland too late to see any fighting, and remain a curious footnote in the Soviet search for a mechanized infantry transporter.

Organization of the Soviet Armoured Force

In 1941 after several months of rapid German advances on the Eastern Front, Adolf Hitler remarked to General Heinz Guderian, 'If I had known that the figures for Russian tank strength you gave in your book (*Achtung, Panzer!* published before the war) were in fact true, I would never have started this war.' Actually, Guderian had estimated Soviet armoured strength at 10,000 tanks, about one-third of its actual strength! The Soviet mechanization programme had resulted in the Red Army receiving armoured vehicles in quantities beyond the wildest nightmares of their German adversaries. Since 1928, the Red Army received 31,000 tanks and 5,000 other armoured vehicles of which about 24,000 tanks and 4,819 armoured cars were still in service in June 1941. Besides these, the RKKA also fielded 272,000 motor vehicles and 21,448 artillery tractors when war broke out. Yet neither these stupendous equipment inventories nor the revival of the mechanized corps in June 1940 could repair the underlying weaknesses of the RKKA. The inventory figures and imposing list of armoured units illustrates only a distorted shadow of an ill-trained, ill-led and ill-maintained army which was about to face Europe's best-led, most confident and most experienced army.

The first nine mechanized corps began forming in August 1940 and by 1941, plans were under way to add a further twenty-one

194. During the siege of Leningrad, a number of T-26 hulls were used to produce improvised mechanized howitzers armed with the 76.2mm Model 1926 regimental gun.

△195 ▽196

△197

195. During the war, a number of improvised tanks were built on tractor chassis, in this case on a KhTZ-5 agricultural chassis.
196. Probably the most famous of the improvised tanks were the so-called Terror Tanks of Odessa which were use with some success against the Roumanians during the fighting around that city. (A. Loder)
197. In Leningrad, a number of assaul vehicles were improvised using lorries, partially armoured and with various gu and mortars mounted on the rear bed. (G. Balin)

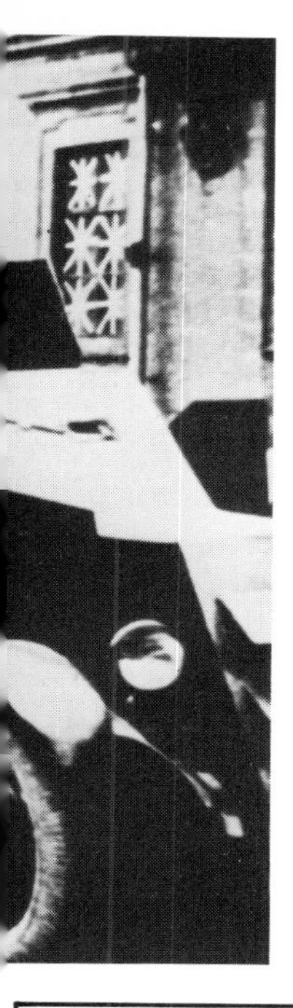

to the roster. The 1940 mechanized corps was a true corps in the Western sense of the word, being composed of two tank divisions, a motorized division and corps troops including an HQ and staff, a motorcycle regiment, communications and engineer battalions and an aircraft co-operation squadron. Each tank division had a paper strength of two tank regiments, a motor rifle regiment, an artillery regiment, a scout battalion, communications battalion, engineer battalion, anti-aircraft battalion, repair battalion and an MP company, totalling 375 tanks, 11,343 men and 60 major calibre artillery pieces. The official table of equipment called for 210 T-34 medium tanks, 63 KV heavy tanks and 102 T-26 or BT tanks. The motorized division consisted of two motor rifle regiments, a tank regiment, an artillery regiment, an engineer battalion, a scout battalion, a communications battalion, and an anti-aircraft and anti-tank battalion. Each of these divisions had a paper strength of 275 light tanks. In total, the official strength of the new mechanized corps was three times the size of the pre-war corps, totalling 37,000 men, 1,031 tanks, 268 armoured cars, 358 guns and mortars in the 76mm–122mm range, 5,000 motor vehicles, 350 tractors and 1,700 motorcycles.

The enormity of these new formations underscored the acute shortage of trained mechanized unit commanders. Only the fielding of a small number of gargantuan formations could prevent the limited pool of even

MECHANIZED EQUIPMENT OF THE RKKA ON 22 JUNE 1941

Tanks					
T-27*	400	T-18M*	400	T-34	967
T-37*	2,400	T-26*	11,000	T-35*	40
T-38*	1,200	BT*	6,000	KV	508
T-40	222	T-28*	500	* Estimates	
Armoured cars	4,819				
Tractors					
STZ-3	3,658	Komintern	1,017		
STZ-5	7,170	Voroshilovyets	228		
Komsomolyets	4,041	Kommunar	504		
Motor vehicles	272,600				

THE SOVIET MECHANIZED CORPS, 22 JUNE 1941

Corps	Tank Divisions	Motorized Division	Commander (Maj-Gen)	Military District	Staging Area	No. Tanks*
1 MK	1, 3 TD	163 MD	M. L. Chernyavskiy	LMD	Pskov	163
2 MK	11, 16 TD	15 MD	Yu. V. Novoselskiy	OMD	Lipkany	350
3 MK	2, 5 TD	84 MD	A. V. Kurkin	SBMD	Vilno	460 (105)
4 MK	8, 32 TD	81 MD	A. A. Vlasov	SKMD	Lvov	860 (460)
5 MK	13, 17 TD	109 MD	I. P. Alekseyenko	RVGK	Vinitsa	700
6 MK	4, 7 TD	29 MD	M. G. Khatskilevich	SWMD	Bialystok	1000
7 MK	14, 18 TD	1 MD	V. I. Vinogradov	MMD	Vitebsk-Kaluga	1000
8 MK	12, 34 TD	7 MD	D. I. Ryabyshev	SKMD	Dubno	600 (170)
9 MK	20, 35 TD	131 MD	K. K. Rokossovskiy	SKMD	Zytomierz	700 (0)
10 MK	21, 24 TD	198 MD	Lavrionovich	LMD	N. of Leningrad	?
11 MK	29, 33 TD	204 MD	D. K. Mostovenko	SWMD	Grodno	204 (27)
12 MK	23, 28 TD	202 MD	N. M. Shestpalov	SBMD	Shauliya	690 (0)
13 MK	27, 31 TD	4 MD	P. N. Akhlyustan	SWMD	Belsk	300
14 MK	22, 30 TD	205 MD	S. I. Oborin	SWMD	Brest	508
15 MK	10, 37 TD	212 MD	I. I. Karpezo	SKMD	Zytomierz	915 (135)
16 MK	15, 39 TD	240 MD	A. D. Sokolov	SKMD	Kamenets-Podolskiy	?
17 MK	25, 54 TD	103 MD	M. A. Petrov	SWMD	Baranovichi	300
18 MK	36, 47 TD	209 MD		OMD		350
19 MK	40, 43 TD	213 MD	N. V. Feklenko	SKMD	Zytomierz	160 (4)
20 MK	26, 38 TD	210 MD	N. Vedeneyev	SWMD	Minsk	300
21 MK	42, 46 TD	185 MD	D. D. Lelyushenko	MMD	Opochka	98 (0)
22 MK	19, 41 TD	215 MD	S. M. Kondrusev	SKMD	Rovno-Dubno	? (31)
23 MK	44, 48 TD	220 MD		RVGK		?
24 MK	45, 49 TD	216 MD	V. I. Chistyakov	SKMD	Proskurov	?
25 MK	50, 55 TD	219 MD	S. M. Krivoshein	RVGK	Kharkov	?
26 MK		12 MD		FEF		?
27 MK				FEF		?
28 MK	6, 54 TD	236 MD	V. V. Novikov	TCMD	Baku	?
29 MK				FEF		?
30 MK	58, 60 TD	239 MD		TBMD		?

Key

FEF	Far Eastern Front
LMD	Leningrad Military District
MD	Motorized Division
MK	Mechanized Corps
MMD	Moscow Military District
OMD	Odessa Military District
RVGK	High Command Reserves
SBMD	Special Baltic Military District
SKMD	Special Kiev Military District
SWMD	Special Western Military District
TBMD	Transbaikal Military District
TCMD	Trans-Caucasus Military District
TD	Tank Division

*Figures in parentheses indicate Nr. new tanks.

marginally competent generals from being totally exhausted. The paradoxical problem faced by the RKKA in 1941 was that although it possessed a vast pool of tanks and motorized equipment, it could not possibly supply the tremendous equipment demands of the new corps. Of the 24,000 tanks available, 4,060 were already committed to the requirements of organic tank units in rifle, cavalry and airborne divisions, leaving about 20,000 tanks for the corps. The corps tables however, called for 31,574 tanks and 8,040 armoured cars. This was about 150 per cent of the available tanks, and 165 per cent of all armoured cars (ignoring for a moment the fact that most of the armoured cars were already committed to use in rifle and cavalry divisions). What made the situation worse was that of the 24,000 Red Army tanks in 1941, 29 per cent required major overhaul and 44 per cent required rebuilding. In other words, only 27 per cent or about 7,000 tanks were in good enough mechanical condition to last more than a few days of fighting before suffering mechanical breakdown. This problem was rooted in the Soviet fascination with annual production statistics to the exclusion of the more mundane matter of manufacturing enough costly spare parts to keep the vehicles already manufactured in running order. Soviet tanks not only had a short running life, but on breaking down, the supply of critical transmissions, engines and other spare parts was often non-existent. Factory managers were responsible (with their lives) for attaining annual production goals, but inadequate attention was paid to future repair requirements of these tanks. Support equipment for the new corps was in equally short supply, about 39 per cent of the lorries, 44 per cent of the tractors, 29 per cent of the repair equipment and 17 per cent of the motorcycles.

As a result of these shortages, many of the new corps were little more than paper formations. None the less, they represented 92 of the RKKA's 303 divisions at the outbreak of the war, and contained most of its most formidable weaponry. Unfortunately, the potent new T-34 and KV tanks were thinly distributed, which both diminished their tactical impact and created training and maintenance burdens as crews had little opportunity to train before the onset of war.

The new corps were hampered as well by a lack of time to conduct vital unit manoeuvres and exercises. Soviet summer manoeuvres too often bore a closer resemblance to belligerent choreography than to military tactics, but even these were difficult to conduct given the late date when many of the formations began to form. Co-ordination of the action of the new corps was hampered by the lack of trained, experienced staffs and by insufficient radios. Tank-infantry co-operation had not been effectively developed owing to a lack of training as well as the absence of a cross-country troop carrier like the German Hanomag Sd.Kfz.251 armoured halftrack. Soviet motorized units rode into action on GAZ-AA lorries which were nothing more than vintage 1930 Ford AA lorries with a coat of dark green paint. Its cross-country capability was mediocre in all but the best of circumstances, and non-existent in mud or snow. Furthermore, it had no armour.

The Summer Catastrophe

In June 1941, the Wehrmacht invaded the Soviet Union with about 3,350 of its 5,640 tanks. In terms of tanks, the Germans were outnumbered 7-to-1. By the end of 1941, the terms were rather more even after the Wehrmacht virtually wiped out the entire Soviet pre-war inventory of armoured vehicles. Nearly a decade's toil and expense was lost in a series of catastrophic defeats, to say nothing of the mammoth troop losses.

Although in many histories of the war, the Soviet tanks of the period have often been derided as obsolete junk, nothing could be further from the truth. The vast bulk of the Red Army's tanks were cannon-armed BT and T-26 which were certainly comparable to the German Pz Kpfw I and Pz Kpfw II in firepower and mobility. Furthermore, the Wehrmacht had nothing to compare to the new T-34 or KV which proved a very frightening shock to German infantry and German tanks alike. The new Soviet tanks were available in sizeable numbers. The weakness of the Soviet mechanized corps lay not in the design of their equipment, but rather in its poor mechanical state, the inadequate training of their crews, and the abysmal quality of Soviet military leadership in the first months of the war.

The fate of the Soviet mechanized corps was brief, brutal and bloody. The 3rd and 12th Mechanized Corps defending the Baltic MD were almost annihilated in three days of

198. The T-50 was designed to replace the T-26 infantry tank, but only a small number were built because of its high cost and complexity. It served with a tank brigade in Karelia fighting the Finns where it was known as the Little Klim, a reference to its similarity in appearance to the KV tank.

fighting from 22 to 24 June. The Red Army's most powerful concentration of armour was in the Special Western Military District, and consisted of six mechanized corps. The corps possessed 313 KVs and 627 T-34s, or nearly two-thirds of the modern tanks in the Soviet inventory at the time. In a series of encircling battles near Bialystok and Minsk, the German Army Group Centre trapped and destroyed these corps. By 8 July, Army Group Centre had destroyed or captured 2,600 tanks, by 11 July a total of 3,300 tanks and by August, more than 5,000 tanks, or nearly a quarter of Soviet tank strength. One of the few areas where the mechanized corps had any significant tactical impact was in the Ukraine where on 25 June the five mechanized corps of the Kiev Special MD counterattacked von Kleist's Panzer Gruppe I beginning in the Brody-Dubno area. By the end of the month however, these units had been decimated and Panzer Gruppe I pressed on.

Soviet tank losses were so overwhelming that on 15 July, the mechanized corps were officially disbanded. Surviving tank divisions were doled out to infantry formations to provide support, and soon disappeared by attrition. The motorized divisions were reorganized as ordinary rifle divisions. After the summer fiasco, the largest tank units were to be brigades, and emaciated brigades at that. Despite the undeniable bravery of Soviet tank troops, German losses were modest: on all fronts in June only 130 tanks, in July 744 and in August 604. In 1941, German losses, including those in the Western Desert, totalled 2,900 vehicles. The annihilation of the Soviet tank force was accomplished not only by the glaring disparity in the tactical and strategic skills of the opponents, but also by the mechanical malignancies which infected Soviet tanks of the time. Besides the poor state of the older tanks, the new T-34s and KVs suffered from teething problems particularly with regard to clutches and transmissions. Mechanical breakdowns accounted for at least 50 per cent of the tank losses in the summer fighting, and recovery or repair equipment was not to be found. Between July 1941 and December 1941, Soviet industry produced 4,800 AFVs in addition to the 29,000 available at the war's outset. Nevertheless, by December 1941, the Red Army could field only 4,495 tanks, of which 2,124 were in the Far East, well beyond German reach.

The German advance in the summer of 1941 succeeded in destroying most of the Soviet tank fleet, and came near to enveloping most of the tank industry which was heavily concentrated in the Leningrad and Kharkov areas. Kharkov fell on 24 October 1941 and Leningrad was surrounded by late September 1941. However, in early September 1941, the new GKO (Main Defence Committee, headed by Stalin) ordered all key defence plants to be evacuated to the Urals. Production at all major tank factories except the Stalingrad Tractor Factory and the Krasnoye Sormovo Zavod Nr. 112 in Gorki was halted. Both of these plants had just initiated T-34 production. The KV assembly lines at the Kirovskiy Works in Leningrad were removed to Chelyabinsk, together with the Izhorskiy Steel Factory (armour plate) from Kolpino, part of Zavod Nr. 75 (V-2 diesel tank engines) where they joined with the Chelyabinsk Tractor Works (ChTZ) to form the new Zavod Nr. 100 Kirovskiy Works, better known later as Tankograd (Tank City). The main T-34 assembly facilities in Kharkov were evacuated to Nizhni Tagil with parts of Zavod Nr. 174 from Leningrad, where they were mated with the Ural Locomotive Factory to form the new Zavod Nr. 183 Ural Tank Works (I. V. Stalin). The remainder of Zavod Nr. 174 was moved to Omsk where it began the much delayed assembly of the new T-50 light tank. The Kolomenskiy Loco-

THE FATE OF THE SOVIET TANK DIVISIONS, 1941

Tank Div.	Corps Attachment	Tank Regiments	Infantry, Artillery and Subordinate Units	Date of Destruction*	Site of Destruction
1 TD	1 MK	1, 2, 124	1 MSP	24 April 42*	
2 TD	3 MK	3, 4, 8	121 MSP, 2 MAP	12 July 41	Minsk
3 TD	1 MK	5, 6	3 MSP, 3 MAP, 3 RB	7 Dec 41*	
4 TD	6 MK	7, 8	4 MAP	4 July 41	Bialystok
5 TD	3 MK	9, 10	5 MSP, 5 MAP, 5 BB	27 June 41	Olita
6 TD	28 MK	11		24 July 41*	
7 TD	6 MK	13, 14, 47	7 MSP, 112 MAP, 97 RB	17 July 41	Disna
8 TD	4 MK	15, 16	8 MSP, 8 MAP, 8 RB	24 Sept 41*	
9 TD		17, 18, 127	9 MSP, 9 MAP, 9 RB, 9 ZB		
10 TD	15 MK	19, 20	10 MSP, 10 MAP, 10 RB	23 Sept 41*	
11 TD	2 MK	21, 22	11 MSP, 13 MAP	8 Sept 41	S. Russia
12 TD	8 MK	23, 24	12 RB, 143 ZB	13 Sept 41	Dniepropyetrovsk
13 TD	5 MK	25, 26	13 MSP, 37 MAP, 13 ZB	4 Aug 41	Smolensk
14 TD	7 MK	27	14 MSP	5 Oct 41*	
15 TD	16 MK			8 Aug 41	Uman
16 TD	2 MK	31	207 RB	8 Aug 41	Uman
17 TD	5 MK	27, 28, 33	17 MSP, 17 MAP, 17 RB	4 Aug 41	Smolensk
18 TD	7 MK	35, 36	18 MSP, 18 MAP	20 Oct 41	Viazma
19 TD	22 MK	37, 38, 58	19 MSP	24 Sept 41	Kiev
20 TD	9 MK	39, 40	20 MSP	29 Sept 41	Kiev
21 TD	10 MK	41, 42	35 MSP, 21 MAP, 21 RB	4 April 42*	
22 TD	14 MK	43, 44	22 MSP, 22 MAP	5 July 41	Slutsk
23 TD	12 MK	45		28 Sept 41*	
24 TD	10 MK	48, 49	24 MSP, 24 MAP, 24 ZB	9 Sept 41	Luga
25 TD	17 MK	50	4 MSP, 25 MIB	28 June 41	Bialystok
26 TD	20 MK		26 MSP	14 July 41*	
27 TD	13 MK				
28 TD	12 MK	55, 56, 125	93, 117 MSP	3 Jan 42*	
29 TD	11 MK	47	106, 128 MSP, 118 MAP	6 July 41	Minsk
30 TD	14 MK			3 July 41*	
31 TD	13 MK			5 July 41	Bialystok
32 TD	4 MK	63, 64	32 MSP	17 July 41	Volodorka
33 TD	11 MK				
34 TD	8 MK	67, 68	34 MSP, 34 MAP, 34 RB	30 June 41	Dubno
35 TD	9 MK	69, 70	35 MSP, 35 MAP	24 Sept 41	Kiev
36 TD	18 MK				
37 TD	15 MK	73, 74		17 July 41*	
38 TD	20 MK	75, 76	38 MSP	15 July 41*	
39 TD	16 MK			6 Aug 41*	
40 TD	19 MK			29 Sept 41	Kiev

motive Works was transferred with parts of Zavod Nr. 37 to Kirov where a new Zavod Nr. 38 was re-established to produce light tanks. A significant portion of the Gorki Automobile Factory was also converted to light tank production.

Although, by Herculean efforts, the Soviets were able to save a good deal of their tank industry, many of the heavy industries which supported it were badly weakened by the German advance. The USSR lost 63 per cent of its coal producing areas to the Germans, and much of the steel industry. In the first half of 1941, steel production had been 11.4 million tons, but by the second half of 1942, this had dropped to a mere 3.9 million tons. The only way that tank production could be expanded in the face of these shortages was to sizeably cut back production of other goods requiring heavy industrial resources. Production of warships, locomotives, railroad cars, machine tools, and other major steel consuming items was virtually halted by 1942 in favour of tank production. Automotive production was drastically curtailed, and Army needs for lorries, motorcycles, cars, tractors and rail equipment was satisfied by draining the civilian sector of this equipment. In later years, these supplies were heavily supplemented by the massive influx of Lend-Lease automotive equipment from the USA, Britain and Canada. Some measure of the switch in focus of Soviet industry can be noted from the fact that in 1937, Soviet tank production absorbed only about 0.6 per cent of Soviet annual steel production, while in 1943, the figure had risen to 17.8 per cent. Although much attention has been paid to the undeniable superiority of the Wehrmacht's tactical skill throughout the war, the Soviet Union's skill in mobilizing its severely damaged and far poorer industrial base, and Germany's failure to do so, proved to be a key margin of victory in the East.

Tank Div.	Corps Attachment	Tank Regiments	Infantry, Artillery and Subordinate Units	Date of Destruction*	Site of Destruction
41 TD	22 MK	81, 82	41 MSP	24 Sept 41	Kiev
42 TD	21 MK	83, 84	42 MSP	18 Aug 41*	
43 TD	19 MK			29 Sept 41	Kiev
44 TD	23 MK				
45 TD	24 MK	89, 134	33 MSP, 144 MAP	8 Aug 41	Uman
46 TD	21 MK	92	21, 46, 91 MSP	2 Aug 41	Chola
47 TD	18 MK	93, 94	47 MSP, 47 MAP	24 Sept 41	Kiev
48 TD	23 MK	95, 96	48 MSP, 48 MAP	26 Aug 41	Velikiye Luki
49 TD	24 MK	97, 98		8 Aug 41	Uman
50 TD	25 MK	99, 100		7 Sept 41*	
51 TD		101, 102		13 Aug 41*	
52 TD					
53 TD					
54 TD	28 MK				
55 TD	25 MK			29 July 41*	
56 TD					
57 TD		114, 115	57 MSP, 57 MAP, 57 MB, 57 ZB	4 Aug 41*	
58 TD	30 MK	116, 117	58 MSP	2 Dec 41*	
59 TD					
60 TD	30 MK	121	60 MSP	10 Feb 42*	
Independent Tank Divisions:					
61 TD				1946*	Far East
69 TD			60, 120, 237 MSP, 118 MAP	20 Oct 41	Viazma
101 TD		202	101 MSP, 101 RB	20 Oct 41	Viazma
102 TD		204	102 MSP, 102 MAP, 102 RB	20 Oct 41	Viazma
104 TD		208, 209	104 MSP, 104 MAP	16 Aug 41*	
105 TD		210, 211	105 MSP, 105 MAP, 105 RB	4 Sept 41*	
107 TD				20 Oct 41	Viazma
108 TD		216, 217	108 MSP, 108 MAP, 108 ZB	29 Nov 41*	
109 TD		218, 219	109 MSP, 109 MAP	1 Sept 41*	
110 TD		220, 221	110 MSP, 110 MAP, 110 RB	12 Sept 41	N. Russia
111 TD				1946*	Far East
112 TD				6 Feb 42*	

Key

BB Armoured Car Battalion
MAP Motorized Artillery Regiment
MIB Motorized Engineer Battalion
MK Mechanized Corps
MSP Motor Rifle Regiment
RB Reconnaissance Battalion
TD Tank Division
ZB Anti-aircraft Battalion

*Indicates that unit was disbanded rather than destroyed.

The priorities facing the Commissariat for Tank Production (NKTP) headed by V. A. Malyshev were threefold: to re-establish the evacuated tank factories in the Urals and restart production as soon as possible; to simplify tank designs as much as possible so as to achieve increased production with unskilled labour; and to cut out redundant tank types. The Soviets were fortunate in having two clearly superior designs, the T-34 and the KV already in service. This avoided the delays which new designs would have entailed.

The T-34 Medium Tank

The combat début of the T-34 in the summer of 1941 revealed it to be unquestionably the finest tank design of its time. The revolutionary combination of thick, angled armour, heavy firepower and superb mobility placed it in a class above its closest German contemporaries, the Pz Kpfw III and Pz Kpfw IV. This forced the Germans to begin a costly programme of up-gunning and up-armouring its tanks, and initiate the development of a new tank, the Panther to serve as an antidote to the T-34. The appearance of the T-34 also forced the Germans to completely revamp their anti-tank arsenal because the existing 37mm and 50mm anti-tank guns were largely ineffective against the T-34 and KV. While the 88mm anti-aircraft gun could be used as a stopgap in limited circumstances, only the arrival of the PAK 40 75mm anti-tank gun could restore the balance. The early T-34 was not without its problems. The early production batches had serious transmission defects, and indeed, probably more T-34s were lost in 1941 to mechanical trouble than to enemy action.

During the evacuation of KhPZ Nr. 183 to Nizhni Tagil, production of the T-34 shifted to the Stalingrad Tractor Factory and to

△199 ▽200

Krasnoye Sormovo Zavod Nr. 112 which began T-34 production in July 1941. The GKB-T-34 (T-34 Main Design Bureau), headed by Morozov since Koshkin's death, was shifted to Nizhni Tagil as well. Two vexing questions remained. The T-34 Model 1940 was armed with the short L-11 gun which did not meet the stated requirements. P. Muraviev of F. Grabin's design team at Zavod Nr. 92 in Gorki had designed a much superior gun, the F-34, before the war, but in the confused state of gun production brought about by Kulik's interference, none of the relevant bureaucrats would authorize its production. Grabin, with the connivance of the director of Zavod Nr. 92 began providing KhPZ with the new F-34 in place of the L-11, and the first unofficial T-34 Model 1941s began to appear shortly before the war started. Used mainly as platoon and company commanders' tanks, they were enormously popular, and letters were sent from a number of units praising the new design. This came to the attention of Stalin and the GKO which finally authorized the F-34. It would remain the main gun of the T-34 until 1944. The second problem was that in 1940 when permission to begin production of the T-34 was sought, its critics forced the design team to agree to develop a more satisfactory design, the T-34M. The more realistic members of the GVS upset an attempt to delay production of the T-34 until the T-34M was ready and in the critical state of affairs in the autumn of 1941, the T-34M project slipped into limbo before a prototype had been completed.

The same conservative critics of the T-34 had also insisted on the production of an infantry tank, the T-50, to supplement the T-34. By the time that T-50 production commenced at Omsk in 1941, however, it became apparent that the infantry tank would cost as much to produce as a T-34, yet clearly did not have equal combat utility. It was a luxury the Red Army could ill afford at the time and was cancelled after a small production run. This left the T-34 as the universal tank that Koshkin had originally proposed, fulfilling the roles previously filled by the T-26 infantry tank, BT cavalry tank and T-28 medium tank.

The main emphasis of the Morozov design team was on simplification of the T-34 to cut costs and make production by an unskilled work force easier. In the spring of 1941, V.

199. Opponents of the T-34 insisted that an improved type be developed before production was permitted. This became the T-34M shown here in the original designer's model. More sensible thought prevailed and T-34 production was initiated despite some teething problems.
200. Experiences in Finland prompted Soviet tank designers to incorporate features in new tank designs to minimize the effects of arctic cold. This photograph of the driver's position in the T-34 shows the compressed air cylinders used to start the engine in cold weather.

Buslov and V. Nitsenko developed a cast turret, similar in outline to the welded turret used on the T-34, but easier to manufacture. It was adopted and both T-34 Model 1940s and Model 1941s used cast and welded turrets. T-34s produced at STZ primarily used welded turrets; those produced at Krasnoye Sormovo used cast turrets. Late in 1941, the GKB-T-34 developed a new version of the T-34 called the T-34 Model 1942. It was very similar in appearance to the earlier models, but many of the components had been simplified. For example the F-34 Model 1941 gun had 861 parts while the Model 42 gun had only 614. In terms of manpower and metal, the cost of a T-34 dropped from 269,500 roubles in 1941 to 193,000 in 1942. New techniques, such as the automatic welding system developed by Professor E. Paton facilitated this effort. The only major external features which identified this new version were the redesigned driver's hatch, the circular access port in the rear and other small details. At the end of 1941 the T-34 Model 1942 was gradually eased into production at STZ and Krasnoye Sormovo, as parts for the earlier Model 1941 were used up. Indeed, STZ produced some tanks which combined features from both the Model 1941 and the Model 1942. Production of the T-34 at Nizhni Tagil resumed in December 1941 despite horrendous conditions. One of the few worthwhile outcomes from the T-34M controversy was the design of a new, larger cast turret which gave the gun crew more room. Use of this new hexagonal turret began

201. The L-11 gun in the T-34 Model 1940 was replaced by a more effective F-34 gun in the months before the war's outbreak. This led to the T-34 Model 1941, a pair of which are seen after having collided in the heat of battle. (National Archives)
202. This interior illustration of a T-34 Model 1942 shows the key crew positions. (National Archives)

△**201** ▽**202**

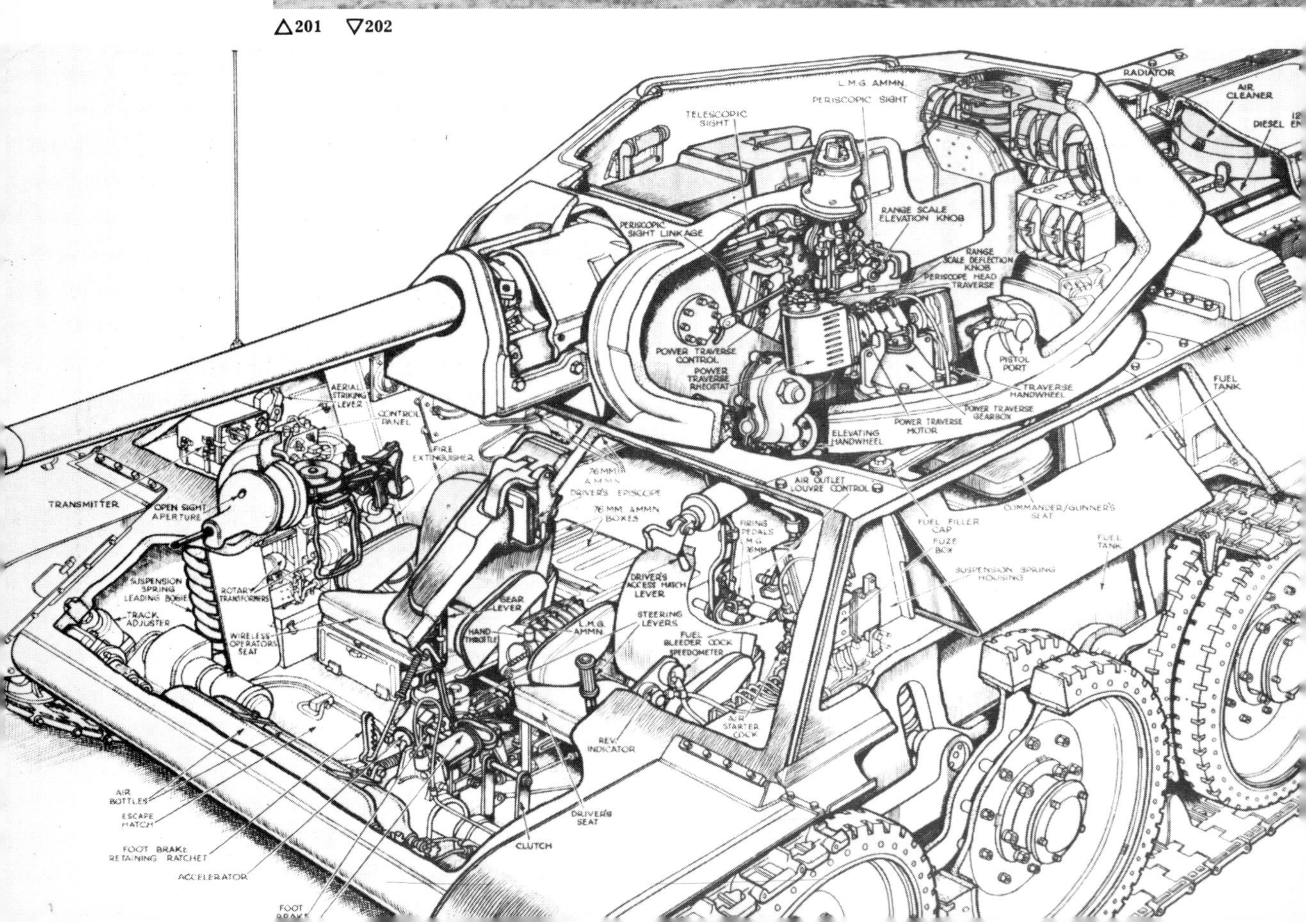

at Nizhni Tagil early in 1942 as the T-34 Model 1943, and it first appeared against the Finns in Karelia in April 1942. Production of the Model 1942 and Model 1943 took place simultaneously, with the other two facilities continuing to manufacture the T-34 Model 1942 until later in 1942. There were a number of production variations between the products of the different factories. Both the T-34 Model 1942 and T-34 Model 1943 had a distinctly rougher appearance than the well-crafted T-34 Model 1940, but the apparent crudity of many of the welds and joints did not detract at any point from the integrity of the armour. Indeed, an inspection of a T-34 Model 1942 provided to the British School of Tank Technology in 1943 found the armour quality to be equal or superior to British armour. Where fine machining was required for moving parts, it was provided.

In 1942, Russia faced a severe shortage of rubber which forced STZ to begin producing its T-34s with all-metal road wheels, and the other plants followed suit. Eventually, rubber-rimmed wheels were used in the first and fifth positions because with all-metal wheels in these positions, harmonic vibrations were set up when the tank was moving

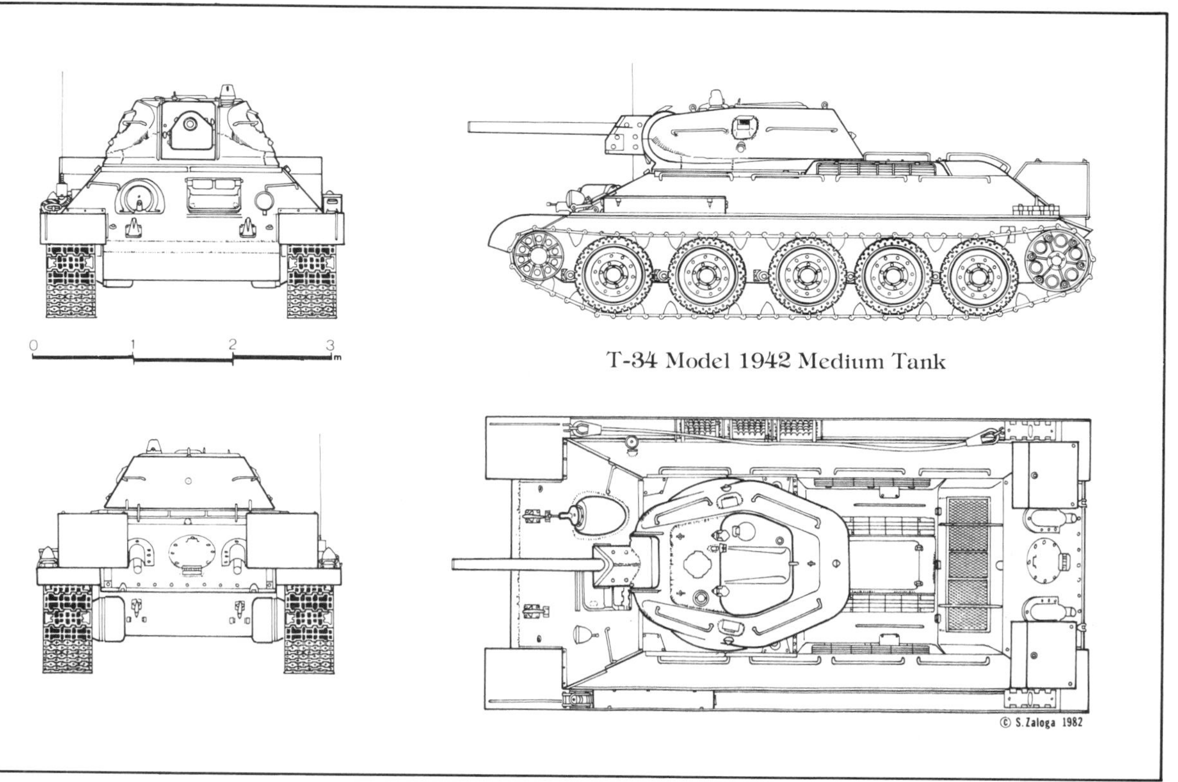

T-34 Model 1942 Medium Tank

△203 ▽204

203. The turret of the T-34 was inefficiently designed and cramped. This interior view shows the gunner's position to the left and the commander/loader's station to the right.

204. During the grim days of the winter of 1941 – 42, little kept the tank forces from all but disappearing but the production of the STZ Factory in Stalingrad which was one of the few not evacuated. In the autumn of 1942 it was the scene of some of the heaviest fighting in the great battle for the city. Here, T-34 Model 41/42 tanks and STZ-5 tractors in the rail marshalling yards outside the factory are inspected before shipment.

205. The T-34 Model 1942 closely resembled the Model 1941, but incorporated a number of detail changes which had been introduced to simplify production and reduce costs. A distinctive feature was the circular access hatch at the rear; on earlier models it had been rectangular.

at high speed, which loosened parts and caused other damage. In the autumn of 1942, STZ's output began to diminish as a result of the heavy fighting enveloping Stalingrad, but in August, production had been extended to Tankograd where T-34 production continued until April 1944. The Ural Heavy Machine Tool Factory (UZTM) in Sverdlovsk began to provide T-34 components in 1942, and began full assembly of T-34s later in the year.

Further improvements were incorporated into the T-34 later in the year. Additional fuel could be carried by using the new exterior fuel panniers at the rear of the vehicle. At the beginning of 1943 these were changed to cylindrical drums, with most tanks being adapted to carry three. Various new tracks were developed for use in snow and mud, and to improve traction.

While Soviet tanks could not be equalled in terms of firepower, armour or mobility, their performance on the battlefield was often sadly lacking. German tank troops found that Soviet tank units seldom took advantage of terrain, acted in an un-coordinated fashion, and tended to attack in rigid geometric formations. Some of these problems can undoubtedly be traced to inadequate training, but poor ergonometric design of the tanks was also to blame. In 1942, it was not unusual for tank crews to receive as little as 72 hours of classroom training apart from basic training. Unit exercises were often perfunctory, but equally damaging was the archaic layout of Soviet tank turrets. German turrets had three-man crews: gunner, loader and commander. The function of the commander was to observe the terrain, direct his crew and co-ordinate the deployment of his tank with that of his unit. In contrast, the Soviet turret had only two men, a gunner and a tank commander. The tank commander not only had the same duties as his German counterpart, but also had to load the main gun and the coaxial machine-gun which could be very distracting in the heat of battle.

205▽

206. In the spring of 1942, Zavod Nr. 183 began producing the first T-34 Model 1943 which used a new, larger two-man hexagonal turret. This did not completely overcome the inefficiencies of the earlier turrets, but it was more spacious and easier to produce. Note that on this vehicle there are steel roadwheels only in the centre three positions. Rubber-tyred wheels were used at front and rear to cut down the harmonic vibrations caused by steel roadwheels. (National Archives)

207. During the production of the T-34 Model 1943, the turret was modified on the later production types to incorporate an all-round vision cupola for the commander. This cupola is very evident in this picture of the T-34 of Lt R. Tesarik, of the Czechoslovak 1st Tank Regiment which fought alongside the Russians on the Eastern Front from 1943. (CTK via Jiri Hornat)

△206 ▽207

▽208

208. There was considerable variation in the details of the turrets produced by the various factories assembling the T-34. These T-34 Model 1943 have the distinctly rounded turrets of the Chelyabinsk production line. (National Archives)
209. A T-34 Model 1943 tank named 'Leningradyets' of the 30th Guards Tank Brigade advances into Krasnoye Selo in January 1944. (Sovfoto)

209△

Furthermore, the turrets of the T-34 and KV were not fitted with a turret basket. The crew sat on stools suspended from the turret ring. Under their feet were ammunition bins covered by a neoprene mat. During combat, the floor became a mess of open bins and matting as the crew began removing ammunition and this degraded performance. Even if not distracted by his loading duties, the Soviet tank commander did not have a 360° vision cupola like his German counterpart. On the T-34 and KV he had only a single traversable periscope with a very narrow field of vision, and a view-slit near his left shoulder. Many German tank troops liked to fight with their heads out of the turret to better see the terrain, but this was impossible in the KV because of the location of the roof hatch, and difficult in the case of the T-34 as the large, single-piece hatch opened forward, blocking the commander's field of view. The relative shortage of radios in Soviet tanks until 1943 also hampered co-ordination of unit operations. Communications between tanks in a platoon had to be conducted by flag which was slow and unreliable. More often, the platoon commander merely instructed the other two tanks to follow his example. Soviet designers had appreciated these faults as is evident in the KV-3 and T-34M designs, but, given the pressures to limit major design innovations for the sake of maintaining maximum production, in order to compensate the staggering battlefield attrition, such improvements were not adopted until the middle of the war.

In the case of the T-34, late in 1942, an interim step was taken by redesigning the roof of the T-34 Model 1943 to incorporate a 360° vision cupola and to equip more tanks with radios.

Light Tanks

At the beginning of the war the Red Army had a small number of the new T-40 amphibious scout tank in service, and its non-amphibious version, the T-60, was on the verge of production. In addition, the T-50 light infantry tank was also about to enter production. The T-40s combat début was unremarkable: it had thin armour and was lightly armed. The Astrov team in Moscow designed a prototype called the T-40S (sukhoputniy: land version) armed with Taubin's new 20mm gun, but because of added armour it was too heavy to be amphibious. It was not a very sensible design because it offered no advantages over the T-60 yet was more complicated to manufacture, and so production never ensued. Production of the T-60 began in July 1941 at Zavod Nr. 37 in Moscow alongside the T-40. In the light of staggering losses at the front, in September 1941 it was decided to drop the T-40 and concentrate on the simpler, better armed and better armoured T-60. Only 230 T-40s were completed; in fact the last batch were used as Katyusha multiple rocket launchers with a BM-8-24 rocket rack in place of the turret. In the autumn, Zavod Nr. 37 was transferred to the Urals, and T-60 production was undertaken primarily by the GAZ in Gorki and Zavod Nr. 38 in Kirov. The Podolskiy Machine Factory (S. Ordzhonikidze) in Podolsk produced T-60 hulls. Further development of the T-60 was entrusted to G. Surenian's team at GAZ because the Astrov design bureau at Zavod Nr. 38 had been assigned to begin work on a T-60 replacement. In the later half of 1942, an improved version of the T-60 entered production. While the T-60 Model 1941 had used spoked road wheels, the T-60 Model 1942 used disc wheels, and had a more powerful GAZ-203 engine. In addition, some of the final batches had armour added to the hull and turret bringing the hull armour up to 35mm on the front and 25mm on the side, and bringing the turret frontal armour up to 35mm. In September 1942, after 6,022 T-60 had been built, production was halted in favour of the improved T-70. By this time, the T-60 had proven completely obsolete; it was too slow to keep up with the T-34 medium tank in cross-country operations, it was too thinly armoured and its gun was virtually useless against German tanks. It had been kept in production so long only because of the desperate need of tanks to fill out

210. The original version of the T-60 light tank was distinctive because of its use of spoked road-wheels. (IWM)

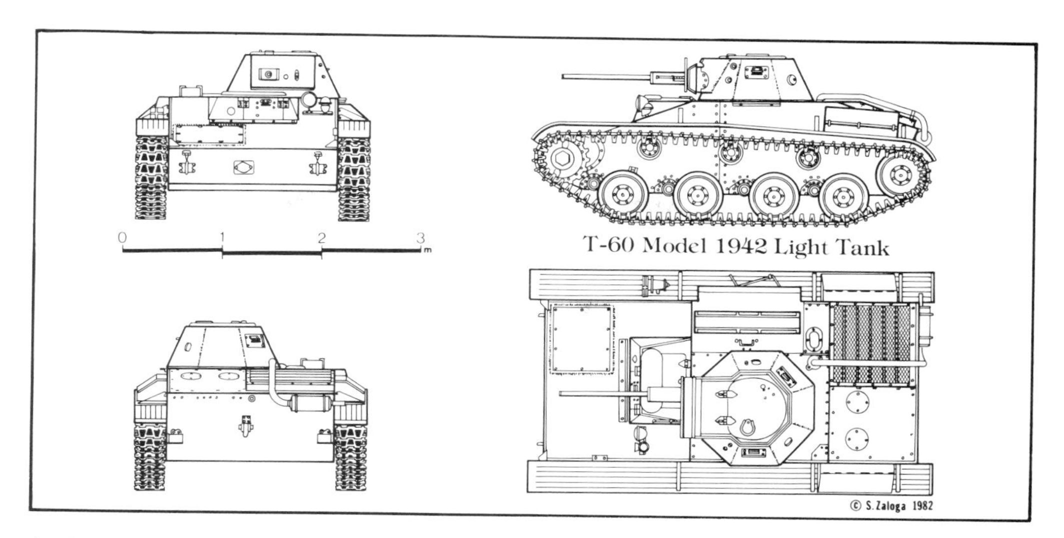

depleted tank units. It could be produced at small factories without facilities for handling larger tanks like the T-34.

As mentioned before, the production of the T-50 light infantry tank was short-lived. By February 1942, only 63 had been finished in Omsk, and of these only 48 were armed. While an excellent light tank, it was simply too complicated and expensive to build. Unlike the T-60 and later T-70, which used readily available lorry engines and components, it required a special new engine and transmission. Despite the disenchantment with light tanks on the part of the troops in the field, the GABTU continued to seek an infantry tank design even after cancelling the T-50. Work on this tank, the T-45, was divided between the Zavod Nr. 174 and Kirovskiy Works teams. A prototype was completed, but by this time, the T-70 was available and the T-45 faded into much deserved oblivion.

211. The later production batches of the T-60 used convex disc roadwheels, and had additional armour on the turret sides and front.

Work on the T-70 by N. Astrov's team began towards the end of 1941. The basic aim was to increase the frontal armour up to 45mm in order to protect the tank from 37mm guns, and to increase the main gun at least to a 45mm gun so as to give the crew a slight chance if enemy tanks were encountered. As debilitating as was the two-man crew on the T-34, the one-man crew on the T-60 and T-70 light tanks made platoon co-ordination virtually impossible to all but the most skilled. However, this feature went unchanged. Like that of the T-60, the hull of the new T-70 was kept simple for ease of manufacture. The engine layout was peculiar, consisting of two GAZ-202 lorry engines, one on each side of the hull, each engine powering one track by means of separate, unsynchronized lorry transmissions. The aim was to use as many available components as possible, but this was to prove a fiasco. The turret was conical like that on the T-30, with a standard 45mm tank gun. A small number of T-70 were produced in the heat of the moment, but even before they could be issued, it was evident that the powertrain layout was completely unacceptable. The Astrov team redesigned it by placing the two engines in a row and using a conventional transmission and differential arrangement. To ease assembly, the turret was also redesigned to use flat armour plate, and it was moved to the left, with the engines to the right. The T-70M was accepted by the GKO for Red Army service in March 1942, but is usually called simply the T-70. Some of the first machines still used the old conical turret, but this was replaced by the flat panel turret after April 1942. T-70 production took place at Zavod Nr. 37 and alongside T-60 production at GAZ and Zavod Nr. 38. It completely supplanted the T-60 in September 1942. The T-70 remained in production until the end of October 1943, by which time some 8,226 had been manufactured. The final production series used the more powerful GAZ-203 engine and had other hull improvements such as a traversable MK-4 periscope for the driver in place of a simple view-slit. In service, the T-70 proved competent but unexceptional.

In 1942, the Astrov team began redesigning it to accommodate a two-man turret crew. This appeared as the T-80 in the autumn of 1943. The T-80 was essentially similar to the T-70 except for the new larger turret, strengthened suspension, wider track and electrical turret traverse. While a very sound light tank design, by this point in the war, Soviet tank troops desired a more heavily armed tank to cope with newer German types. The resources devoted to a T-80 could be better spent on manufacturing the SU-76 which used the same components but had heavier firepower. Moreover, by this time, adequate numbers of Lend-Lease light tanks like the Valentine had become available for use in roles earlier satisfied by the T-70 and T-60. Only about 120 T-80s were completed before production was halted. This was the last light tank adopted by the Red Army during the war, although towards the war's end, work began on a new amphibious light tank, the K-90.

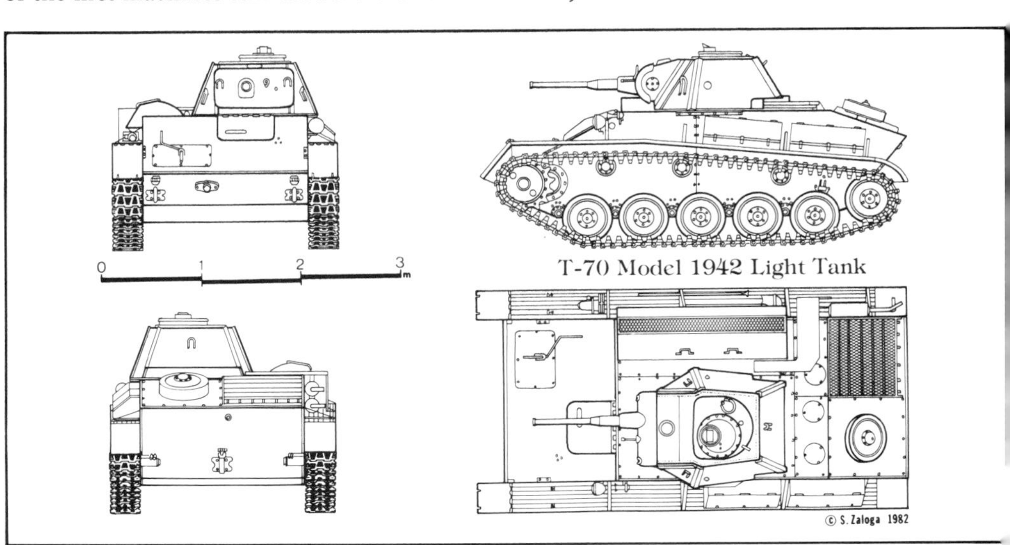

T-70 Model 1942 Light Tank

212. The T-70 light tank was developed because of the sluggishness of the T-60 in rough terrain, and its inadequate gun. Even the 45mm gun of the T-70 was hardly adequate against German tanks in 1943. This T-70 served with the Polish LWP forces which fought alongside the Russians from 1943.
213. This T-70 has been disabled by a mine. It is of the later production batch with the MK-4 periscope for the driver. (National Archives)
214. One of the main problems with the T-70 was that it had only a single turret crewman. This problem was addressed in the T-80 which had a two-man crew, but only 120 were produced. By this time, the Red Army had grown dissatisfied with the small gun carried on light tanks and preferred the SU-76M assault gun version of this vehicle instead.

212△

213△ 214▽

215. Following the use of *appliqué* armour on the KV-1E, a new welded turret was developed for use on late-production KV-1 Model 1941s. It was nearly identical in appearance with the earlier type except in the contours near the turret overhang.

Aside from officially sanctioned light tank development and production, there were a number of improvised light tank designs built during the war. In August 1941, Odessa was surrounded and cut off from supplies of tanks. P. K. Romanov of the January Uprising Factory proposed that tractors and tramcars be armoured as improvised tanks. The tram idea was dropped, but 3 STZ-5 tractors were fitted with boiler plate sandwiched with wood or rubber sheeting to provide more protection from small arms. The armament on these tanks varied. Some used small subturrets from T-26 Model 1931 tanks, others had new turrets armed with 37mm Model 15 R mountain guns or 45mm anti-tank guns. Eventually, a total of 68 of these Odessa Tanks were built. They were eventually called NI Tanks (Na Ispug: Terror Tanks). Fighting against Roumanian infantry, they were surprisingly effective, even if their armour proved to be rather suspect. Other improvised tanks were built on KhTZ-3 tractors. Unlike the NI Tanks which had turrets, the Kharkov Tractor Tanks had fixed superstructures armed with 45mm guns. It is not known where these vehicles were built, but photographs exist of several vehicles which were all obviously based on a standard plan.

The KV Heavy Tank

At the outbreak of the war, at least three problems with the KV heavy tank had to be settled: technical flaws in the design, inadequate armament, and the adequacy of its armour. The early KVs had serious clutch and transmission problems. The clutch was so bad that the tank had to be stopped to change gears, so of course its projected maximum road speed of 35km/hr could not be met. This problem was solved by various improvements. The KV-1 Model 1939 had been armed as a stopgap measure with the inadequate L-11 gun. On the KV-1 Model 1940, this was replaced by the improved F-32 gun. The controversy stirred up by Kulik in 1941 led to the development of Grabin's new 85mm gun for the KV-3 being permanently postponed. A secondary effect of Kulik's fantasies was a directive to thicken the armour of the KV. The original turrets had 90mm frontal armour and 75mm side armour. At the time, the Izhorskiy Works could not provide any thicker armour, so instead, 35mm appliqué armour was bolted to the turret sides and to portions of the hull front and side. This version was called the KV-1 Model 1940 s ekranami (with appliqué) or KV-1E. The final batch of KV-1 Model

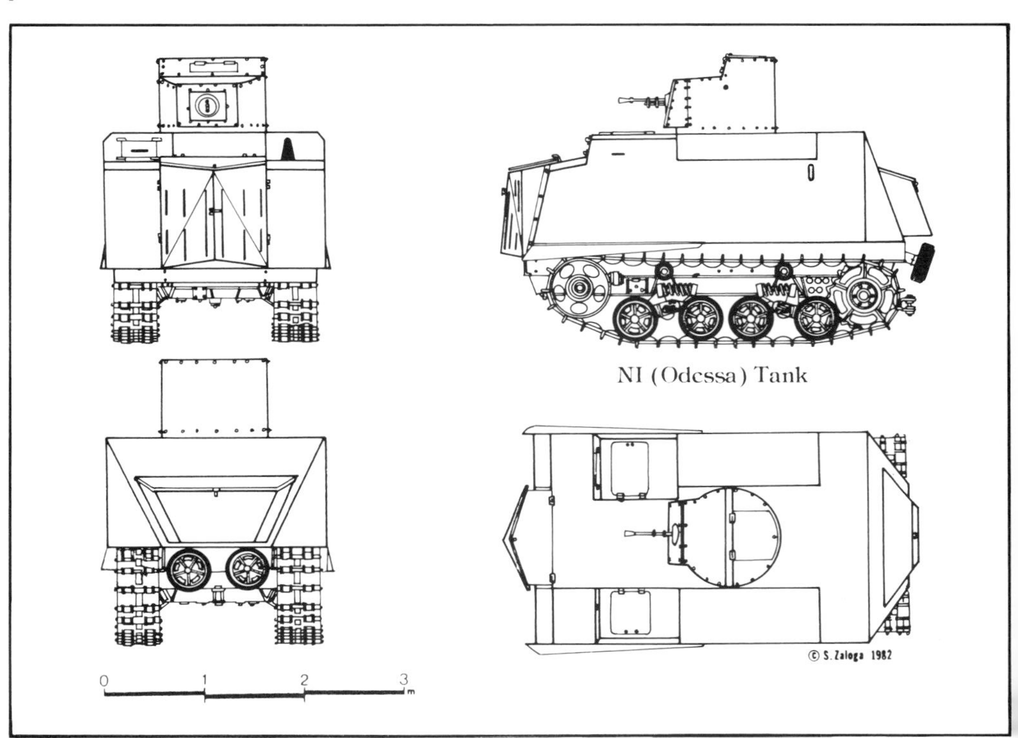

215△

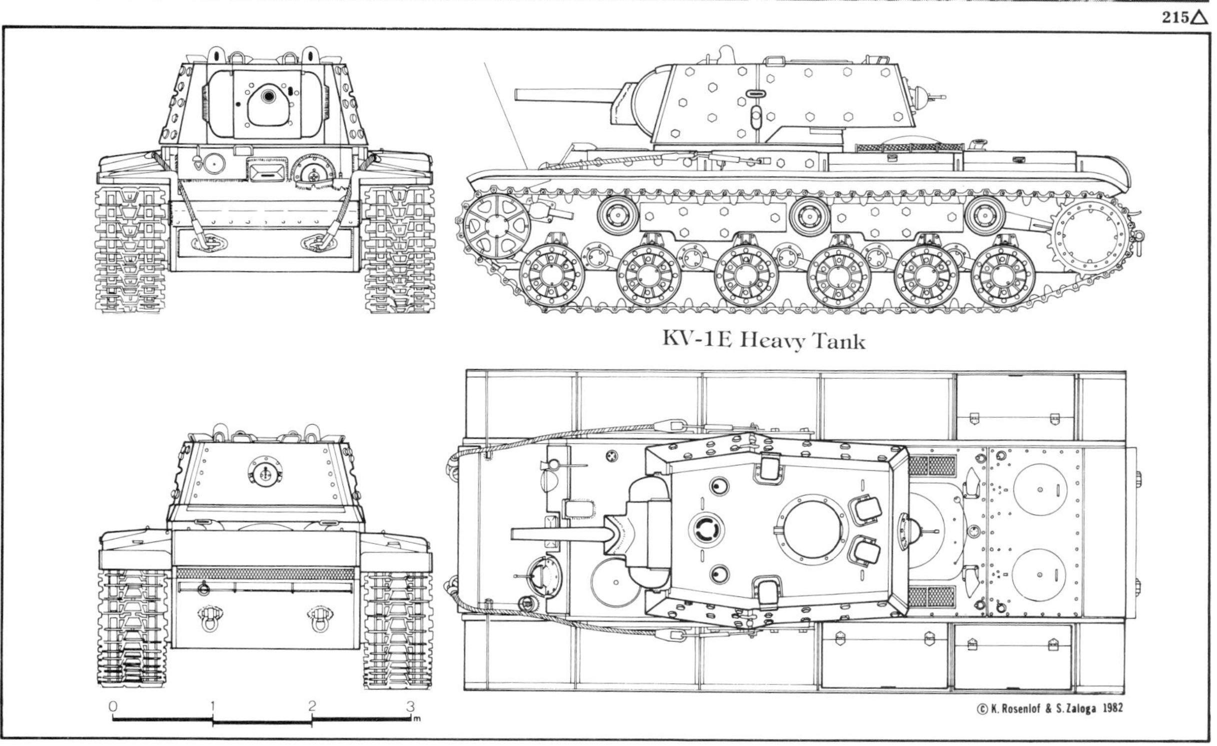

△216 ▽217

216. The KV-1 Model 1942 was almost identical in appearance with the earlier Model 1941 but had thicker turret and hull armour. This model can be identified by the sharply angled rear deck and by the thickened collar around the rear turret machine-gun. This vehicle is now preserved at the Finnish armour museum in Parola and has several of the early resilient steel wheels found on the KV-1 Model 1940 and Model 1942. These were added by the Finns to replace damaged spoked wheels and were not ordinarily seen on this version.
217. Although the turret interior of the KV-1 Model 1941 was more spacious than that on the T-34, it was no more efficiently arranged and still had the commander doubling as a loader which impaired the effectiveness of the tank in action. (National Archives)

218△

218. Problems with excessive weight on the KV-1 Model 1942 and the inefficient turret layout resulted in the redesign of the KV as the KV-1S. This vehicle of the 6th Heavy Tank Regiment shows the new turret, new road-wheel design and the changes to the engine deck. This version had extensive hand-holds to permit the use of 'tank desant' infantry riders.

1940 had a new welded turret which incorporated thicker armour and made the appliqué unnecessary. These were nearly identical in appearance with the earlier production batches without appliqué, the only visual difference being a simpler configuration of the turret side in the lower rear.

The war cut short the plan to field the KV-3 tank. The 107mm gun which Kulik had insisted upon was never completed, and the KV-3 prototype was fitted with an 85mm naval gun and used in the defence of Leningrad. When production facilities for the KV were finally re-established in Chelyabinsk, it was decided to drop the KV-2 Dreadnought in favour of the KV-1. In action the KV-2 had proved a mixed blessing; its 152mm howitzer was impressive, but its primary role as a bunker buster was no longer relevant in the grim winter of 1941–42. Also, its turret was so massive, that it was almost impossible to traverse unless on level ground. The strange predicament that resulted was that the KV-1 Model 1940 with its F-32 was less well armed than the contemporary T-34 Model 1941 medium tank which had the more potent F-34 gun. As a result, Kotin's team prevailed upon the GKO to permit use of the F-34 on the KV, since this would have the added benefit of standardizing tank guns. The new KV-1 Model 1941 had either the F-34 gun, or the ZiS-5, which was simply a redesigned F-34 gun which mated better with the KV turret fire controls. The re-established production line at Chelyabinsk also concentrated on simplifying the design in much the same fashion as the T-34 programme. A new cast turret which was easier to manufacture than the welded turret was developed. A simpler road wheel was designed, and the use of hull appliqué armour was simplified and standardized. In 1942, Kotin's TsKB-2 (Central Design Bureau -2) introduced other changes to the KV. On the assumption that one cannot have too much of a good thing, the hull armour was boosted from 75mm to 90mm. This variant, the KV-1 Model 1942, was nearly identical in appearance with the earlier Model 1941, the only major distinguishing

219. This rear view of the KV-1S prototype shows the all-round vision cupola for the commander on the left turret side and the more steeply angled rear engine deck. At this stage in the war, most Soviet tanks began carrying external fuel cylinders to increase their effective range. These were generally not connected internally and fuel had to be hand-pumped into the main internal tanks.

feature being the angled rather than rounded overhang at the hull rear. A new, thicker cast turret with 120mm at the front was introduced, although the KV-1 Model 1942 could be seen with either the thicker cast turret, or the thicker welded turret. Of course the thicker armour degraded the vehicle's automotive performance since no corresponding engine improvements had been made. As a result, the KV-1 Model 1942 was looked upon as a mixed blessing by some of its crews.

Tank Unit Organization

On 15 July 1941, the annihilation of the mechanized corps in the frontier battles forced the Soviets to disband them. Glavkom K. E. Voroshilov, Stalin's deputy and a dominant force in the Red Army since the 1920s, saw the decision as a vindication of his opposition to the mechanization of the cavalry and boasted: 'Now we'll put the matter straight.' Fortunately for the Red Army, Voroshilov and other cronies of Stalin such as Budenny and Kulik quickly showed themselves totally incompetent during the 1941 fighting and were demoted and disgraced. Others, like the former head of the ABTU, D. G. Pavlov, were simply shot. The new spirit in the Red Army sprang from men such as Georgi Zhukov, who had so skilfully used armoured units against the Japanese in 1939. Several of the mechanized corps commanders like Ryabyshev, Rokossovskiy and Lelyushenko would soon take command of armies and fronts, while talented young brigade commanders like Rotmistrov and Katukov would be elevated to divisional, corps and army commands.

The tank divisions which survived the initial frontier battles were lost in the fighting soon afterwards or were disbanded. Several tank divisions were still stationed in the Far East. The staggering losses of July and August forced STAVKA to abandon any plans to raise divisional-sized armoured formations. Instead, tank brigades were adopted as the largest armoured formations as of August 1941. The new tank brigade had a nominal strength of 93 tanks, consisting of a tank regiment and a motor rifle battalion. The tank regiment had a KV heavy tank company, a company of T-34s and two companies of whatever light tanks were available. By September 1941, shortages led to

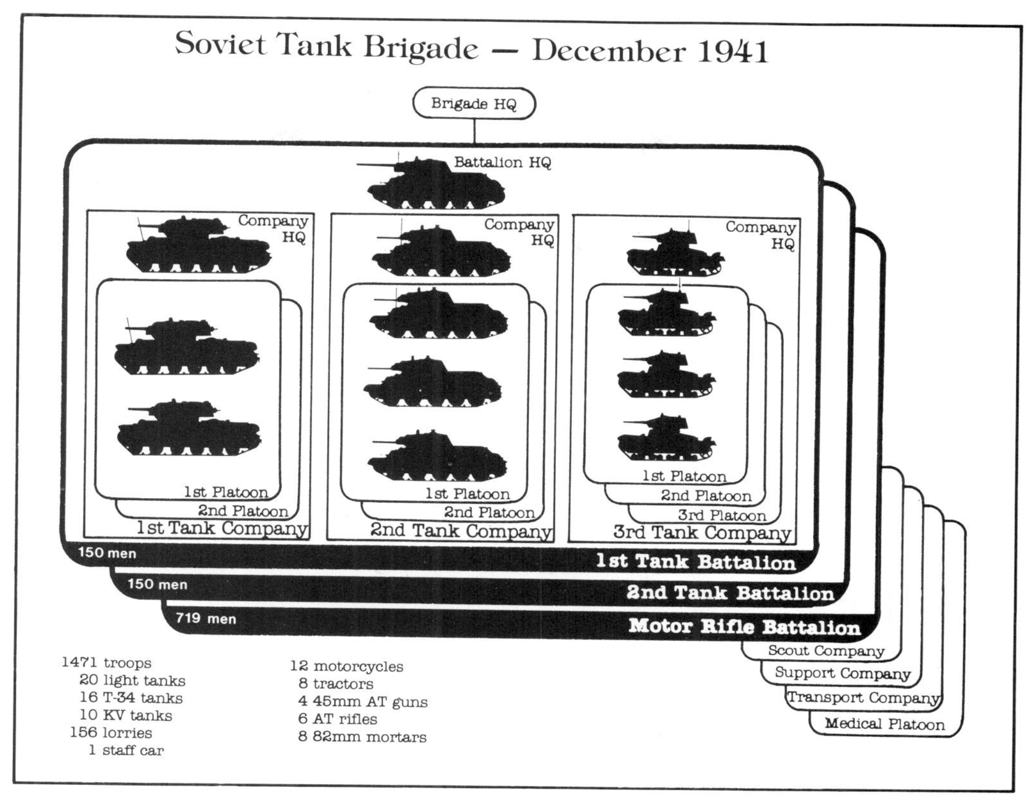

reduction in the paper strength of these units to 67 tanks, though most brigades didn't even have that many tanks. In September, independent tank battalions were formed which could be assigned to cavalry or infantry units for support. They consisted of one medium tank company and two light tank companies with 29 tanks. These units were not entirely well received because they lacked any of the KV heavy tanks which had proved so successful in terrorizing ill-equipped German infantry units. As a result, in November, they were reorganized and were supposed to consist of five KV, eleven T-34 and twenty light tanks. Severe shortages of tanks in the winter of 1941–42 from attrition and the evacuation of the factories forced the paper strength of the tank brigades even lower. The January 1942 table of equipment was only 42 tanks, and those assigned to support cavalry units were not supposed to have the precious KV tanks. By February 1942, the official tables of equipment reached their nadir at a mere 27 tanks. By early spring, the situation began to improve as the factories resumed production and Lend-Lease tanks became available in small numbers. The April 1942 tables of equipment returned the tank brigades to the January levels of 46 tanks, but more importantly, the T-34 strength was proportionately higher at the expense of the less valuable light tanks. The most significant change brought about by greater availability of tanks was the GKO decision to begin forming the new tank corps. The term 'tank corps' is misleading. By Western standards, the corps were in fact tank divisions and weak ones at that. Each had three tank brigades and a motor rifle brigade, but possessed only twenty KVs, 40 T-34s and 40 light tanks. Nevertheless, Soviet tank corps strength continued to grow throughout the war, while the strength of the Panzer divisions shrank. In July, the establishment of the tank corps was raised to 168 tanks, and a battalion of the potent BM-13 Katyusha multiple rocket launchers was added.

The combat débout of the tank corps was also matched by the formation of the new tank armies which, in fact, were more comparable to a British or American corps. They were of varied composition, usually being based on two tank corps and a rifle division. The new tank corps and tank armies went into action in May 1942, and were not an unqualified success. The tank corps were often used in a timid, defensive fashion with little co-ordination between sub-units. As mentioned earlier, Soviet tank tactics were usually quite poor, stemming from lack of training and inherent design flaws in the tanks. The potentially powerful tank armies were also a disappointment and could not prevent the shocking defeat at Voronezh. Several of the new tank corps were wiped out. The fighting highlighted the incompatibility of the heterogeneous tank brigades. General Pavel Rotmistrov, who would head the Soviet armoured force after the war, candidly explained this to STAVKA: 'The difficulty is that while there isn't much difference in speed between the light (T-60) tank and the medium (T-34) tank on the roads, when moving across country, the light tanks are quickly left behind. The heavy (KV) tank is already behind and often crushes bridges which cuts off units behind it. Under battlefield conditions, this has meant that too often the T-34 alone arrived; the light tanks had difficulty fighting the German tanks anyway, and the KVs were delayed in the rear. It was also difficult to command these companies because occasionally they were equipped with different types of radios or none at all.'

The head of the Armoured Force (GABTU), Colonel-General Ya. N. Federenko set about improving the situation in a number of ways. Crew training was increased, especially unit training. Technical improvements were suggested such as three-man turret crews, improved vision devices and provisions for more radios. To ensure closer support of infantry and tanks in the absence of armoured troop carriers, hand-holds were to be welded to tanks to permit them to carry tank raiders (tank desant). In

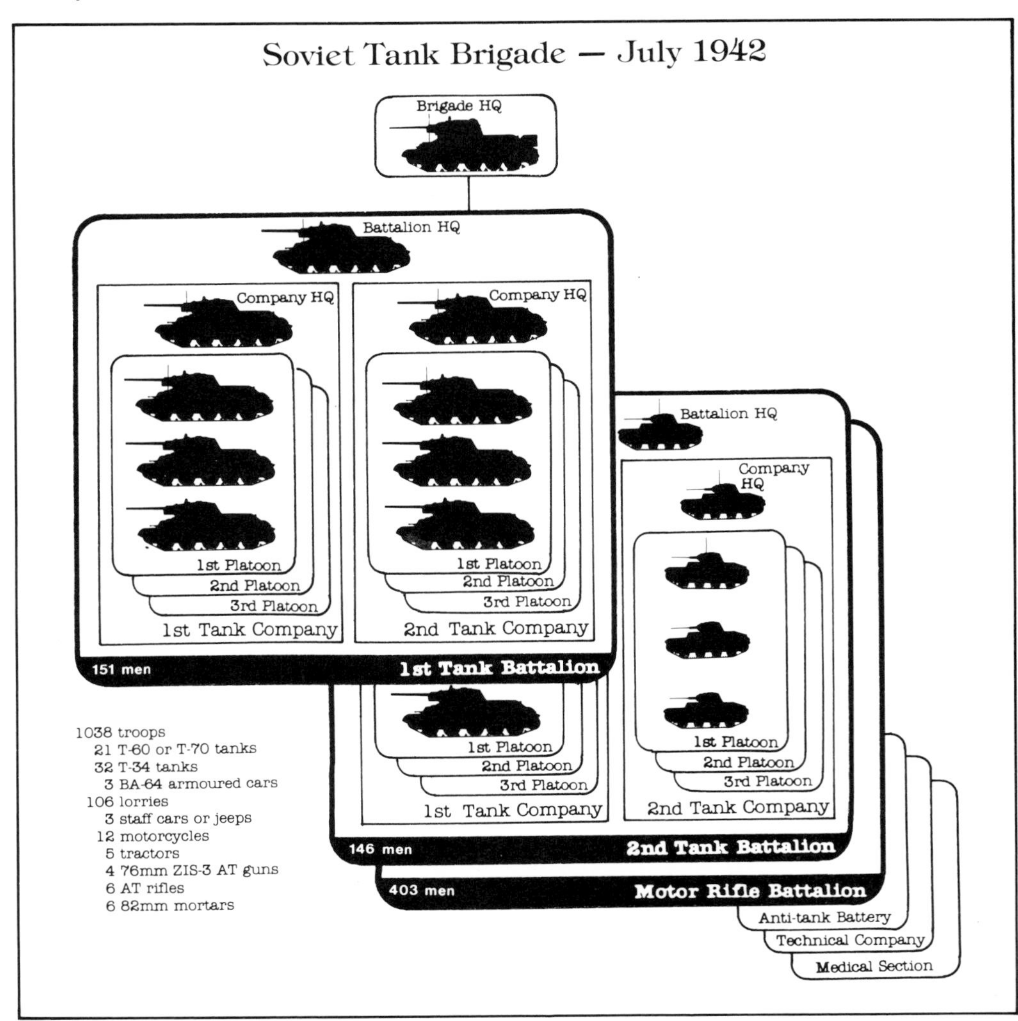

July 1942, the new tank brigade table dropped the KV; by this time, its armour was no longer invulnerable, and the increased armour of the KV-1 Model 1942 had slowed it so much that it could not operate properly in combination with the fleeter T-34 and T-70. The new tank brigades had 53 tanks. The KVs were shifted to independent tank regiments where they could be used for infantry support. The July changes also dropped the cumbersome tank regiment headquarters from the tank brigade organization in favour of a simpler configuration. In October 1943, some of the brigades began to be enlarged to 65 tanks by adding an additional company of the much prized T-34.

Another important change in Soviet mechanized doctrine was marked by the introduction of the new mechanized corps in September 1942. This differed from the tank corps by reversing the composition of the brigades. A mechanized corps had three mechanized brigades and only one tank brigade. However, owing to a lack of armoured infantry transporters, the mechanized brigades needed an entire tank regiment to help lift the assault infantry into action, and as a result, the mechanized corps had more tanks than the tank corps. Each mechanized brigade had three motor rifle battalions plus a tank regiment. Besides the independent heavy tank regiments mentioned earlier, in September 1942, GABTU also introduced independent tank regiments composed of T-34s and light tanks. These were used to reinforce tank or mechanized corps, or could be attached to rifle and cavalry divisions to provide support. They replaced the earlier independent tank battalions which now began disappearing.

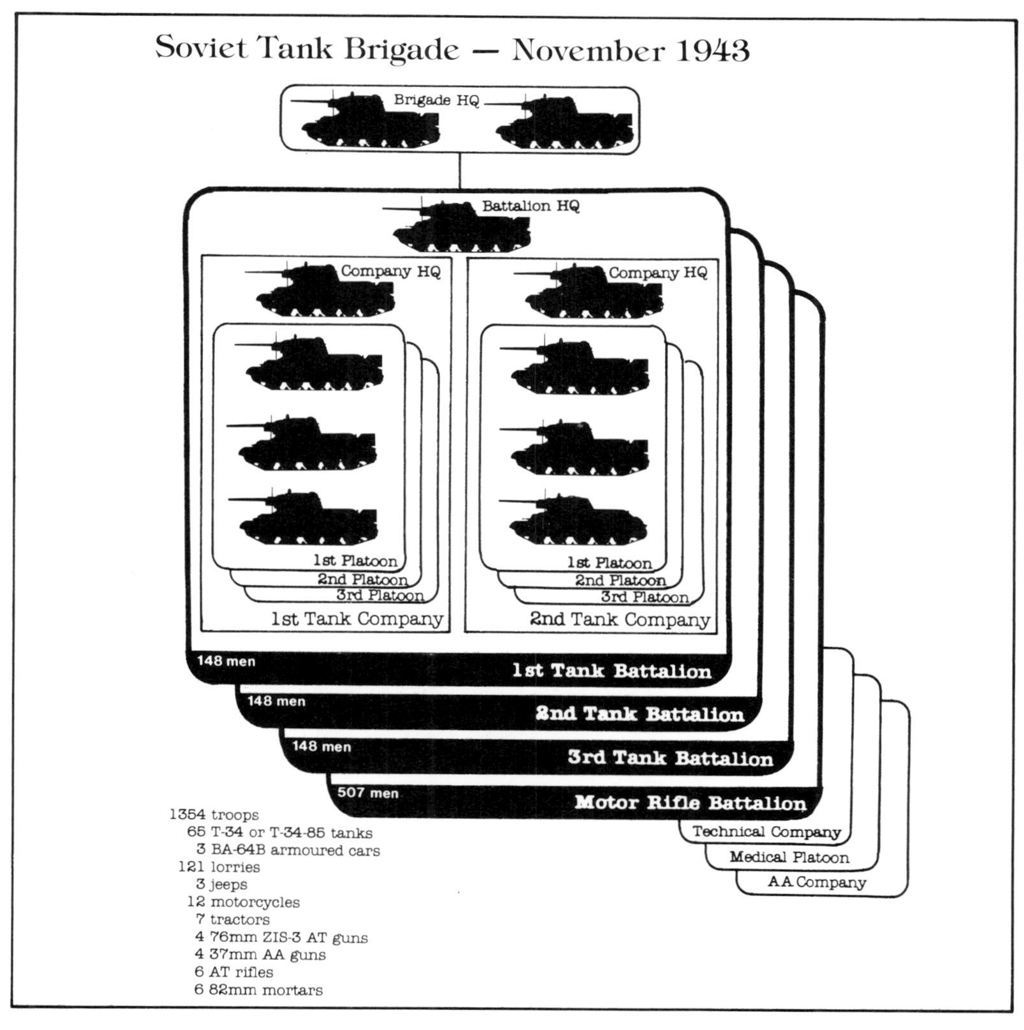

220. Hungarian troops make a prize catch of a disabled Katyusha BM-13 multiple rocket launcher. These weapons were so secret in the first months of the war that they were kept under the direction of the NKVD. (National Archives)

221. Besides the BM-13, the Katyusha batteries also used the smaller M-8 rockets fired from BM-8-48 launchers like this one. (Terry Gander)

222. There were a number of tracked versions of the BM-13 produced in small numbers including this version based on the STZ-5 artillery tractor. (US Army)

Mechanized Artillery Development

The employment of the new tank corps and mechanized corps in 1942 revealed the need of mechanized artillery to support the new formations. Mechanized artillery development had languished in the pre-war years, being subordinate to the conservative and powerful Artillery Directorate (GAU) and because of the inability of the design teams to develop mechanized artillery weapons that could justify their high cost by offering significant advantages over motor towed artillery. In the early months of the war, there was a good deal of scattered improvisation of self-propelled artillery on a small scale. In August 1941, F. Grabin's design team in Gorki's Zavod Nr. 92 mated some of the new ZiS-29 57mm anti-tank guns and Komsomolyets artillery transporters, resulting in the small ZiS-30 tank destroyer. Apparently several dozen were built, but the vehicle was clearly a hasty improvisation and availability of both the chassis and jinxed 57mm gun was limited. In Leningrad, a number of T-26 chassis were modified by the addition of a 76.2mm regimental gun Model 27 on a platform with an armoured shield. Small numbers were produced together with at least a prototype on a T-34 chassis. A small number of GAZ-AA and ZiS-5 lorries were partly armoured and mortars were fitted on their rear flat beds.

Katyusha Rocket Launchers

The first self-propelled artillery weapons produced in quantity in the USSR were not guns at all but novel rocket weapons. In June 1938, GAU had authorized the RNII (Jet Scientific Research Institute) to develop multiple rocket ground launchers for firing the RS-132 aircraft rocket. A design team under I. Gvay developed a 24-rail launcher firing the modified M-132 rocket over the side of a ZiS-5 lorry. The mounting proved unstable during firing, leading to a second prototype called the MU-1 (Mechanized Assembly-1). This was also a failure, which prompted V. N. Galkovskiy to propose that the rockets be fired longitudinally on the chassis. This lead to the BM-13 (Combat Machine for M-13 rockets) which was completed in August 1939. Field tests with a variety of different rocket types were con-

▽220

221△ 222▽

△223

223. The T-60 light tank was used as the basis for a BM-8-24 launcher. This illustration shows the main frame assembly (1 – 7), the crew station (8) and the added platforms for loading the rockets (9, 10).

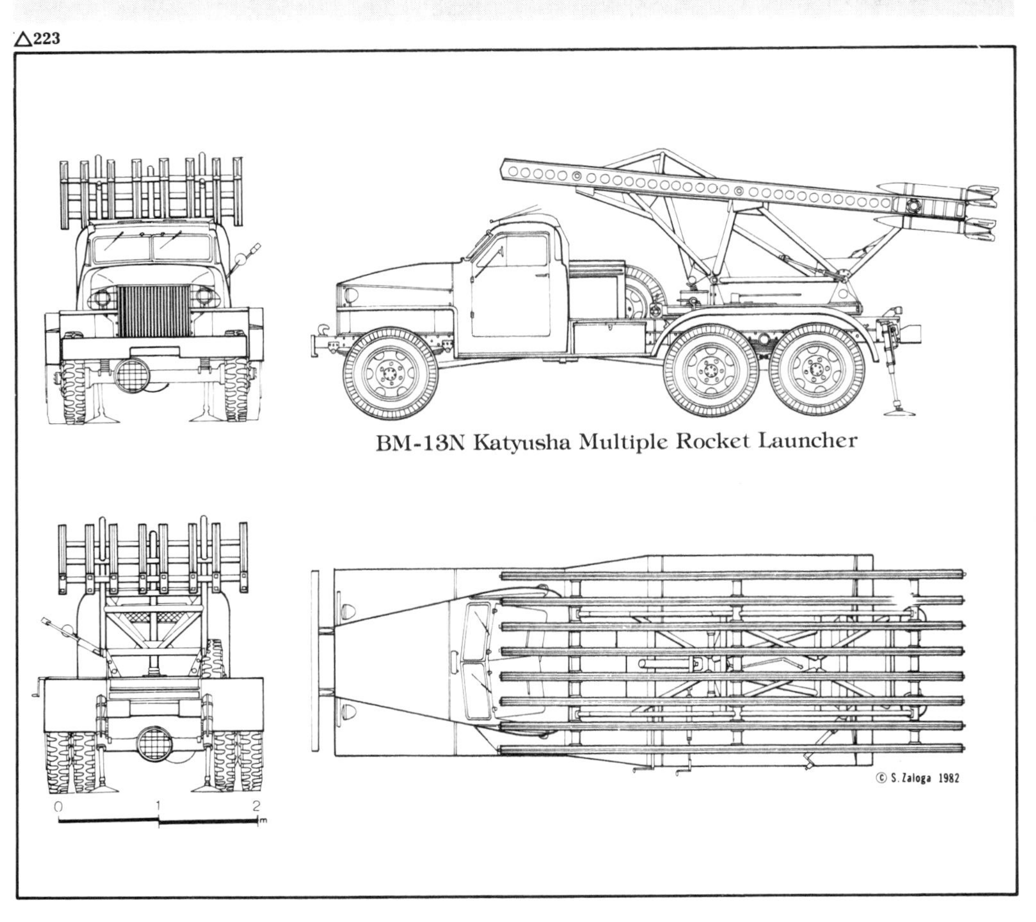

224. A BM-13N mounted on a Studebaker US6 chassis launches its M-13 rockets during the fighting for Berlin. The rockets could be salvoed in series, or fired individually.

ducted throughout 1940, with the GAU finally approving the vehicle as the BM-13-16 (Combat Vehicle for M-13 rockets with sixteen launch rails), but only 40 were completed before the war started. The new weapon was guarded with the greatest secrecy and at the outbreak of the war a special unit was formed under NKVD direction. The first battery went into action near the Orsha railway station on 7 July 1941 and proved an immediate success. The GAU was duly impressed, and ordered production to begin on a crash basis. The rocket launchers were still so highly classified that they received a variety of bogus names such as Kostikov guns, etc. Eventually they were officially designated Guards Mortars, but the name which stuck was the popular nickname, Katyusha, the diminutive form of the name Katerina, after the Isakovskiy tune of the same name, popular in Russia at the time. The scream of the rockets led the Germans to call them Stalin's Organs. Although originally lorry mounted, attempts were made in 1941 to develop other carriages for better cross-country performance. Some BM-13 mounts were mated to the STZ-5 artillery tractor and produced in small numbers. There was also a version mounted on the KV tank, the KV-1K, but this was not produced in any quantity as it wasted a perfectly good heavy tank in a role easily satisfied by a less

▽224

225. In 1944, the heavy M-30 rockets were adopted by the mobile Katyusha batteries with the development of the BM-31 launcher seen here mounted on a Studebaker US6 at a Moscow victory parade. (Sovfoto)

expensive carriage. In August 1941, a second type of Katyusha rocket was developed, the M-8 82mm rocket which was smaller and had shorter range. These were mounted on lorries as the BM-8-36, or on turretless tank chassis, such as the T-40 and T-60, as the BM-8-24. In 1942, the Soviets developed a version of the M-13 rocket with a larger, bulbous warhead, the M-30. Unlike the other two types, the M-30 was not fired from a self-propelled launcher, but from rama (frame) launchers. Self-propelled versions, the BM-31, were not fielded until 1944.

The main attraction of the Katyusha launcher was that it was cheap to manufacture and could be turned out by small factories without the elaborate machine tools needed for conventional tubed artillery. A BM-13 salvo dropped 4.35 tons of rocket and high explosive into a 10-acre area in a terrifying 7–10 second strike. Although not so accurate as conventional artillery, the Katyusha was much more feared by German soldiers than conventional artillery. By the end of the war, about 10,000 Katyusha launchers had been manufactured, mostly for the Army, but some for the Navy's river flotillas as well. The majority of the Army launchers were self-propelled. The BM-8, BM-13 and BM-31 were all initially mounted on the ZiS-6 truck or its derivatives such as the ZiS-5 and ZiS-5V. In 1942 as Lend-Lease trucks became available, the launchers were mounted on a variety of American, British and Canadian lorries, such as the Chevrolet 1 ½ ton, International K, Ford WOT-8, GMC 2 ½ ton and Studebaker US6 2 ½ ton truck. The Lend-Lease types were sometimes distinguished as BM-13S. The superior cross-country performance of the Studebaker US6 led the GAU to standardize this mounting for the BM-13, which was designated BM-13N (N-normalizovanniy: standard). The BM-8 could be mounted on smaller chassis such as the BM-8-8 on the GAZ-67 jeep. However, it was also mounted on larger vehicles with more rails, such as the BM-8-48 on the Studebaker US6. The large BM-31 frame launcher was invariably mounted on larger lorries, first the ZiS-6, but more often on the Studebaker US6. Katyusha launchers were also mounted on armoured trains.

Following the first success of the BM-13 battery at Orsha, the Red Army hastened to form new guards mortar units. The initial guards mortar batteries each had seven

226. The first attempt to develop a mechanized gun during the Great Patriotic War was the OSU-76 which mated a ZIS-3 76.2mm divisional gun to a T-60 light tank chassis. The chassis proved to be too small for the gun.

BM-13, but in July 1941, this was standardized at four launchers per battery. They were usually deployed in support of rifle divisions and initially were kept under NKVD control for security. Once the Germans Nebelwerfer rocket launchers became commonplace, this control was relaxed. In August 1941, Stalin personally ordered the formation of special guards mortar regiments which were to be kept under the direction of high command reserve (STAVKA-VGK). These consisted of three firing battalions of three batteries each, for a total of 36 BM-13 or BM-8 launchers. At the same time, independent guards mortar battalions were also formed with 36 launchers in three batteries. By the end of 1941, there were 554 launchers in service with 8 regiments, 35 independent battalions and 2 independent batteries. In June 1942 with the arrival of the first M-30 heavy rockets, heavy guards mortar battalions were formed, but these had static, not mobile launchers. They also had three batteries, but each battery had 36 frame launchers while the self-propelled units had only twelve launchers per battery. When the lorry-mounted BM-31 finally became available in 1944, the motorized heavy guards mortar battalion had only 48 launchers compared to 96 launchers in a static battalion. There were 3,237 launchers manufactured in 1942, bringing total strength up to 57 regiments. Counting the smaller independent battalions, the equivalent of 216 batteries were in service. Of these 23 per cent were M-30 heavy units, 56 per cent were BM-13 units and 21 per cent were the light BM-8 units. In 1943, guards mortar brigades were formed, equipped with static launchers, and later, divisions were formed. By the end of the war, the equivalent of 518 batteries were in service.

The SU-76 Light Mechanized Gun

In April 1942, the GAU proposed a programme for the development of mechanized artillery, but the tank force, tired of the GAU's lagging, had already undertaken steps to design such weapons. Malyshev's Commissariat for Tank Industry set up a Mechanized Artillery Bureau (BAS) at UZTM in Sverdlovsk, under the tank designer L. Troyanov who was working in co-operation with the

227. The OSU-76 was followed by the SU-76 based on a lengthened T-70 tank chassis. This version entered production in 1942, but was so plagued with engine and transmission problems that it had to be completely redesigned. A small number of SU-76s saw combat in the winter of 1942–43, but were quickly withdrawn from frontline service until the improved SU-76M became available.

main artillery design teams of Generals Petrov and Grabin. Development of a light mechanized gun was entrusted to Zavod Nr. 38 in Kirov; of a medium mechanized gun to UZTM in Sverdlovsk, and of a heavy mechanized gun to Tankograd.

Early in 1942, the design team at Zavod Nr. 38 in Kirov began its work on the light mechanized gun based on a T-60 chassis, known as the OSU-76 (Opytnaya Samokhodnaya Ustanovka: Experimental Mechanized Mounting). This vehicle used the standard ZiS-3 76.2mm divisional gun mounted on the rear of a modified T-60 in a partly armoured casemate mount. The OSU-76 project was dropped because of the inadequate size of the chassis and because of the work being done on the larger T-70 at the time. In the spring of 1942, the Grabin team at Zavod Nr. 92 in Gorki, in co-operation with the Zavod Nr. 38 design team, began work on the SU-12, a mechanized 76.2mm gun mounted on a lengthened T-70 chassis. The general configuration of this vehicle was much the same as the earlier OSU-76, except that it was considerably larger. Trials were conducted later in the summer of 1942. The GKO accepted it for production in December 1942 as the SU-76 light mechanized gun. It was intended to provide fire support for rifle and tank formations, and to act as a tank destroyer. A total of 26 were completed in 1942. Curiously, the SU-76 retained the awkward twin-engine arrangement of the early T-70 which had already been terminated on the T-70 assembly line. It is not clear why this unacceptable arrangement was permitted, unless there was a significant shortage of transmissions and differentials of the type being used on the T-70. Not surprisingly, the system proved every bit as unreliable as on the early T-70, leading to denunciations of the vehicle from the hapless crews who received it. In the spring of 1943, design responsibility was shifted to Astrov's bureau, where the problem was rectified by employing the modified configuration of the T-70M with the two engines in-line. This forced a redesign of the forward hull, and at the same time, some improvements were made in the rear casemate. The improved type was designated the SU-76M and production began immediately at GAZ and Zavod Nr. 38. GAZ became the predominant manufacturer of the type, and eventually Zavod Nr. 40 in M'tishchi near Moscow also

▽227

228. The SU-76B was an attempt to provide full armour coverage on the SU-76. It was deemed unnecessary and too heavy, and was not adopted
229. A rear view of a Polish SU-76M shows how exposed the crew was at the rear which limited the effectiveness of the vehicle as a close support weapon. Nevertheless, the SU-76M had excellent firepower for its small size and was cheap to produce. After the ubiquitous T-34, it was the second most common Soviet armoured vehicle type of the war.

230. Although a handy infantry support weapon, the SU-76M was not altogether popular with its crews who nicknamed it 'Suka' (Bitch). Here, an SU-76M battery wait for instructions in the streets of Budapest in 1945. (Sovfoto)

231. Late production batches of the SU-76M had a slightly different rear hull configuration as is evident in this photograph of two SU-76Ms captured in Korea in 1950. The vehicle to the right is the standard wartime production model, the one to the left is the late production type which did not have the pronounced clipped corner at the rear. (US Army)

△230 ▽231

became involved in SU-76M production. All of the earlier SU-76 were withdrawn from front-line service once the SU-76M became available. Although the SU-76M did not prove to be an entirely successful tank destroyer, because of the growing trend towards heavier tanks in the Wehrmacht, the SU-76 proved useful as an assault artillery vehicle, and was produced in greater numbers than other Soviet armoured vehicles of the War excluding the T-34. It was doled out in generous quantities to support rifle divisions, and in many respects became a successor to the infantry tank. It was never very popular with its crews; it had very thin armour, and was one of the few Soviet AFVs not to have full armoured coverage. The open rear made it very unpleasant to serve in during harsh weather, and made it vulnerable to small arms fire and grenades. The driver's station was adjacent to the engines without a bulkhead which was unpleasant in summer. Its nickname in service was 'Suka' which was both the diminutive form of its acronym SU (pronounced 'soo' by the troops), and the Russian word for 'bitch'. In 1943, the Astrov team attempted to correct the complaints about the lack of overhead armour by building a fully-armoured version on an old SU-76, called the SU-76B, but the added weight affected performance adversely, and it was not accepted for service use.

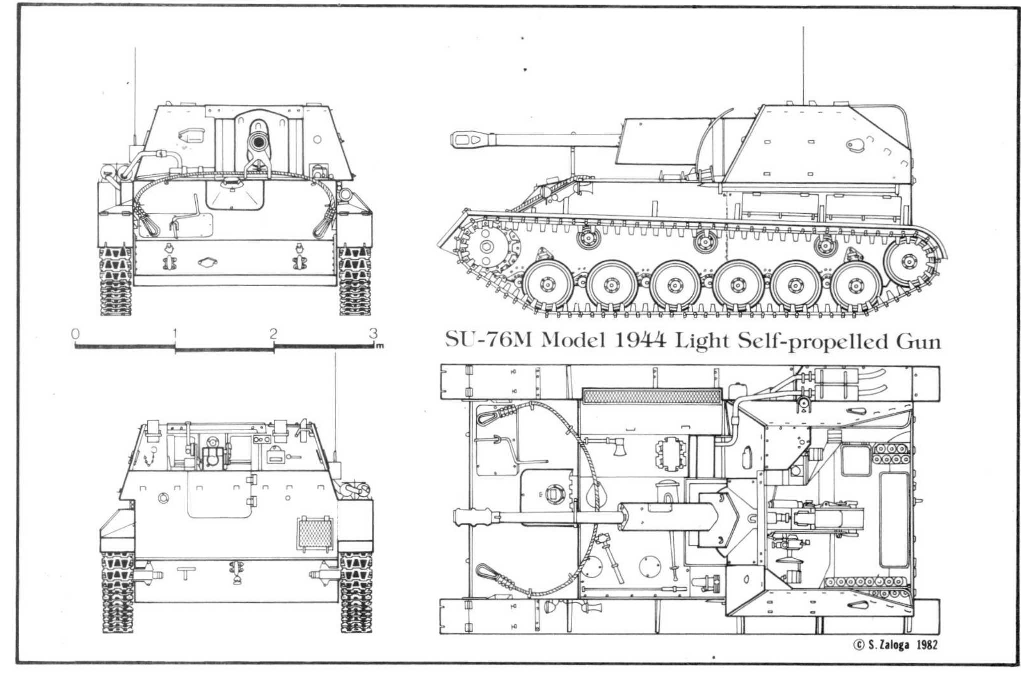

232. The first assault gun version of the T-34 was the squat SU-122 armed with a 122mm howitzer. The Red Army hoped it would double as a direct support weapon and tank destroyer, but the performance of its HEAT anti-tank round was less than expected. This particular SU-122 was captured by the Germans and sent to Prague for trials. (Ivan Bajtos)
233. Late production batches of the SU-122 used the same ball socket mantlet of the SU-85.

The SU-122 Medium Mechanized Gun

In the summer of 1942, the design office at UZTM, in conjunction with the special NKTP team of Z. Kotin, L. Gorlitskiy and E. Shilnishchkov, began design work on a medium mechanized gun, the SU-35, which consisted of an M-30 122mm howitzer mounted in a fully-armoured casemate on a T-34 hull. The conversion was quite straightforward, requiring far less redesign of the basic tank hull than was represented by the T-70/SU-76 conversion. The SU-35 was accepted by the GKO in December 1942 as the SU-122 and was ordered into production immediately at UZTM. The SU-122 was envisaged as an assault gun, along the lines of the German Sturmgeschutz, for direct fire support of infantry or tank formations against defended strongpoints. It could be used in support of infantry formations against tanks, although its HEAT round never lived up to expectations. In 1943, a tank destroyer version called the SU-122P was built, using the long-barrelled 122mm Model 1931/37 gun, but this weapon proved too massive for the chassis and was not accepted for production. The first SU-122 were produced at the end of 1942 and went into action the following January.

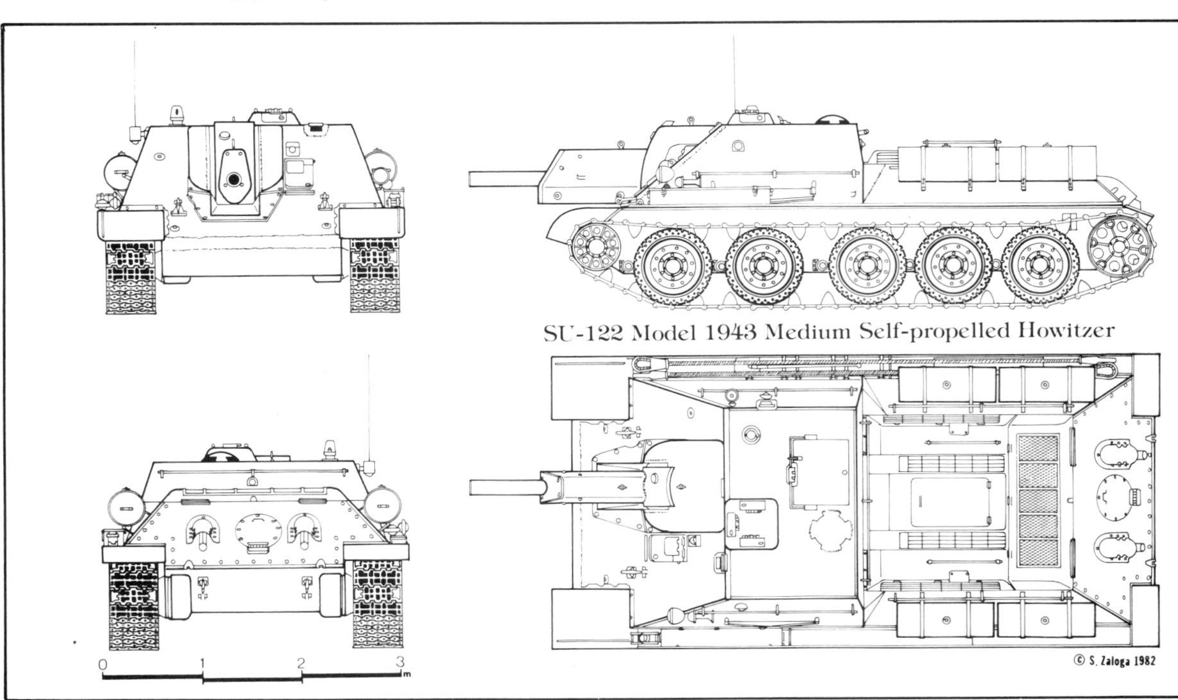

SU-122 Model 1943 Medium Self-propelled Howitzer

232△ 233▽

234. Among the most peculiar mechanized guns developed for the Red Army in the Great Patriotic War was the KV-6 armed with a 76.2mm gun and two 45mm guns. It is unclear what advantage this arrangement was presumed to enjoy; the equally peculiar KV-7 had essentially the same configuration with two 76.2mm guns.

The KV-7 Mechanized Gun

Of all the mechanized guns spawned by the NKTP efforts, the projects developed by Z. Kotin's team at Tankograd on the KV chassis were the most peculiar. Two types were examined, the KV-6, armed with a 76.2mm gun and twin 45mm guns, and the KV-7, armed with twin 76.2mm guns. These guns were fitted in large ball mounts attached to fixed casemates. It is unclear what advantage the NKTP saw in these monstrosities beyond the slightly greater ease of manufacture compared to conventional turreted tanks. In January 1942, trials were conducted which led the NKTP to grant provisional permission to begin production of the KV-7. Before production ensued, however, either someone came to his senses or technical difficulties cropped up, but quantity production never took place. Shortly afterwards, the Kotin team was diverted to work on the KV-8 flame-thrower tank which put an end to these curiosities. So ended the initial attempt to develop a heavy mechanized gun.

Mechanized Artillery Units

The first self-propelled gun regiments were formed in December 1942 with the new SU-76 and SU-122 mechanized guns. These regiments had four batteries of SU-76 and two batteries of SU-122. The first two regiments were committed to the Volkhov Front east of Leningrad in January 1943, and two further regiments were committed to the Western Front in March 1943. The units were placed under the control of Front or Army command, but proved to be a failure. In their assessment of the new units, the front commanders were quick to point out that they did not feel there was any inherent problem with mechanized artillery units, and indeed, they praised the concept. Rather, the presence of two vehicle types in a single small unit proved awkward to support logistically and the new SU-76 proved unreliable because of its unsynchronized transmission arrangement. Both vehicles proved incompatible in action because the SU-76, lacking overhead armour, had to engage targets from a distance, while the SU-122 with its thicker and more complete armour could attack defended infantry positions at very close ranges without fear of small arms or grenades. As a result, in May 1943, the mechanized artillery regiments were divided into light and medium regiments, each equipped with only a single vehicle type. This configuration proved much more successful in action, and the arrival of the improved SU-76M solved the technical problem faced by the light regiments.

The German Response

In the face of the glaring superiority of the T-34 and KV, the Wehrmacht began a hasty modernization of its armoured force. Both the Pz Kpfw III and Pz Kpfw IV were modernized with better guns and armour, and most of the light tanks were withdrawn and rebuilt as tank destroyers, mounting the new PAK 40 75mm anti-tank gun or captured Soviet F-22 76.2mm divisional guns in lightly armoured casemates. This did not completely restore technical parity, and some German officers in 1941 urged that the Wehrmacht swallow its pride and simply build copies of the T-34. Instead, the Germans developed two costly new tanks, the Tiger heavy tank and the Panther medium tank. The Tiger was the first to arrive, and a single battalion was dispatched to the Leningrad Front in December 1942. This was not a particularly wise move, because in January a Tiger was captured by the Russians. Inspection of the captured Tiger gave the Soviet tank designers an excuse to shake the NKTP from its single-minded preoccupation with maximum production and to force a resumption in qualitative improvements, particularly in the area of tank firepower. Unfortunately, this came too late to have much effect on the 1943 production programme.

The one vehicle which needed the most serious attention was the KV heavy tank. Since the re-establishment of the Kirovskiy Works in Chelyabinsk, Kotin's design team, the TsKB-2 (Central Design Bureau-2) had introduced a number of modest improvements to the KV-1. On the assumption that one cannot have enough of a good thing, the new KV-1 Model 1942 had even thicker armour on the hull and turret than the earlier KV-1 Model 1941. The new version boasted hull armour up from 75mm to 90mm, and a new cast turret was designed which had frontal armour 120mm thick. The KV-1 Model 1942 was built in two forms; with the earlier thick welded turret, and with this latter type of thickened cast turret. It was nearly identical in appearance with earlier models, the only distinct external change being the angled overhang at the rear, which had been round on the Model 1941. Unfortunately, the added armour on the KV-1 Model 1942 made the KV even slower and less manageable. With the advent of new German anti-tank rounds such as the 75mm arrowhead projectile, and new, shaped-charge warheads, even the thicker armour was vulnerable to the new generation of German tank and anti-tank guns. As mentioned earlier, this forced the GABTU in the summer of 1942 to remove the KVs from the tank brigades and place them in separate regiments where their slow speed did not hinder the operations of T-34s. N. Dukhov, the chief engineer of TsKB-2, was assigned to redesign the KV under intensely contradictory pressures.

The KV-3 design would clearly have satisfied the needs of the GABTU because it would have restored a more logical situation where the army's heavy tank design was better armed than its medium tank. Furthermore, the KV-3 was better engined and, therefore, more mobile than the current KV-1, but adopting the KV-3 would have meant opening a new engine production line and new gun and ammunition lines. This was clearly unacceptable to the NKTP which in the summer of 1942 was barely managing to keep tank production ahead of battlefield losses. Since neither a new gun nor a new engine were acceptable alternatives, Dukhov was forced to improve the mobility of the KV by thinning the armour back to the level used on the KV-1 Model 1941. At the same time, however, Dukhov made much needed improvements in the turret layout of the KV. While the KV-1 had a three-man turret crew, it suffered from the same type of ergonometric flaws as the T-34 mentioned earlier. This resulted from the fact that the third turret crewman served in the archaic role of rear turret machine-gunner, while the commander was still overburdened with loading duties. In fact the situation was even worse on the KV, because its commander did not have immediate access to the single roof hatch which was above the rear gunner's station, and so could not direct the tank in action from an open turret hatch. The KV-3 Obiekt 222 had recognized this problem, but like the Obiekt 220 had not affected the production model.

Dukhov's new version, the KV-1S (skorostniy: speedy) corrected this problem by siting the commander behind the gunner, giving him a 360° cupola and re-deploying the rear turret gunner as a loader. The new KV-1S also incorporated much needed transmission improvements and entered production in August 1942. This still left the Red Army with a heavy tank slower than the T-34, 150 per cent more costly, fitted with the same gun and with armour that was not significantly less vulnerable to the increasingly common German 75mm guns. The sentiment of the tank crews was summarized by General M. E. Katukov who commanded the First Soviet Guards tank brigade: 'The T-34 fulfills our hopes and has proven itself in action. But the heavy KV tank . . . the soldiers don't like it. It is very heavy and clumsy and not very agile. It surmounts obstacles with great difficulty. It often damages bridges and becomes involved in other accidents. More to the point, it is armed with the same 76mm gun as the T-34. This raises the question, to what extent is it superior to the T-34? If the KV had a more potent gun, or one of greater calibre, it might be possible to excuse its weight and other shortcomings.'

As a result of these views, in the summer of 1943, Stalin decided to cancel heavy tank production altogether, but the designers and Malyshev of the NKTP convinced him that the KV-1S would at least alleviate the speed problem, and that cancellation of the KV would drastically affect tank production at a key moment. Stalin relented, but Kotin realized that a major revision of the KV would be necessary if the heavy tank concept was to survive. He divided his group into two: one section headed by Dukhov, who would be responsible for modernization of the KV beyond the KV-1S, and the other, Shashmurin, Yermolayev and Tsiets, which would begin work on a drastically revised design called the KV-13. The most serious constraint on the KV-13 was the NKTP's insistence on remaining with the outdated F-34 gun. The appearance of the Tiger outside Leningrad, and use of the Tiger during the winter battles around Kharkov finally forced the NKTP out of its complacency, and made it realize that the 76.2mm gun equipping all medium and heavy tanks and light mechanized guns was about to become inadequate. As a short-term solution, the Dukhov team mounted an M-30 122mm howitzer in a KV as the KV-9 but, as in the case of the SU-122, the anti-tank performance of this weapon was disappointing.

What was needed were new long-barrelled tank guns like the German 88mm gun. Both the Grabin and Petrov design bureaux were directed to develop new 85mm guns based around the ammunition already in use in the 85mm anti-aircraft gun. Before these became available, the NKTP instructed the design teams to examine other alternatives. Morozov's team recognized that the 57mm ZiS-2 anti-tank gun had better armour penetration than the F-34 76.2mm. The 76.2mm BP-350P HVAP rounds could penetrate 94mm of armour at 500m whereas the 57mm BP-571P HVAP round could penetrate

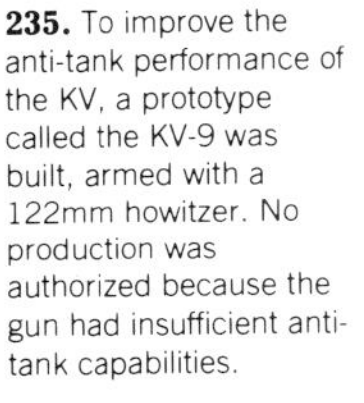

235. To improve the anti-tank performance of the KV, a prototype called the KV-9 was built, armed with a 122mm howitzer. No production was authorized because the gun had insufficient anti-tank capabilities.

236. The prototype for the SU-152 was completed in barely a month and was in action for the first time at Kursk where it earned the nickname 'Zvierboy' (Animal Hunter) for its ability to deal with the new Panther, Tiger and Elefant armoured vehicles.

140mm of armour at this range. The ZiS-2 was experimentally mounted in a T-34, but the main drawback of such a change in guns was that the excellent high explosive round of the 76mm gun was lost. The 57mm gun had been optimized for anti-tank performance, compromising its ability to fire large, high explosive rounds. This deficiency doomed this project. It is a popular misconception that tanks are used primarily against other tanks. In fact they are used against a wide range of targets, and Soviet designers correctly appreciated the detrimental effect the weakening of the high explosive capability of the T-34's armament would have on this balance. Another alternative to cope with the Tiger was to thicken the T-34's armour. A prototype, the T-43, was built with 90mm armour, but even this was vulnerable to the new German 88mm tank gun. At the same time, the thicker armour severely compromised the T-34's mobility and was considered unacceptable. As a result, attention turned to improving the firepower of the T-34's and KV's mechanized gun counterparts.

Tank Destroyers

The attempt to mount the 122mm A-19 gun in the SU-122 as the SU-122P proved to be a dead-end, and instead in April 1943 the design group of L. Troyanov from BAS, L. Gorlitskiy from Tankograd and General F. Petrov, set about mounting Petrov's new D-5 85mm gun in the SU-122. There was general dissatisfaction with the gun mounting on the SU-122, and so a new ball mounting was developed which gave better protection and better traverse. This was used on the final production batches of the SU-122 in 1943, and on the new tank destroyer version, the SU-85. However, this was not completed until August 1943, so the new SU-85 did not enter production in time to participate in the climactic battles at Kursk and Orel in the summer of 1943.

The TsKB-2 team under Kotin, in co-operation with the BAS under L. Troyanov, also began a crash programme to develop a tank destroyer version of the KV. Two types were to be developed, the KV-12, mounting the massive 203mm B-4 Model 1931 gun howitzer, and the KV-14, mounting the 152mm ML-20 Model 1937 gun howitzer. The KV-12 was cancelled and this designation was later used for a small series of smoke-generating tanks on the KV-1 chassis. Prototypes of the KV-14 on modified KV-1S chassis, were designed in a record 25 days, and on 7 February, barely a month after the capture of the Tiger, perfunctory trials were completed. On 14 February 1943, the GKO accepted the KV-14 for production as the SU-152. The first heavy mechanized gun regiments were formed in May 1943, but the first regiment had only twelve SU-152 heavy mechanized guns when it was rushed to the Kursk battlefield. It was reinforced during

237. The T-34-85 Model 1943 remedied the need for better anti-tank firepower with its new D-5T 85mm gun, and finally corrected the inefficiencies of the turret layout with a new three-man configuration which also provided an all-round vision cupola for the commander. The T-34-85s of this unit were purchased with contributions from the Orthodox Church and named after the legendary Prince Dmitri Donskoi.
238. The initial production run of the T-34-85 used the D-5T gun because of difficulties with the preferred ZiS-S-53 gun. This version can be distinguished by the circular collar on the gun mantlet, and the retention of the radio and antenna in the hull. The standard production model of the T-34-85 with the ZiS-S-53 gun, the T-34-85 Model 1944, had the radio moved into the turret.

the fighting to bring it up to full strength of 21 SU-152. The SU-152 proved to be one of the few Soviet armoured vehicles that could fight with the new German armour on even terms, and quickly earned the nickname Zvierboy-Animal Hunter for its reputed abilities to kill Tigers, Panthers and Elefants!

The Battle of Kursk-Orel

By ruthlessly restricting armoured vehicle production to a minimal number of vehicle types and by channelling design efforts to simplify production rather than firepower or mobility innovations, the Red Army approached the summer battles of 1943 with a significant advantage in tanks. The availability of Lend-Lease tanks, though many were of mediocre quality, also helped to strengthen the Soviet inventory. In November 1942, at the height of the Stalingrad fighting, the Red Army could field 6,600 armoured vehicles. By the summer of 1943, this had risen to 9,500 vehicles. Of equal importance, the level of crew training was on the rise, more tanks were being fitted with radios and there was a growing number of experienced tank units and experienced and skilled unit commanders. The Soviets, anticipating a German drive on the Kursk salient, concentrated 7,500 armoured vehicles in the fronts in and around the Kursk salient, or about 78 per cent of their total armour. By comparison, the Germans concentrated about 61 per cent of their armour on the Eastern Front, in the drive on the salient, about 2,700 tanks and other armoured vehicles. A significant portion of the Soviet strength was secretly hoarded in reserve for an anticipated counter-offensive. It is ironic that the critical tank battles of the Kursk campaign were won by the Soviets at a time when Soviet armour was qualitatively weaker than German armour. Throughout 1941 and 1942, the Soviets had maintained a qualitative edge, albeit ever narrowing, against the Germans, which was often offset by the Wehrmacht's tactical skill. At Kursk, the Germans introduced the new Tigers and Panthers in large numbers, and these vehicles could engage and destroy any Soviet tank at ranges far in excess of the capabilities of the ubiquitous F-34 76.2mm gun. Even at close ranges, the thick new armour of the Panthers and Tigers was very difficult to defeat. Fortunately, like the T-34 and KV in 1941, the new German tank designs were plagued by teething problems which diminished their tactical effectiveness. Key battles like that at Prokhorovka were won by the Soviet tank units engaging German armour at close ranges where the Germans could not take maximum advantage of their superior firepower, and where the advantage of their superior armoured protection was sizeably diminished. German losses in July 1943 amounted to 580 armoured vehicles, including 83 Panthers, 23 Tigers and 39 Elefants. A great many more tanks and other armoured vehicles were knocked out during the fighting, but were recovered and repaired by the vigorous German armoured vehicle recovery teams. Soviet tank losses were probably double, but the Soviets could absorb their losses more easily. At Kursk the Germans lost the strategic initiative on the Eastern Front. Now, the Soviet armoured force had to prove that it had learned the lessons of mobile mechanized warfare in its advance towards Berlin.

The T-34-85 Medium Tank

The inability of the T-34 adequately to deal with the new German armour forced the NKTP to accept the fact that major improvements in Soviet tank design would have to be accepted no matter what disruption they caused the tank industry. The GKO intervened, having been deluged by complaints from the field that Soviet tanks needed 'a longer arm' to reach out and smash German armour. Four gun design teams were assigned to a crash programme to field an up-armed T-34. Besides the Grabin and Petrov teams already working on 85mm guns, Grabin's bureau at Zavod Nr. 92 in Gorki was turned over to 23-year-old A. Savin when Grabin was shifted to the Central Artillery Design Bureau (TsAKB) in Moscow, and K. Siderenko's team also began design work on their S-18 85mm gun. The new guns were tested at the Gorokhovieskiy Proving Grounds outside Gorki, where Grabin's ZiS-53 was declared the winner. Unfortunately, the new turret, designed by V. Kerichev at Krasnoye Sormovo in Gorki, did not mate properly with the new gun, apparently being designed around Petrov's D-5 gun which had been available earlier since it was already in production for the SU-85. Two unarmed T-34-85s were

237△ 238▽

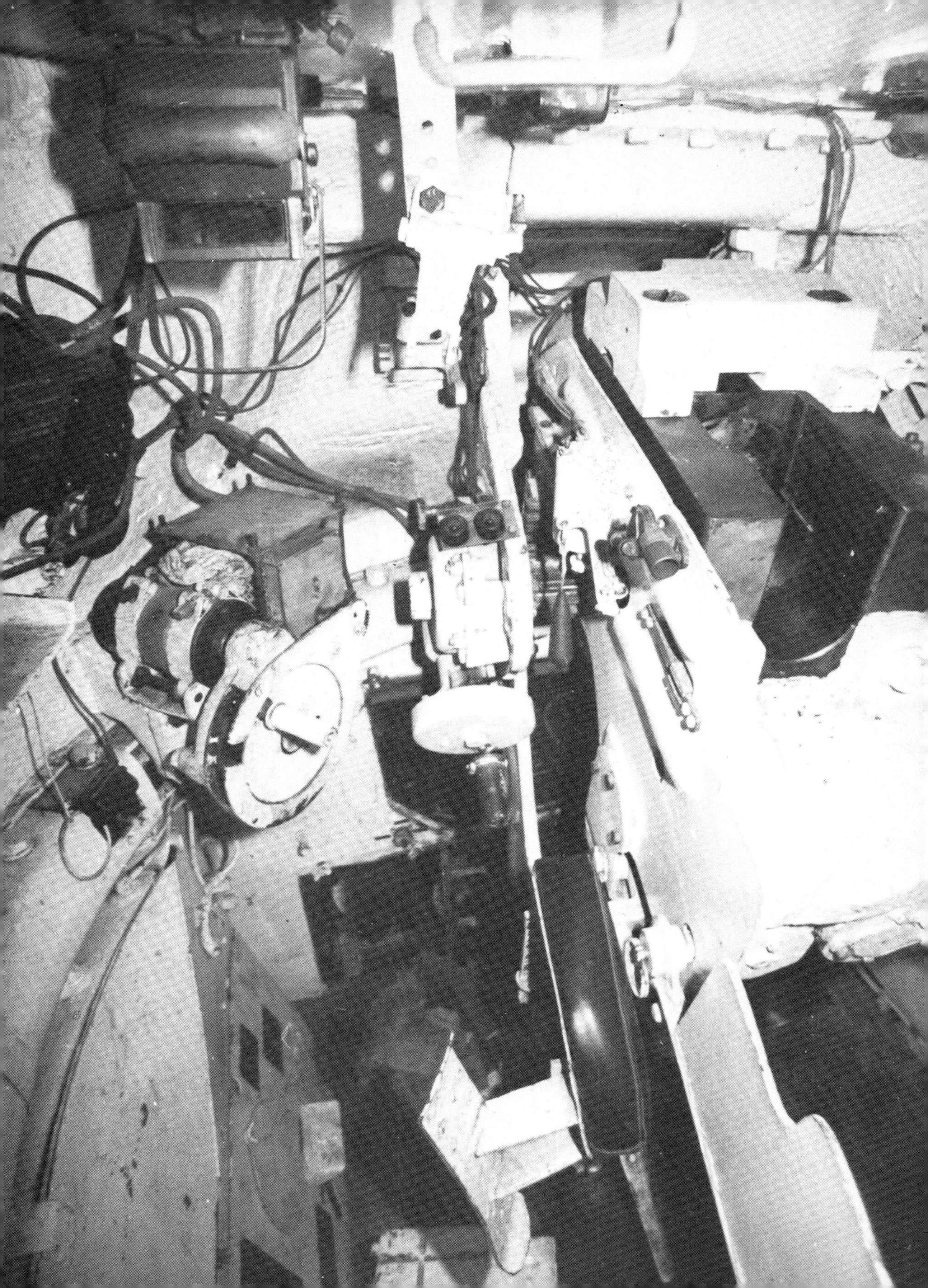

240△

239. This interior view of a T-34-85 was taken from the commander's station looking forward towards the gunner's controls.

240. The crew of a T-34-85 chat with Czech civilians in Prague, May 1945. There were a number of turret variations on the T-34-85 Model 1944, differing mainly in casting and moulding details. (CTK via Jiri Hornat)

completed on 15 December 1943, and the GKO approved the type for Army service despite the problems. To circumvent any further delays, the NKTP ordered the T-34-85 into production on an interim basis, using the runner-up D-5T gun. This entered production at Zavod Nr. 112 Krasnoye Sormovo in December 1943. In the meantime, Grabin's gun was adapted to fit the new turret by Savin, who incorporated other improvements. The modified gun was designated ZiS-S-53, in acknowledgement of Savin's contributions to the design. It supplanted the D-5T on the new T-34-85 Model 1944 in the spring of 1944. The T-34-85 Model 1943 and T-34-85 Model 1944 differed in a number of respects. The most obvious external difference was the gun mantlet, but the Model 1944 also had the commander's cupola moved back to give more room to the gunner and to allow the radio to be moved from its previous position near the hull machine-gunner up into the turret in front of the commander so that he had more control over it. The T-34-85 represented not only an important leap forward in firepower, but finally the T-34 turret was reconfigured for a three-man crew with full vision facilities for the tank commander and with full radio equipment. T-34-85 production did not completely supplant production of the T-34 Model 1943 armed with the 76mm gun at all factories, but did make up the bulk of the 1944 production. It was initially misidentified by the Germans as the T-43, which has led to some reports that the aborted, up-armoured T-43 had been in action, which in fact was not the case.

In October 1943, the NKTP finally cancelled any further light tank production after only 120 T-80s had been built. By this stage in the war, they were completely inadequate against German tanks, and remaining requirements for scout tanks could be satisfied by existing inventories and Lend-Lease shipments of such types as the Valentine. In connection with this decision, in November 1943, the tank brigades were again reorganized: all light tanks were removed from the table of equipment, and the new brigades were composed solely of T-34s and T-34-85s. The mixture of T-34 and T-34-85 was arbitrary depending upon what type was available, though guards units were favoured with the better equipment when possible. Light tanks were retained in mechanized artillery units and some other formations for scouting and liaison duty.

241. The KV-13T was the last of the KV tank line, laying the groundwork for the succeeding IS heavy tanks. The hull configuration was almost identical with the KV-13 and the IS-2.
242. A last-ditch attempt to prolong KV production was undertaken with the KV-1S-85 project, which re-armed the tank with an 85mm gun. The KV-85, however, was deemed more satisfactory.

△241 ▽242

The IS-2 Heavy Tank

During the summer fighting, Kotin's design teams developed several versions of the new KV-13, experimenting with new suspensions, new hull layouts and new turrets. As an interim step, a KV-1S was up-armed with an 85mm gun as the KV-1S-85, but this was not accepted for production because the turret was too small to accommodate the gun and its recoil. A new tank design was developed, based on the KV-13 research and named the IS-1 or IS-85 (after Iosef Stalin; K. Voroshilov having been in disgrace since the beginning of the war).

This mounted an 85mm gun, and was as thickly armoured as the KV-1 Model 1942. However, by redesigning the hull and turret

243. The KV-85 was a stopgap until the IS series entered production; it consisted of a slightly modified KV-1S hull and an IS-1 turret with 85mm gun. Only 130 were built.
244. The IS-1 offered a completely new hull and turret with better armour layout than the KV-1S, but as the 85mm gun was also being adopted by the T-34, IS-1 production was halted in favour of the more heavily armed IS-2 with a 122mm gun.

and by introducing transmission and power-train improvements, the new IS-1 was nearly as mobile as the lightened KV-1S. The prototype was displayed to Stalin in August and won considerable admiration from the GKO. Production would take time to initiate, and there was some concern that the IS-1 was only armed with the same gun as the new T-34-85. To bridge the gap until IS-1 production began, the NKTP ordered the Kirovskiy Works to build a modest number of KV-1S with the more heavily armed turret of the IS-1 as the KV-85. In September and October 1943, 130 KV-85s were manufactured. The Chelyabinsk team adapted two heavier guns to the IS-1, the BS-3 100mm anti-tank gun and the A-19 122mm gun, and these were known respectively as the IS-100

245. This dramatic shot of an IS-2 clearly shows the enormous new gun adopted for it. These tanks were taking part in the attack around Budapest by the 2nd Ukrainian Front in December 1944. (Sovfoto)

246. The IS-2m had a new front bow casting and improvements to the gun fire control system. These IS-2m, probably of the 85th Heavy Tank Regiment, are patrolling a rubble-strewn street in Berlin.

and IS-122 heavy tanks. In November 1943, they were put through firing trials at NIIBT in Kubinka. A captured Panther was used as the target and a 122mm round crashed through the frontal armour and clear through the rear armour as well. However, the 100mm gun had better armour penetration (185mm at 1,000m as compared to 160mm for the 122mm gun). But the 122mm gun was selected because there was a surplus of 122mm tube production facilities and an adequate ammunition base, while the opposite was true for the 100mm gun. A small number of IS-1 with 85mm guns were completed before this decision was made, but with acceptance of the IS-122 for Red Army use by the GKO as the IS-2, the IS-1s were re-gunned before being issued. A total of 102 IS-2s and the prototypes were completed in 1943. The type was in such great demand after its début that in April 1944, the NKTP ordered construction of a new assembly facility at Tankograd to increase production. It first saw action with the 11th Guards Heavy Tank Regiment following the Korsun-Shevchenkovskiy battles in the early spring of 1944.

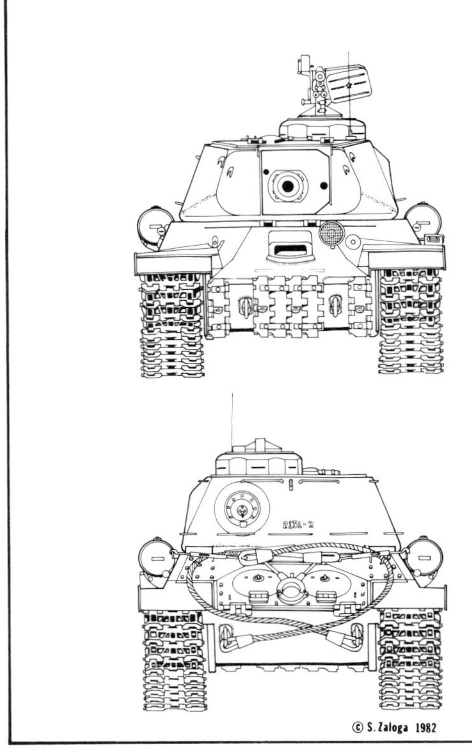

▽245

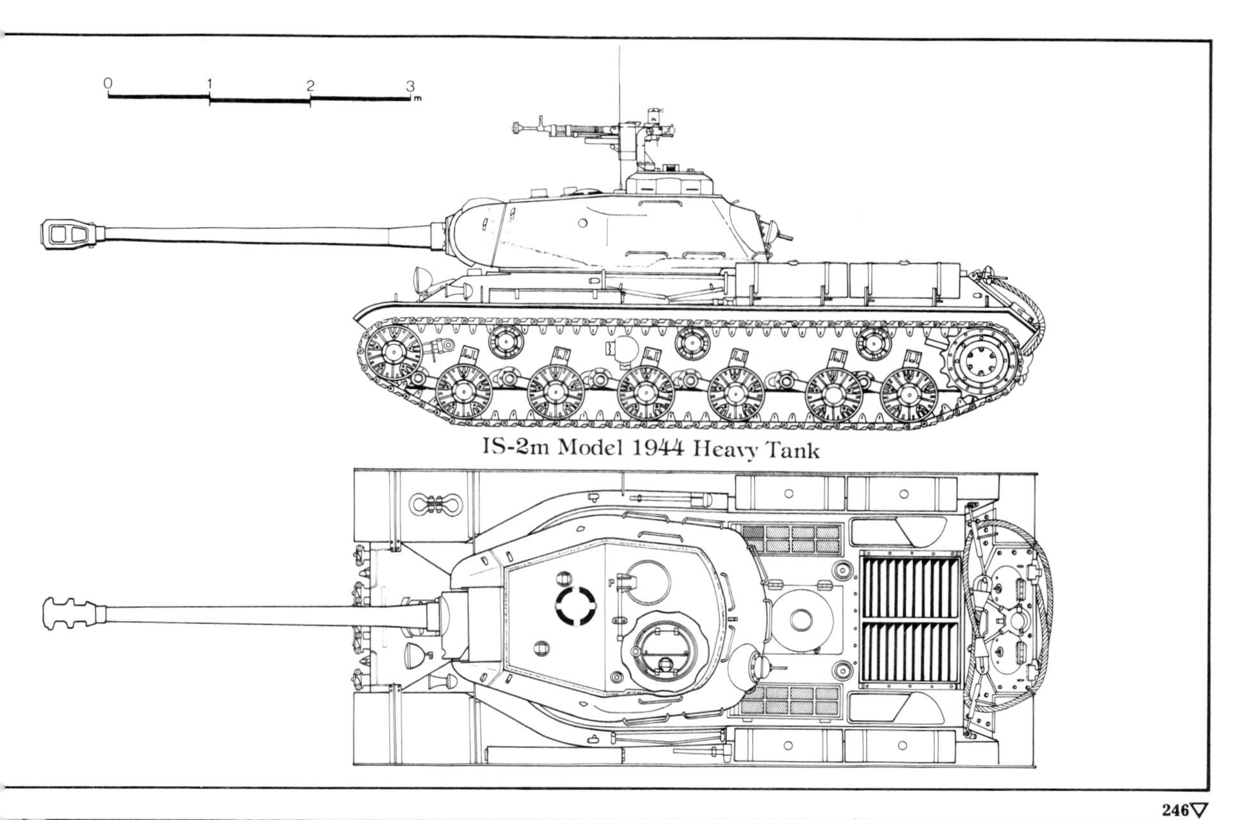

IS-2m Model 1944 Heavy Tank

246▽

247. The IS-2 retained the rear turret machine-gun that had characterized Soviet heavy tanks throughout the war.
248. The sleek lines of the IS-3 heavy tank strongly influenced world tank design after its initial public appearance in September 1945 in Berlin. A small number of them had been in action around Berlin in the spring of 1945. (Sovfoto)

The redesigned hull and layout of the IS-2 gave it better ballistic protection than the KV, and maximum turret armour was an impressive 160mm. Far more appreciated by its crews was the anti-tank capability of the new gun. It delivered 3.5 times more kinetic energy on impact than the 76mm round, and even in the rare case where this was not sufficient to penetrate the armour, the force of the impact and explosion of the high explosive filler was usually enough to blow a turret off almost any tank. The most serious disadvantage of the IS-2 was that its small internal size permitted stowage of only 28 rounds of ammunition, and these were of the split type which slowed the rate of fire. The IS-2 has been compared unfavourably to both the Tiger and later Royal Tiger in terms of armour and firepower, though it should be kept in mind that in terms of weight, size and cost, it was much more comparable to the Panther medium tank than to the much larger and heavier Tiger. Indeed, the Germans' decision to adopt so large, heavy and complex a tank as the Panther for their medium tank was one of the factors which limited German tank production to levels far lower than Soviet production, and helped the Soviets to build up a decisive quantitative advantage in tanks during the final year of the war.

In the spring of 1944, the IS-2 was further improved with the introduction of the IS-2m (m: modifikatsirovanniy). Apart from fire control improvements and other internal changes, the main difference was the use of a

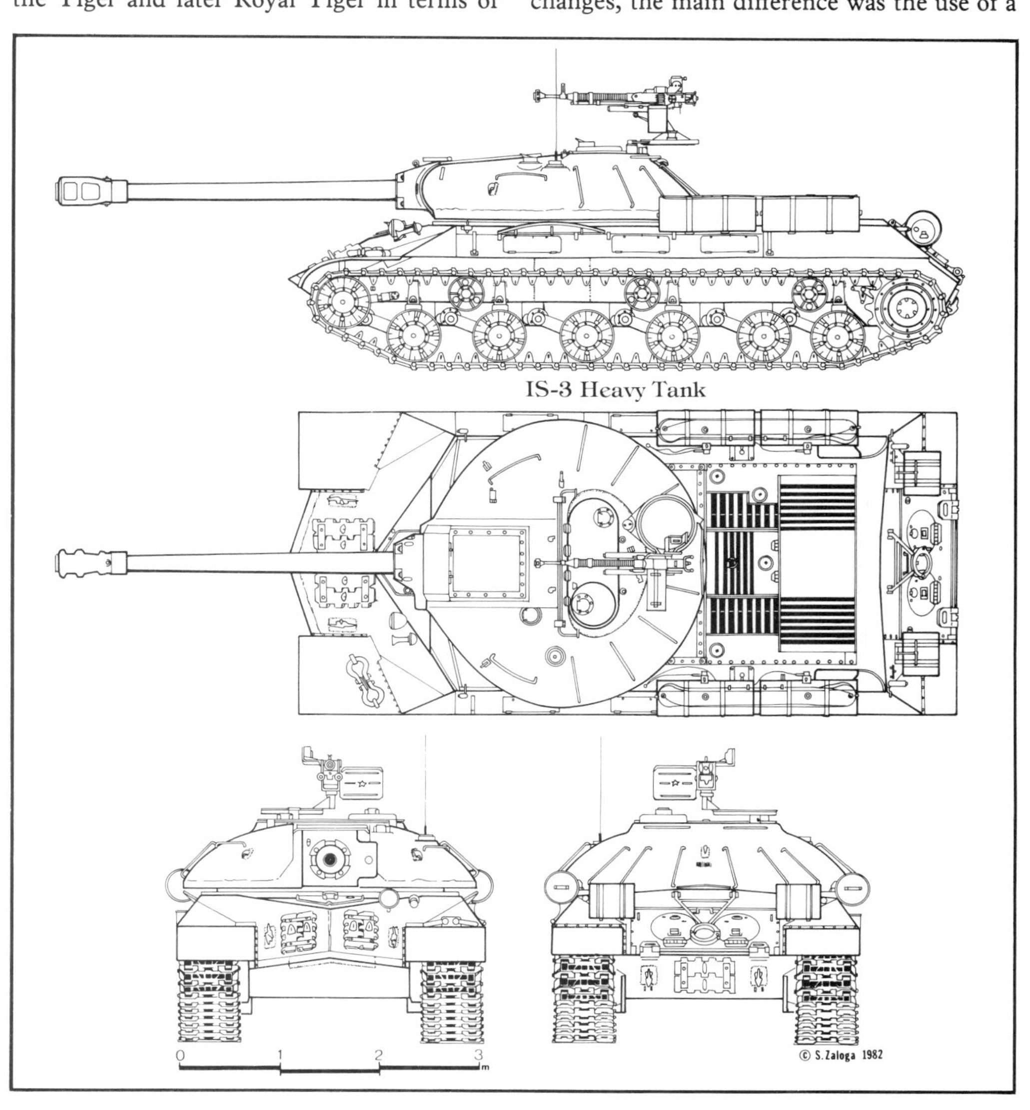

HEAVY TANKS, 1941–45							
Designation	**KV-1 Model 41**	**KV-1 Model 42**	**KV-2 Model 41**	**KV-1S Model 42**	**KV-3 Obiekt 220**	**KV-85 Model 43**	**IS-2 Model 45**
Crew	5	5	6	5	5	4	4
Weight (tonnes)	45	47	52	42.5	63	46	46
Length (cm)	675	680	680	680	840	860	990
Width (cm)	332	332	332	325	325	325	309
Height (cm)	271	271	328	264	310	290	273
Armament	F-34	ZiS-5	M-10T	ZiS-5	F-39	D-5T	D-25T
Gun calibre (mm)	76.2	76.2	152	76.2	85	85	122
Main rounds stowed	111	114	36	114		70	28
Secondary armament	4×DT	4×DT	3×DT	4×DT	3×DT	3×DT	2×DT, DShK
Engine type	V-2	V-2	V-2	V-2	V-2PUN	V-2	V-2
Horsepower	600	600	600	600	850	600	600
Fuel (litres)	600	600	600	975	600	975	820
Max road speed (km/h)	35	28	26	45	33	40	37
Max road range (km)	335	250	225	250	250	250	240
Max terrain range (km)	170	180	150	160	180	180	210
Armour (mm)							
turret front	90	120	110	82	100	160	160
turret side	75	120	75	82	75	110	110
turret rear	75	90	75	82	75	100	100
turret roof	35	40	35	30	35	30	30
hull glacis	75	110	75	75	100	75	120
hull side	75	90-130	75	60	75	60	95
hull rear	60-75	60-75	60-75	40-75	60-75	40-75	60
hull top	30	30	30	30	30	30	30
hull bottom	40	20	40	40	40	40	30
Radio type	71-TK-3	9R	71-TK-3	9R	71-TK-3	9R	10R

249. The ISU-122, like this one of the 1st Polish Army (LWP) crossing the Oder River into Germany in 1945, was the tank destroyer version of the IS-2 tank. In fact, more ISU-122 and ISU-152 assault guns were built than the tank version.
250. The successor to the SU-152 Zvierboy was the ISU-152, based on the IS-2 chassis. It carried the same main gun as the SU-152, but had a slightly higher superstructure. This ISU-152 unit pauses in the streets of Berlin in 1945. (Sovfoto)

new, simpler and better angled bow casting. Also the improved D-25T gun was introduced which was nearly identical with the A-19, but had a drop-breech which speeded loading. A number of experimental versions of the IS-2 were built, with various guns, the most drastic variant being the IS-1E with a new electrical transmission and a new road wheel configuration. None of these were accepted for production. While experiments with the IS-2 were being conducted, TsKB-2 was divided to permit a team under Dukhov to examine a radically re-configured IS-2. Two versions were proposed: the IS-3, with a new hemispherical turret, and the IS-4, with a longer hull and thicker armour. The IS-3 project continued and a prototype was completed in November 1944. It had extremely thick and heavily-rounded turret armour, a heavily sloped bow, and a peculiar side hull construction with large stowage bins over the tracks which offered stand-off protection against the shaped charges of new infantry anti-tank weapons such as the German Panzerfaust. With the prospects of victory, so sanguine, the GKO allowed the Red Army the luxury of a second heavy tank type. About 350 IS-3s were produced up to the end of the war in Europe and about 250 IS-4s were built later. Production of the IS-3 was concurrent with the IS-2m. The IS-3 saw limited action during the final weeks of the war in Germany, and was quickly nicknamed Shchuka (Pike) after its pointed bow. Automotively, the IS-3 and IS-2m were virtually identical, and they also shared the same gun and fire controls. The suspension was based on the same components, and only the armour layout was different.

Heavy Assault Guns

With production of the KV-1S terminated in April 1943 and production of the KV-85 completed in October, the NKTP ordered the design teams at Chelyabinsk to develop an improved derivative of the SU-152 based on the IS-1 hull. The design was straightforward and was undertaken by the BAS with the co-operation of General F. Petrov. This vehicle received the factory designation Obiekt 249 or ISU-249, and was very similar in appearance to the SU-152 except for a higher superstructure. The prototype used the ML-20 gun howitzer accepted for production at the end of 1943 as the ISU-152. By the end of the year, 35 had been produced. The A-19 and ML-20 shared the same carriage and recuperator assembly, so later in 1943, Chelyabinsk developed a version of the ISU-152 with a 122mm gun, simply by switching the barrels and changing the internal ammunition stowage. This was also accepted for production in 1943 as the

249△ 250▽

ISU-122. Externally, both vehicles were identical except for the gun tubes; the ISU-122 had a longer barrel without a muzzle brake.

The ISU-122 and ISU-152 were used by independent heavy mechanized gun regiments in the same way as the SU-152. They were earmarked primarily for use by the tank corps, and were kept in the second line of attack behind tanks to provide long-range cover fire against heavy German tanks or strongpoints. Although nominally an artillery weapon, they were used almost exclusively in the direct fire role, and the regiments were often raised on the basis of existing heavy tank regiments with tank rather than artillery training. As a result of their success in action, additional independent regiments were formed to support rifle and mechanized formations, and finally in December 1944, Guards Heavy Mechanized Artillery Brigades were formed. These were configured like tank brigades with 65 ISU-152 or ISU-122, and attached to tank armies for heavy fire support. Like the earlier regiments, they were often raised on the basis of

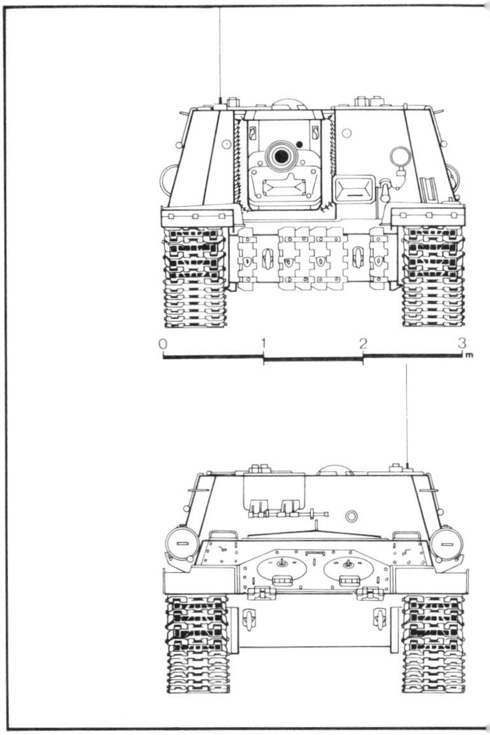

251. In 1945, the ISU-122 was improved with a new ball mantlet and the improved D-25S gun; it was designated the ISU-122S.

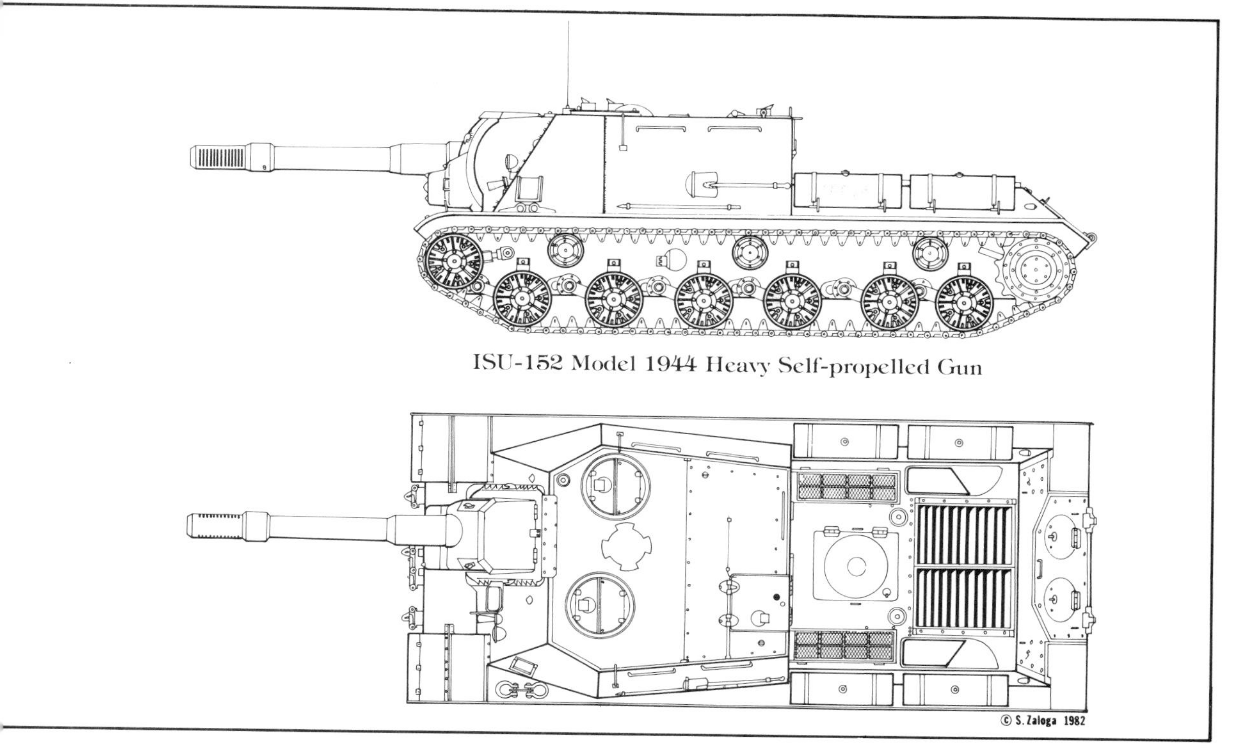
ISU-152 Model 1944 Heavy Self-propelled Gun

© S. Zaloga 1982

existing tank units because their direct fire tactics were closer to tank operations than to any sort of artillery operation. There was no tactical distinction between the ISU-122 or ISU-152. Both types were kept concurrently in production simply because of the availability of 122mm tubes and ammunition, even though the ISU-152 was preferred for most assault roles because of its larger, high explosive rounds. The better anti-tank performance and longer range of the ISU-122 were seldom taken advantage of because of the type of tactics used by these units. The final production series of the ISU-122, the ISU-122S, used the improved D-25 gun with its faster drop-breech, but also had a new ball mantlet and a muzzle brake to reduce recoil. In response to the appearance of the Royal Tiger in August 1944, work was begun on a longer barrelled version of the 122mm gun on both

MECHANIZED GUNS, 1942–45

Designation	SU-76	SU-76M	SU-85	SU-100	SU-122	SU-152	ISU-122	ISU-152
Crew	4	4	4	4	5	5	5	5
Weight (tonnes)	11.2	10.2	29.2	31.6	30.9	45.5	45.5	46
Length (cm)	500	500	815	945	695	895	985	918
Width (cm)	274	270	300	300	300	325	307	307
Height (cm)	220	210	245	225	232	245	248	248
Armament	ZiS-3	ZiS-3	D-5S	D-10S	M-30S	ML-20S	A-19S	ML-20S
Gun calibre (mm)	76.2	76.2	85	100	122	152	122	152
Main rounds stowed	60	60	48	34	40	20	30	20
Engine type	2 × GAZ-202	2 × GAZ-203	V-2	V-2	V-2	V-2	V-2	V-2
Horsepower	70 + 70	85 + 85	500	500	500	600	600	600
Fuel (litres)	400	420	810	770	810	975	860	860
Max road speed (km/h)	44	45	47	48	55	43	37	37
Max road range (km)	265	320	400	320	300	330	220	220
Max terrain range (km)	160	190	200	180	150	120	80	80
Armour (mm)								
hull front	35	35	45	45	45	60	90	90
hull side	16	16	45	45	45	60	90	90
hull rear	16	16	45	45	45	60	60	60
hull roof	10	10	20	20	20	30	30	30
hull bottom	10	10	20	20	20	30	30	30
Radio type	9R	9RM	9R	10-RF-26	9R	9R	10RF	10RF

the IS-2 and ISU-122, and on a longer 152mm gun on the ISU-152 for better armour penetration. The new BL-7 122mm gun was mounted in prototypes of the ISU-122BM and the BL-8 152mm gun was mounted in the ISU-152BM. Neither type was accepted for production because it was soon realized that the few Royal Tigers that did appear were easily dealt with by IS-2s or by the heavy assault guns. Another experimental type was the ISU-122E which had heavier armour and widened tracks to protect it from the latest German 88mm guns, but it was not accepted for service because its mobility was excessively degraded by the armour weight. Just before the war's end, Dukhov's team developed the ISU-130, with a 130mm naval gun on an ISU-122 chassis, but this was not produced until after the war. Instead, the final production batches of the ISU-152 were built on the IS-2m chassis as the ISU-152K with a number of modifications, including an IS-3 engine deck and external stowage bins. This type did not enter production until after the war.

Light Mechanized Guns

Although the SU-76M was no longer viewed as entirely adequate in the tank destroyer after 1943, it remained in production until the end of the war because of its utility as a light assault gun to support infantry. In 1943 it was joined in small numbers by the SU-76i, an assault gun armed with the 76.2mm ZiS-5 gun based on captured Pz Kpfw III and StuG III chassis. Large numbers of these had fallen into Soviet hands, particularly at Stalingrad, and Zavod Nr. 38 converted about 1,200 of them by adding a new, fully-armoured superstructure and gun. The SU-76i first went into action in the autumn of 1943, and seems to have been issued to tank regiments as well as to light mechanized gun regiments.

In an attempt to enhance the anti-tank capability of the SU-76, at least three versions of the SU-76 were built, using a 57mm ZiS-2 gun instead of the usual 76.2mm ZiS-3. The SU-74 was a fully-armoured version with the 57mm in the rear casemate mount. The SU-76D was also fully armoured, but had the 57mm gun and casemate located in a forward position on a shortened chassis with only five road wheels per side. There was also the SU-57B, of which there are few details. None of these were accepted for production because by the time they had been developed and tested, the 57mm anti-tank gun had become less effective against German armour. This led to attempts in 1945 to mount an 85mm anti-tank gun on the SU-76 chassis, and two different prototypes were built, the SU-85A and SU-85B. These did not enter production.

Tank Destroyers of 1944

Unlike the other mechanized guns developed by the Red Army in the Second World War, which were dual-purpose weapons suitable for both anti-tank operations and direct fire support, the SU-85 was developed exclusively as a tank destroyer. In August 1944, the first 100 SU-85 entered service with the

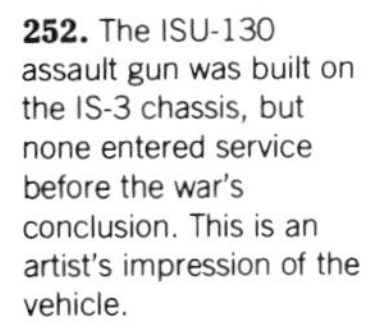

252. The ISU-130 assault gun was built on the IS-3 chassis, but none entered service before the war's conclusion. This is an artist's impression of the vehicle.

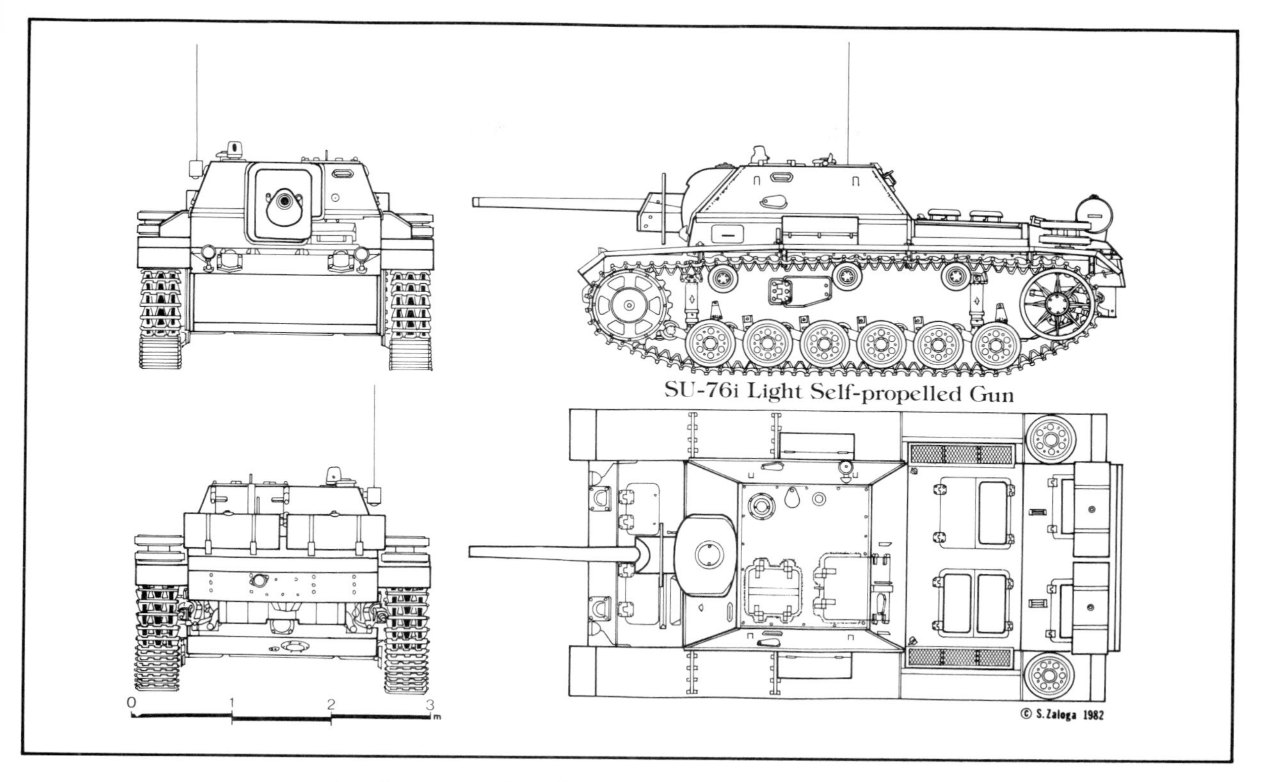

new tank destroyer battalions. These battalions had 16 SU-85 in three batteries, and in 1944, their strength was raised to 21 SU-85. The SU-85 proved reasonably successful in attacking tanks, but care had to be exercised in its deployment because it had no defensive machine-guns. Soviet tank destroyer tactics stressed using these for overwatch of attacking tanks, as they were not suited to close assault tactics. Production of the SU-85 was terminated in the summer of 1944 because by this time, production of the T-34-85 was in full swing and it was pointless to continue to manufacture a tank destroyer on a T-34 hull that was no more potent than the basic tank version. In the meantime, a group headed by General F. Petrov developed a suitable mounting for the new D-10S Model 1944 100mm gun in the form of an improved casemate ball. This new vehicle,

253. The SU-85 was among the best tank destroyers of its day, though it arrived too late to participate in the crucial battle at Kursk. This view of the SU-85 prototype shows the slight detail differences from the production models, particularly with regard to the mantlet.

△254 ▽255

254. A formation of SU-85 of a Polish LWP mechanized gun regiment in action in the winter of 1944–45.
255. The final tank destroyer version of the T-34 was the SU-100. Armed with a long 100mm D-10S gun, it was the most effective tank destroyer developed during the war. A very small number entered service before the war ended.
256. The T-44, one of the most advanced medium tanks of the Second World War, was the culmination of an attempt to improve the T-34. Although it retained a turret very similar to that on the T-34-85, and shared the same roadwheels, track and engine, the hull and engine layout was completely redesigned and a new torsion bar suspension was added. A very small number saw action in the final months of the war.
257. The T-34-100 was an unsuccessful attempt to mount a 100mm gun in a modified T-34-85 turret. The gun proved too large for the chassis.

the SU-100, closely resembled the SU-85 and was identifiable by the improved commander's station with its new vision cupola, and by the longer gun barrel. The final production batches of the SU-85 also had this new vision cupola. SU-100 production began in September 1944 at UZTM in Sverdlovsk. They were employed in new tank destroyer battalions in place of the SU-85, and in the new Guards Mechanized Artillery Brigades, formed in December 1944, each of which had 65 SU-100.

The T-44 Medium Tank

In the summer of 1944, with production of the T-34-85 under way at three tank assembly plants, the Morozov design team began investigating potential improvements. A prototype was built, armed with a 100mm gun as the T-34-100. This vehicle disposed of the hull gunner in favour of carrying more ammunition, but with work on the replacement for the T-34 taking place, interest turned in this direction instead. T-34-85 production continued even after the war until the late

256△ 257▽

LIGHT AND MEDIUM TANKS, 1941–45

Designation	T-60 Model 42	T-70 Model 42	T-80 Model 43	T-34 Model 41	T-34 Model 42	T-34 Model 43	T-34-85 Model 44	T-44 Model 45
Crew	2	2	3	4	4	4	5	4
Weight (tonnes)	6.4	9.2	11.6	26.5	28.5	30.9	32	31.9
Length (cm)	410	429	442	668	668	675	815	765
Width (cm)	430	232	250	300	300	300	300	315
Height (cm)	174	204	218	245	245	245	260	245
Main armament	TNSh	Model 38	Model 38	F-34	F-34	F-34	ZiS-S-53	D-5T
Gun calibre (mm)	20	45	45	76.2	76.2	76.2	85	85
Main rounds stowed	780	94	94	77	77	100	60	58
Secondary armament	DT	DT	DT	2 × DT	2 × DT	2 × DT	2 × DT	2 × DTM
Engine type	GAZ-203	2 × GAZ-202	2 × GAZ-203	V-2	V-2	V-2	V-2	V-44
Horsepower	85	70 + 70	85 + 85	500	500	500	500	500
Fuel (litres)	320	440	440	460	610	790	810	642
Max road speed (km/h)	45	45	45	53	55	55	55	51
Max road range (km)	450	360	320	400	400	465	360	300
Max terrain range (km)	250	180	235	260	260	365	310	210
Armour (mm)								
turret front	25	60	60	52	65	70	90	120
turret side	15	35	35	52	65	52	75	75
turret rear	15	35	35	45	47	52	60	75
turret roof	7	10	10	20	20	20	20	20
hull glacis	35	45	50	45	47	47	47	90
hull side	25	45	25	45	47	60	60	75
hull rear	25	35	25	47	47	47	47	30-90
hull top	13	10	10	20	20	20	20	15
hull bottom	13	10	10	21	21	21	21	20
Radio type	9R	9R	9R	71-TK-3	9R	9R	9R	9R

258. The T-44-100 was an attempt to mount a 100mm gun in the T-44. As with the T-34-100, the turret was too small, and the Red Army had to await the advent of the T-54 two years later before it was equipped with such a heavily-armed medium tank.

1940s, and was resumed in 1953 in Poland and Czechoslovakia where a further 9,000 tanks were manufactured. During the Great Patriotic War alone, some 53,000 T-34s were manufactured, not counting the mechanized gun derivatives, more than all tanks produced by Britain and Germany combined.

At the end of 1943, the T-34M programme was resumed at Nizhni Tagil, although it was quickly redesignated T-44. The archaic Christie suspension with its large internal springs was replaced by a more economical torsion bar suspension. The engine was reoriented in a novel transverse mounting, and a sleek and simple new hull shape was adopted. The first T-44 prototype was completed in the summer of 1944. It used a turret derived from the T-34-85, but without the prominent collar at the base, and with thicker frontal armour. Trials were initiated, but before they were completed it was decided to return the Morozov design team to Kharkov where the former Zavod Nr. 75 Diesel Factory was to be re-established as a tank assembly plant. Further design work continued there and the T-44 was accepted for production in 1945 as an eventual replacement for the T-34-85. The T-44 offered numerous advantages over the T-34-85. It was lower and sleeker, better armoured, and

259. The K-90 was an experimental amphibious tank developed during the closing months of the war. After the war, it would be developed by the Kirovskiy Works in Leningrad into the famous PT-76. Artist's impression.

potentially even easier to manufacture. An attempt was made to fit it with a 100mm gun as the T-44-100, but like the similar T-34 effort it was abandoned because of newer developments, in this case a new turret specially designed for the 100mm gun which would result in the T-54 in 1945–46. About 150–200 T-44s had been completed at Kharkov by the end of the war. The T-44 formed the basis for the post-war dynasty of the T-54, T-55 and T-62, and T-55 production did not cease at Zavod Nr. 13 in Omsk (formerly Zavod Nr. 174) until 1981. In many respects, the T-44 was the most advanced medium tank to have emerged from the Second World War. The initial versions had transmission problems which were rectified in the modernized T-44M after the war. It did not completely replace the T-34-85 on Soviet production lines until 1947 when the improved T-54 entered production.

The K-90 Amphibious Tank

The problem with light scout tanks such as the T-70 and T-80 was that their main guns were ineffective against German tanks of the period so that they could not be used in roles where they would confront enemy armour. For less demanding scouting or liaison roles, inexpensive light armoured cars like the BA-64B could be used instead. Nevertheless, the Red Army was still interested in scout tanks, and in 1944 the NKTP assigned a new design team to study an amphibious tank that could mount a 76mm gun. A prototype, the K-90, was built, but trials revealed that more work was needed. This was undertaken by N. Shashmurin at the Kirovskiy Works after it had been re-established in Leningrad in 1945. This project resulted in the famous PT-76 amphibious scout tank after the war.

Light Fighting Vehicles

Probably the most unusual fighting vehicles to be employed by the Red Army during the Great Patriotic War were the aerosans. These were light sled vehicles, propelled across snow by old aeroplane engines and propellers. The OSGA-6 and KM-5 aerosans were used during the war against Finland. They were of plywood construction and were used mainly to transport supplies when the snow was too deep for wheeled or tracked transport. Some of the OSGA-6 (also known later as the NKL-6) had small machine-gun ring mounts added to the roof and were used for raiding. Four or five men could be carried inside and four men could be towed on skis. During the war, the improved NKL-16/41 and NKL-16/42 aerosans were produced at the Narkomles Factory in Moscow. They

△260 ▽261

proved so useful in the winter of 1941–42 that responsibility for their design and production was transferred to the GABTU. Production was undertaken by the ZiS and GAZ automobile factories as well as by smaller firms such as the Bekietovskiy Wood Works in Stalingrad. In December 1941, GABTU commissioned the Narkomles Factory to design an armoured version of the NKL-16 which could be used in the winter for scouting and raiding in snow too deep to permit the use of tanks or armoured cars. The design team headed by M. Andreyev developed the NKL-26 armoured aerosan. Its armour was limited to 10mm armour plate on the front, because the limited tractive force of the propeller would not permit greater weight. Aerosans, like tanks, were generally organized into battalions, the usual strength being 45 aerosans in three companies. The NKL-26 was usually deployed in company strength formations. In 1942, the Narkoryechflota in Gorki developed an even smaller, unarmoured aerosan, the RF-8 (GAZ-98), powered by a GAZ-M1 lorry engine. It was completely open and armed with a DT

260. The NKL-26 was a lightly armoured aerosan used for winter raiding, and was armed with a single DT machine-gun in an open scarf-ring on the roof.
261. An NKL-16/41 aerosan in operation in 1942. Although this version of the aerosan was used mainly for transport, a machine-gun ring could be fitted to the roof for raiding and patrolling.

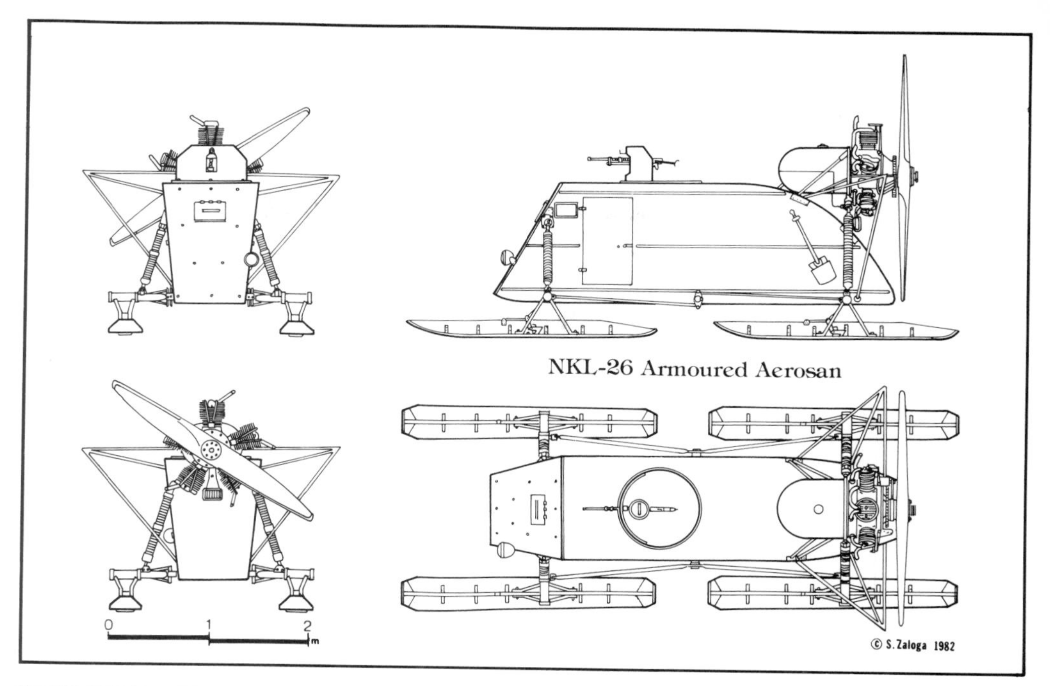

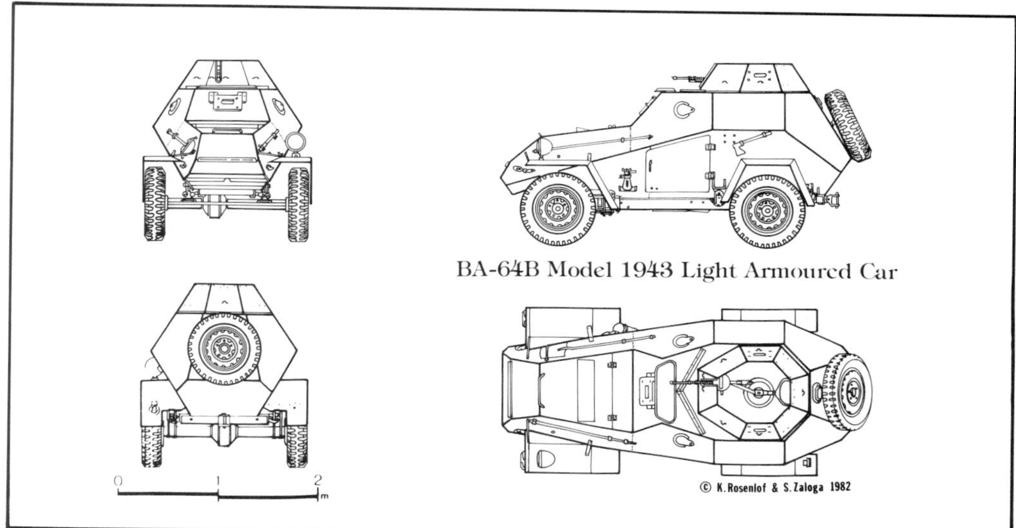

machine-gun in a forward gun tub. Like the NKL-26, it was used for scouting and raiding but had no armour at all. The aerosans were especially prominent in northern areas, and areas featuring frozen lakes or rivers were favoured because the aerosans had very limited ability to climb even shallow hills.

Besides unconventional scout vehicles like aerosans, the Soviets also developed armoured cars during the war, though certainly not so vigorously as before the war. There was a large reserve of BA-10s in the Far East and these were gradually brought into action against the Germans. Indeed, BA-10s could still be seen in action in 1943, long after its contemporaries such as the T-26 or BT had disappeared. The first new armoured car design of the war was the BA-64, developed by Grachev's design team at GAZ on the basis of the GAZ-64 jeep. They were produced in very small numbers at the end of 1941 and into 1942. The BA-64 had a 'coffin'-style hull and was armed with a single DT machine-gun fired from an open pulpit. Development of a troop-carrying version, the BA-64D (desantniy: raider) was

262. The initial version of the BA-64 had a fixed pulpit mount for the roof machine-gun.
263. The BA-64D was intended as a small troop carrier for raiding parties, but only a prototype was built. In appearance it was similar to the BASh-64 staff vehicle.
264. The BA-64B was the most common version of the BA-64, and had a small turret open-topped for its DT machine-gun. In this picture, the two armoured cars have canvas covers over the turret.

△262

△263 ▽264

265. The Ba-64SKh was an experimental version of the BA-64B with skis and a rear track assembly for travelling in deep snow.
266. Two rail versions of the BA-64ZhD were built, but none of these experimental rail scouts were accepted for service use.

265△ 266▽

also undertaken; this could carry six men, but it was not accepted for production. Production of the BA-64 was slow because of more pressing priorities at GAZ and because of the technical shortcomings of the GAZ-64 jeep on which it was based. In 1943, the improved GAZ-67B jeep, which had a wider wheel base, entered production. The armoured car derivative was the BA-64B which became the standard production model of the BA-64. The most noticeable change on the BA-64B was the small turret for the machine-gun. The usual armament was a 7.62mm machine-gun, but in 1944, small numbers of BA-64DShKs were built armed with 12.7mm DShK heavy machine-guns. In some units, improvised armament was used including 14.5mm PTRS anti-tank rifles, and various captured German 20mm cannon. Total production of the BA-64 during the war is uncertain, but was probably about 3,500 vehicles. Several specialized versions were developed but not produced in any quantity. The BASh-64 was a staff vehicle with a variety of armoured rear configurations for map-reading, storing radios and so on. The BA-64SKh was a half-tracked version based on the experimental GAZ-60. There were two rail versions, the BA-64ZhD, which were developed competitively by GAZ and the Vykunskiy Factory. The BA-64B was widely used throughout the Red Army for transporting officers, scouting, liaison duty and other tasks. It was known popularly as the 'Bobik' by its crews, based on the diminutive form of its acronym.

267. The PT-34 was a T-34 tank fitted with a Mugalev mine roller. Seen here is a T-34 Model 1943 of the Polish Army in this role.
268. The mine roller assembly was also fitted to T-34-85s.

Engineer Tanks

In the wake of the fiasco in Finland, the Red Army laid down requirements for a mine-clearing vehicle based on a tank, which would permit engineer units to clear heavily protected minefields from within a tank without exposing themselves to fire. It was to be designed to withstand the blast of heavy anti-tank mines. A team was formed under P. M. Mugalev at the Dormashina Factory in Nikolayev. In 1940, a prototype, using a T-28 tank was completed, but no production ensued, probably because of problems uncovered during testing. Further work was interrupted by the outbreak of war, but in 1942, Mugalev began investigating a new design for various sizes of tanks, including the T-60, KV and T-34. The new unit consisted of a fork on a multi-wheeled axle. Each wheel consisted of a solid centre disc with H-beam girders radiating outwards like a starfish. The whole unit was quite heavy, and on contact with a mine would detonate it, losing an arm or two in the process. Production versions used large cast wheels. Because of the detrimental effect on the clutch and transmission, only the T-34 was adjudged suitable for the role. The first mine-rolling detachments were formed in May 1942. During the Voronezh fighting in August, the 233rd Tank Battalion of the 86th Tank Brigade had at least two experimental units of mine trawls in action. Further development work was undertaken to improve the system, and the first major commitment of an entire unit took place in October 1943 with the 166th Independent Engineer Tank Regiment attached to the 3rd Guards Tank Army. These regiments had 18 trawls and 22 T-34 tanks. Only a portion of the tanks had the trawls fitted and were designated PT-34, while the other tanks provided covering fire. A trawl could withstand from eight to ten detonations of 5–10kg anti-tank mines. At least five of these regiments were formed: the 148th and 253rd Engineer Tank Regiments with the 3rd Byelorussian Front, the 92nd Engineer Tank Regiment with the 5th Shock Army and the 119th and 166th Engineer Tank Regiments with the 1st Byelorussian Front. They were used throughout the war, and the Mugalev system is not only still in use with Soviet tank units, but is being adopted by US and Israeli tank units in the 1980s.

△267 ▽268

269. Here, a T-37 tank is attached to the belly of a TB-3 bomber for delivery during an airborne attack. This curious means of reinforcing an airborne landing was reportedly used in 1940 in Roumania.

Airborne Fighting Vehicles

Designs proposed for Soviet airborne units included some of the most bizarre in the history of fighting vehicles. This menagerie got off to a good start in 1930 when the Grokhovskiy OKB (Special Design Bureau) was assigned the task of developing 'air buses'. The problem was that silk was expensive and rare in Russia at the time, so there was some interest in developing techniques to drop troops without the need for parachutes. Apart from experiments in dropping men from low altitudes into snow drifts, the air bus offered the most promising alternative. Two designs were put forward, the G-45 and an amphibious version called the hydro airbus. The G-45 was a large wing aerofoil section with bicycle wheels suspended on large springs. The idea was to carry one of these, with twelve men inside, under the belly of a TB-1 bomber, approach over the target area low and slow, and drop the airbus which, theoretically would skid to a stop. It was a silly idea and after the prototype of the amphibious version disintegrated on landing during trials over water, the designer and his assistant were strapped into the land version for trials; they survived but the concept did not.

The next venture of the intrepid air pioneers was to strap T-27 tankettes under bombers, and land them on airfields. This concept was straightforward, and later airborne divisions were usually equipped with special airborne tank companies whose T-37 amphibious tanks were also carried under bombers. In 1935, there were more attempts to drop these vehicles without parachutes, this time into water. The results are unrecorded. There are reports that during the 1940 seizure of Bessarabia from Roumania, the airborne units assigned to capturing airfields were reinforced by light tanks which were dropped from only a few metres by slow-flying TB-3 bombers. They were apparently without crews, and one hopes the clutches were in neutral. Some of the airborne units received T-40 tanks in 1941.

The dubious results of these early ventures led to a Soviet Air Force (VVS) assignment to the famous O. Antonov in 1942 to design a glider to land tanks in support of airdrops. Disdaining the conventional approach, as in the British Hamilcar glider for the Tetrarch tank, Antonov used the tank itself as the fuselage, and added a biplane wing assembly and forked tail attached by a special detachable cradle. The design, the A-40T Krylia Tank (Flying Tank), used a T-60 light tank. Trials of the prototype were unsuccessful; even with the clutch in neutral, the tracked suspension was very difficult to tow at the high speeds necessary to get the glider to take

▽269

270. The A-40T, seen here as the designer's model, was a bizarre attempt to fly in light tanks to support airborne formations. It proved impracticable because the tank suspension could not stand up to the high speeds at take-off or landing.
271. The KSP-63 was an attempt to develop a light mechanized gun to support airborne or scout units, and mounted a ZiS-3 76.2mm divisional gun. The chassis was too small to absorb the recoil and series production was not undertaken.

off, and so the project was abandoned. Work on other airborne projects during the war were not given great priority because of the lack of sufficient transport aircraft to mount major airborne operations. In 1943 the NKTP sponsored an attempt to develop a wheeled assault gun, the KSP-76, for use by airborne units and to provide support to wheeled scouting units. The vehicle was based on a GAZ-63 chassis and armed with a 76.2mm ZiS-3 divisional gun like the SU-76. However, the chassis proved too light to withstand the repeated recoils of the gun, and the project was discontinued. Further airborne vehicle development was postponed until after the war.

270△ 271▽

272. The OT-34 had a flame-thrower fitted in place of the hull machine-gun and is identifiable from the stubby flame projector which replaced the usual DT machine-gun.
273. The KV-8 flame-thrower tank had the flame projector mounted in the turret in place of the main gun. To provide some protection, a 45mm gun in a larger dummy sleeve was also fitted.
274. The KV-8S was a similar flame-thrower tank based on the improved KV-1S chassis.

△272

Flame-thrower Tanks

During the 1930s, the Red Army pioneered the use of flame-thrower tanks, based primarily on the T-26, but because of the defensive tactics of the Soviets during the first year of the war, the type fell into disuse. In 1942, interest revived, and a new tank flame-thrower, the ATO-41 was developed. It was mounted in KV tanks as the KV-8 and in the T-34 tank as the OT-34. When used in the KV it replaced the main gun although a smaller 45mm gun was carried next to the flame projector in a false gun barrel which simulated the usual 76mm gun barrel. This was done to prevent German anti-tank gunners singling out the vulnerable flame-thrower tanks for special attention. The T-34 version also had the fuel internally stored, but the flame projector was placed in the hull machine-gun position, leaving precious little room in the turret for the gun crew. These original types were not entirely successful because of the small amount (100litres) of fuel carried and other problems. An improved flame-thrower was developed, the ATO-42, which was mounted in KV-1S as the KV-8S and in the T-34 Model 1943 as the OT-34. It was also later fitted into the T-34-85 as the TO-34. The ATO-42 could fire four to five bursts every ten seconds, each burst consuming ten litres of fuel. The range varied from 60 to 120 metres depending on the mixture. Few of the KV-8S were built. The original independent flame-thrower battalions had three companies, two of KV-8 with ten tanks and one company of OT-34s with eleven OT-34s. These units were put at the disposal of fronts or armies for special operations. Later in the war the units were re-configured. Due to the lack of KV-8 flame-thrower tanks, the units consisted of two companies of OT-34s and one company of T-34 gun tanks to provide covering fire.

mm M.G. in
Kugelblende
7,62 mm Fla.M.G.-Ha
auf drehbarer Turm
Waffenblende
90 mm
30 mm+
Decke
40 mm
25 mm
40 mm
Boden: 40mm
30 mm+
B 736
1494.4

273△ 274▽

275. A small number of T-34s were also modified as recovery tractors by removing their turrets. These were generally built on tank chassis which had been knocked-out in combat but were too badly damaged to rebuild as tanks.

276. In 1945 a small number of worn-out KVs were used in a turretless form for tank repair and recovery.

△275 ▽276

277. The only armoured vehicle used by the Red Army specifically for recovery purposes was the Lend-Lease M-31. This one was transferred to the Polish 24th Tank Repair Battalion by the Soviet Army in November 1944.

Armoured Recovery Vehicles

The Soviets developed few specialized armoured recovery vehicles during the war. Recovery operations were usually conducted by caterpillar tractors such as the S-60, but towards the end of the war some damaged T-34 and KV tanks were rebuilt without turrets and used for vehicle recovery. These usually had the turret ring plated over, and in some cases, a small cupola was added for vision. The USSR received US M31 ARVs which had full facilities such as winches and cranes. These were the only purpose-built recovery vehicles used by the Soviets.

Bridging Tanks

In the 1930s, the Red Army experimented with bridging tanks based on the T-26, BT and T-28, but none were produced in any significant numbers. During the Great Patriotic War, there were no standardized bridging tanks, but there were a number of local attempts to develop improvised bridging tanks for special operations. The most common configuration was the building of a bridge section on a turretless T-34 hull which would then be driven into the gap or river it was supposed to cover. If a longer bridge were needed, more T-34 bridging vehicles would be driven over in succession until the gap was bridged. The use of bridging tanks in water ruined the tank, so they were used only in extraordinary circumstances. The first reported case of their use was in the Donets River south of Belograd, when several dozen bridge T-34s were used to form a concealed underwater crossing on 3 August 1944 for a surprise attack on the German 320th Infantry Division.

277▽

△278 ▽279

280△

278. The original version of the ZSU-37 was based on the failed SU-76 chassis. Necessary corrections to the powertrain delayed development of this anti-aircraft tank.
279. A small number of the ZSU-37 anti-aircraft tank were built in 1944 and 1945, but it was never entirely successful because of inadequate turret traverse speed.
280. The only artillery tractor built in significant numbers during the war was the YA-12 based on T-60 tank components.

Anti-Aircraft Vehicles

At the outset of the war, the standard Soviet air defence vehicle was the quad Maxim machine-gun mount, the 4M on the GAZ-AAA lorry. This was supplemented by smaller numbers of ZiS-42 self-propelled 25mm anti-aircraft cannon. Additional air protection was offered by the DT machine-guns carried on some tanks. The first serious attempt to develop an armoured vehicle specifically for air defence took place in 1942 on the basis of the T-60 light tank. A new turret was designed, armed with twin 12.7mm DShK heavy machine-guns and with optical sights. It was envisaged that such a vehicle could be used both for air defence and for attacking unarmoured ground targets. No further work took place on this vehicle because in the meantime, the T-70 light tank had become available. The turret system was transferred to the T-70 chassis, and the resulting vehicle was designated the T-90 light tank. The programme was terminated in 1943 in favour of mounting a heavier 37mm anti-aircraft gun on a modified SU-76 chassis, the ZSU-37. About 6 per cent of Soviet tank losses could be attributed to enemy aircraft, averaging about 90 tanks monthly by 1944.

The ZSU-37 was developed from the beginning of 1942 at Zavod Nr. 37. The first prototypes were based on the original SU-76, with the attendant transmission problems. The original prototype also had problems with turret traverse speed which led to a complete redesign in 1943 on an improved SU-76M hull. This was finally accepted for production in 1944. Full-scale production of the ZSU-37 was prevented because of the inadequate turret traverse speed, and only a few hundred vehicles were produced. A derivative, mounting two 25mm automatic cannon, the ZSU-25 was also developed, but this was built in even smaller numbers in 1945. For air defence needs, Soviet mechanized columns relied on towed weapons, on small numbers of lorry-mounted 37mm guns, or on American Lend-Lease types such as the M15 and M17. The M17 was the most common air defence vehicle in tank units.

Artillery Transporters

As a result of the priority afforded to tank production during the war, development of artillery transporters was sharply curtailed. Serious work did not begin until 1943, after the turning-point in the war had been reached. The design bureau at YAZ began development of an artillery transporter that could be used to tow and support the 152mm ML-20 gun howitzer. It was designed to use redundant suspension components from the T-60 light tank which was no longer in production. The original version, the YA-11 was powered by a GAZ-204 engine. This engine was inadequate, and an improved version, the YA-12, was designed using Lend-Lease GM 4-71 engines. This was accepted for production and in 1943 285 were built; in 1944,

△281

281. The ATP artillery transporter was intended to fulfil the same role as the earlier Komsomolyets. After the war it was produced in modified form as the AT-PM. An artist's conception of the prototype is shown here.
282. Armoured trains built during the war often used tank turrets on the artillery cars. This train, built in Moscow, used the turrets from a T-28 medium tank. (Sovfoto)
283. This small armoured rail trolley uses an old T-26 Model 1931 turret for its armament. These self-propelled trolleys were used to scout the rails in front of an armoured train checking for booby traps and enemy troops. (Sovfoto)

982; and in 1945, 399. A similar effort was launched to develop a medium artillery transporter on the T-34 chassis, using a standard lorry cab and flatbed rear. A prototype, the AT-45 was built, but no production ensued. By 1944, with pressure on the tank industry lessening, some attention was paid to the need for light artillery tractors akin to the pre-war Komsomolyets. At Zavod Nr. 75 in Kharkov, a light 200hp tractor, the ATK was designed, and at Zavod Nr. 40 in M'tishchi several similar light tractors were developed including the ATD-D, ATD-K and the AT-P. There were several other transporter projects at the time, such as the K-75 and K-78, but few details are available. None of these were accepted for production during the war, but the AT-P served as the basis for the AT-PM which entered Red Army service after the war.

Armoured Trains

Armoured trains did not play as prominent a role in the Great Patriotic War as in the Civil War, but were still operated in very large numbers. By 1941, they had become extremely vulnerable to air attack, and did not fare very well when opposed by tanks. There were several instances in the 1942 Crimea fighting between tanks and Russian armoured trains, with the trains usually being the victim. The main role played by conventional armoured trains was as mobile artillery batteries providing indirect fire. They were seldom used in their Civil War role providing direct fire support or being used in combined train-infantry attacks. For example, during the battles in the Stalingrad area, there were eight armoured train battalions in action, mainly offering artillery support. Apart from pre-war armoured trains that survived the 1941 disaster, most of the armoured trains used during the Great Patriotic War were armed with tank turrets, most commonly from the T-34, but also from KV heavy tanks. Another important role in which armoured trains were employed was air defence of transport lines. Special anti-aircraft armoured trains were developed with anti-aircraft guns and machine-guns. These escorted important rail shipments, or were used around major rail junctions.

282△ 283▽

284. Air defence trains, like this one, armed with 12.7mm DShK heavy machine-guns, were one of the major new roles undertaken by armoured trains during the Great Patriotic War.
285. This armoured train used the turret and hull section from a T-34. The slogan reads 'Death to the German Occupiers'. Such trains did not play a central role in the Eastern Front fighting comparable to their role in 1917–1920, and were mainly used to provide indirect artillery support. (Sovfoto)
286. 'Soviet Armenia' is fairly typical of the armoured trains built in the 1930s. Each turret is armed with a 76.2mm regimental gun.

△**284**

△**285** ▽**286**

СМЕРТЬ
НЕМЕЦКИМ ОККУПАНТАМ.

287. This armoured trolley uses a T-26 turret with a 45mm gun as its armament. These trolleys could carry a small infantry detachment for scouting.
288. This snow-camouflaged vintage 1930 armoured train was equipped with a 76.2mm divisional gun in each turret.

△287 ▽288

289. The armoured train 'Baltiyets' was equipped with two KV turrets on its artillery cars, and played an important role in the fighting in the Leningrad siege.
290. Besides armoured trains, the Soviets also used armoured rail batteries which differed in that they were fitted with much heavier guns, often taken from ships, and were not fully protected. This armoured battery is typical. The slogan on the side reads 'Blood for blood! Death for death!'

289△ 290▽

Lend-Lease Tanks

Besides its own tanks, the Red Army used extensive quantities of Lend-Lease tanks and other armoured vehicles from the USA, Great Britain and Canada. A total of 22,800 armoured vehicles were supplied to the Red Army during the war, of which 1,981 were lost at sea on the dangerous Arctic convoys. In total, Lend-Lease armoured vehicles amounted to about 20 per cent of the total number of armoured vehicles manufactured by the Soviet Union during the Great Patriotic War. These shipments were the equivalent of 16 per cent of Soviet tank production, 12 per cent of self-propelled gun production, and all of Soviet armoured troop transporter production, because the Soviet Union did not produce armoured troop carriers during the war. The first shipments of tanks were dispatched in 1941, amounting to 487 Matildas, Valentines and Tetrarchs from the UK and 182 M3A1 light tanks and M3 medium tanks from the USA. In 1942, Britain provided a further 2,487 tanks and the USA 3,023 tanks. The first units equipped with Valentines and Matildas went into service in the Staraya Russa and Valdai areas in December 1941 and January 1942. It is interesting to note that these brigades were equipped with Lend-Lease and captured German tanks. Although the Soviets had hoped to form homogeneous Lend-Lease units, the Lend-Lease tanks were used in conjunction with Soviet tank types throughout the war. Usually tank brigades or regiments were allotted a single type of Lend-Lease tank to simplify logistics. A typical example of Soviet units equipped with Lend-Lease tanks was the 38th Tank Brigade which in 1942 was equipped with thirty Matildas and sixteen T-60 light tanks. In 1943, the composition of Soviet tank brigades varied. Brigades equipped solely with Russian tanks amounted to about 61–68 per cent of the force; mixed brigades (Russian and Lend-Lease), 19–22 per cent; solely Lend-Lease equipped, 10–17 per cent. At the beginning of 1943, there were 1,023 Lend-Lease tanks in Soviet units although 6,179 had been received since 1941. In 1944 and 1945, with a major influx of American M4A2 Sherman medium tanks, some tank corps and mechanized corps were equipped entirely with this tank type. For example, in 1945, the 1st Guards Mechanized Corps was equipped entirely with M4A2 Shermans in its tank units.

The role of Lend-Lease equipment in the Soviet war effort has been the source of bitter controversy, with some Western histories attributing to it a decisive impact on the war on the Eastern Front, and Soviet historians generally denigrating it as inconsequential. While the supply of Lend-Lease armoured vehicles was hardly decisive, it played a very useful role, particularly in 1941 and 1942 when the Soviet armoured force was recovering from the disastrous defeats of the summer of 1941, the evacuation of the tank factories and slump in Soviet tank production in the autumn and winter of 1941, and in the wake of the defeats in the Caucasus in the summer of 1942. Lend-Lease tanks during this period played a vital role in preventing the tank strength of the Red Army from stagnating or actually decreasing. Neither should it be forgotten that Britain sent the Russians 14 per cent of her own tank production, even though the Soviet Union out-produced Britain threefold in tanks, and this in 1941 and 1942 when the British Army was very short of tanks in the Western Desert. Far more critical to the Soviet war effort was the supply of tactical vehicles, primarily from the United States. During the war, the Soviet Union produced only 343,624 cars and lorries due to the heavy commitment of major automobile factories like GAZ to armoured vehicle production. The USA alone provided the Soviets with 501,660 tactical wheeled and tracked vehicles, including 77,972 jeeps, 151,053 1–½-ton trucks, and 200,662 2–½-ton trucks. This massive influx of vehicles provided the tank and mechanized corps with vital mobility in the 1944 and 1945 drives into Central Europe, and allowed the Soviet automobile industry to concentrate on armoured vehicle manufacture. The aid was vital, not only because of the sheer quantity, but because of the quality. While Soviet automotive production concentrated almost exclusively on antiquated copies of American 1930 lorry designs, the vehicles provided under Lend-Lease were modern military designs with multiple powered axles and useful cross-country capability. The enormous influence of these designs on Soviet post-war vehicle design is very evident. Indeed, US trucks with their 'USA' serials still visible became so commonplace in Eastern Europe during the later years of the war that common folk-lore in the region interpreted these stencilled letters as meaning 'Ubiyat Sukinsyna Adolfa' (Kill that Son-of-a-Bitch Adolf).

Besides criticising the .quantity of Lend-Lease armoured vehicles provided to the Red Army, Soviet historians have belittled the quality of the tanks provided. The Valentine and Matilda in particular have been singled out as being inferior to the T-34. This was evidently the case, but it should be remembered that the British Army did not have any better tanks at the time, and furthermore, the Valentine and Matilda were far superior to the dreadful little T-60 and certainly comparable to the later T-70 which the Soviets were building in very large numbers. While the Soviet Army was unhappy with the American M3 medium tank, the same complaints were voiced by American tank crews who were also using it at the same time in Tunisia. The M3A1 Stuart light tanks were easily comparable or superior to Soviet T-60 and T-70 light tanks, and the M4A2 Sherman, while not as brilliant a design as the T-34, was far more durable and reliable than its Soviet counterpart. In the post-war encounters between the M4 and the T-34 in Korea and the Middle East, the Sherman was invariably the victor despite the superiority of the T-34 on paper.

Valentine Infantry Tank. The Valentine was the most common type of tank shipped by Britain and Canada to the Soviet Union, totalling 1,388 Canadian and about 2,394 British vehicles. This accounted for nearly all Canadian production of this type, and about 29 per cent of British production. The Soviets received most of the variants of the basic tank including both the 2pdr and 6pdr armed versions, and a small number of bridge-layers. The Valentine proved the most popular British tank in Soviet service, preferred to the Matilda because of its better mobility. In fact, in 1943 when the British offered the Soviets the Cromwell in place of the older types, it was refused in favour of the Valentine. There had been plans to terminate Valentine production in 1943 on the grounds of obsolescence, but production was continued into 1944 solely to satisfy Soviet requirements. In 1942 the Soviets tried to re-arm the Valentine with a 76.2mm gun, but this was unsuccessful because the turret was too small.

291▽

291. Numerically the most important British and Canadian tank supplied to the Soviet Union through Lend-Lease was the Valentine. This Valentine was taking part in Soviet operations during the Rzhev fighting in the winter of 1942–43.

292 (overleaf). Here, a Valentine Mk VIII with 6pdr gun awaits unloading in Iran during transit to Russia. (US Army)

123

173

293. A Soviet tank commander instructs his driver on a Valentine Mk V.
294. A Matilda infantry tank goes into action in support of Soviet infantry in 1942. The Matilda was not as popular as the Valentine because of its sluggish performance, especially in winter.
295. A Russian Churchill Mk IV during the summer of 1943. The Churchill was considered a heavy tank by the Russians, and so was compared unfavourably with the KV. (National Archives)

△293

Matilda Infantry Tank. The Matilda was the second most common type of British tank in Soviet service. It was not as popular as the Valentine because it was slow and performed poorly in winter. Many Russian Matildas had sections of steel bar welded diagonally to their tracks for better traction in snow. General Federenko, head of the Soviet armoured force during the war, recommended to the British advisory teams that the Matilda be redesigned without the outer side armour so as to reduce its weight and prevent snow and mud from accumulating and damaging the suspension. The Matilda was far more heavily armoured than the T-60 or T-70 and so was more useful as an infantry support tank despite its indifferent speed.

Churchill Infantry Tank. Small numbers of Churchills were supplied to the Red Army from May 1942. These were all the 6pdr armed versions. The Soviets regarded the Churchill as a heavy tank and, in fact, during the critical fighting at Prokhorovka during the battle of Kursk, the 5th Guards Tank Army's only heavy tanks were 35 Churchills. The Russians showed no enthusiasm for the Churchill, and none were provided after 1942.

294△ 295▽

296. A Russian Churchill Mk III disabled during the fighting in the summer of 1943. (National Archives)
297. Only 20 of the Tetrarch light airborne tanks were supplied to the Red Army, and they made little impression.

△296 ▽297

298. The Universal Carrier was supplied to the Red Army by Britain, Canada and the United States and was used mainly as a command vehicle, scout vehicle and transporter rather than as an infantry carrier. Here, however, it is being used in its intended role as a Soviet rifle squad disembarks.

299. An M3 Stuart light tank captured by Hungarian troops in 1943. Some of these early versions were shipped from Britain in 1941. Most of the American shipments were of the diesel M3A1.

298△ 299▽

Tetrarch Airborne Tank. A total of twenty Tetrarchs were supplied to the Red Army via Iran in 1941. They were much photographed for propaganda purposes, but played a minuscule role in the Lend-Lease programme.

Universal Carriers. A total of 2,656 Universal Carriers were sent to the Soviet Union during the war from the UK, Canada and the USA. They were used mainly as troop transporters, scout and liaison vehicles. They were not as popular as the American halftracks because they did not have the carrying capacity and had poor performance in snow because of their narrow tracks.

M3A1 Light Tank. A total of 1,676 M3A1 Stuart light tanks were shipped to the Red Army during the war, nearly all of them being the diesel powered version. A small number of earlier M3s were shipped from UK stocks in 1941. The Stuart was criticized by the Soviets for its high silhouette, and the hull machine-guns were ridiculed as being useless. While both these complaints were justified, the Stuart was superior to the T-60 in nearly all respects, and comparable or superior to the T-70. Five M5A1s and two M-24 Chaffee light tanks were provided as samples, but the Russians requested more M4A2 Shermans instead.

M3 Medium Tank. A total of 1,386 M3 Lee Medium tanks were shipped to the Red Army during the war, nearly all being the M3A3 and M3A5 diesel powered versions. Its high silhouette and archaic configuration made it less popular than the later M4 Sherman tanks. It was sometimes derisively referred to as a 'Grave for Seven Brothers'. The M31 armoured recovery version was also supplied.

300. A Soviet M3A1 Stuart and T-34 Model 1943 of the 5th Guards Tank Army rest in Lenin Street, Byelgorod during the winter counter-offensive in February 1943. This tank army played a critical role in the summer encounter at Prokhorovka during the battle of Kursk. (Sovfoto)

301. An M3A3 Lee medium tank burns after having been disabled during fighting in the summer of 1943. The tank was not terribly popular because of its archaic configuration. (National Archives)

300▽ 301△

△302 ▽303

302. An M4A2 (75mm gun) rests in Brno in May 1945 with its crew happily posing with Czechoslovak resistance fighters. (Ivan Bajtos)
303. A column of Russian M4A2 (76mm) Sherman tanks line the streets of Brno on 26 April 1945. Shermans were the single most common type of Allied tank supplied to the Soviet Union, and played a prominent role in the 1944–45 fighting. (CTK via Jiri Hornat)
304. An M4A2 (76mm) passes over the Emms River bridge at Leizen, Austria at the end of the war. (US Army)

M4A2 Medium Tank. The M4A2 Sherman medium tank was supplied in larger numbers than any other American or British tank during the war. A total of 4,252 were sent, about evenly divided between the version with the 75mm gun and the improved version with the 76mm gun. All those supplied were the M4A2 version with diesel engines. The Soviets tried re-arming some of 75mm version with the F-34 gun, these becoming known as the M4M. This conversion does not appear to have been very widespread because there were ample supplies of US 75mm ammunition, but the Germans captured at least a small number of this version. The Sherman was widely used during the last year of the war, and as mentioned earlier, some tank and mechanized corps were equipped entirely with this type. The tank destroyer version of the Sherman, called the M10, was supplied in small numbers.

304▽

Halftracks. The USA provided the Soviets with 2,278 halftracks including the troop carrier versions, and various gun motor carriage types. The troop carrier versions such as the M2, M3, M5 and M9 were used mainly as command vehicles. Probably the most popular halftrack types supplied were the M17 Multiple Gun Motor Carriage armed with quad 0.50cal machine-guns and the M15A1 Multiple Gun Motor Carriage armed with a 37mm automatic cannon and twin 0.50cal machine-guns. These were the only armoured anti-aircraft vehicles available to the Red Army during the war in any quantity. They were used mainly by tank and mechanized corps for air defence. The T-48 tank destroyer was an M3 halftrack armed with a 57mm anti-tank gun. The majority of the production run was sent to the Red Army where it was called the SU-57. It was used to form special tank destroyer brigades, each having about 60 SU-57 in three battalions. The first of these was the 16th Tank Destroyer Brigade which first went into action in August 1943. These units remained in action until the end of the war. Some of the US halftracks were later turned over to the Polish Peoples Army which fought on the Eastern Front in 1943–45. These included troop halftracks as well as M17s and T-48s.

M3A1 Scout Car. A total of 3,340 M3A1 scout cars were sent to the Red Army during the war. They were used mainly as scout vehicles, command cars and radio vehicles to supplement the BA-64.

Foreign Tanks. Besides Lend-Lease tanks, the Red Army used a number of other foreign tank types during the war, mostly captured German armoured vehicles. Some units were formed entirely of captured German tanks or assault guns, while others, particularly during the first year of the war, used small numbers of German tanks to supplement their strength.

305. The most numerous version of the US halftrack supplied to the USSR was the T-48, known in the Red Army as the SU-57. It was used by tank destroyer brigades such as this one arriving in Prague in May 1945. (CTK via Jiri Hornat)

309. By the end of the war several Soviet tank units were equipped entirely with captured German Panther tanks. (Sovfoto)

310. A pair of captured German vehicles in use with Soviet forces in 1944. In the lead is a Pz Kpfw IV, followed by a Marder II tank destroyer. (Sovfoto)

309△ 310▽

Soviet Tanks in Retrospect

Soviet victory in the Great Patriotic War was inextricably bound up with the success of the Soviet tank industry in providing the Red Army with a constant flow of high-quality armoured vehicles. Although most Western histories of the war accept the German view that the defeat of the Wehrmacht on the Eastern Front in 1944 and 1945 was due to overwhelming superiority in *matériel*, they have not appreciated how formidable a task it was to produce this equipment. It is frequently overlooked that Soviet industrial capability during the war was considerably smaller than Germany's consequent on the loss of the key industrial regions in European Russia in 1941 and 1942. For example, in steel production, Germany out-produced the Soviet Union three-fold. In spite of this, during the war the Soviet Union manufactured more than 102,000 armoured vehicles compared to 76,000 for Germany. Only the United States with its production of 287,000 armoured vehicles exceeded Soviet production. The Soviets were able to accomplish this by superior industrial management and by the considerable sacrifices of the Russian people. From the outset of the war, Soviet war industry ruthlessly concentrated on only the most essential weapons. Tank production reached such high levels despite the weak industrial base because ship, locomotive, tractor and automotive production was cut out or sharply cut back in its favour.

More startling is the disparity between the USSR and Germany in tank production. During the war, the Soviet Union produced 79,611 tanks as compared to 25,006 tanks produced by Germany. Soviet armoured vehicle production was heavily weighted in favour of tank production, amounting to about two-thirds of total production with most of the remainder being mechanized assault guns. By contrast, German armoured vehicle production was almost evenly divided into thirds between tanks, self-propelled guns and armoured troop carriers. Similarly, both

THE ARMOURED EQUIPMENT OF RED ARMY MECHANIZED UNITS IN THE SECOND WORLD WAR

Tank Battalions	Date	Troops	Tanks (Total)	Tank Coys	T-38	T-26	BT	T-28	T-60, T-70	T-34	KV	IS
Infantry Tank Bn	1940		38	2	16	22	—	—	—	—	—	—
Paratroop Tank Bn	1940		50	3	50	—	—	—	—	—	—	—
Ind Tank Bn	1940		50	3	—	—	15	35	—	—	—	—
Ind Tank Bn	Sept 41	130	29	3	—	(29)	(29)	—	—	—	—	—
Ind Tank Bn	Nov 41	202	36	3	—	—	—	—	20	11	5	—

Tank Regiments	Date	Troops	Tanks (Total)	Tank Coys	T-38	T-26	BT	T-28	T-60, T-70	T-34	KV	IS
Cavalry Tank Regt	1940		64	6	—	—	64	—	—	—	—	—
Ind Tank Regt	Sept 42	339	39	3	—	—	—	—	16	23	—	—
Ind Heavy Tank Regt	Oct 42	214	21	3	—	—	—	—	—	—	21	—
Ind Tank Regt	Jan 43	572	39	3	—	—	—	—	7	32	—	—
Ind Tank Regt	Feb 44	386	35	4	—	—	—	—	—	35	—	—
Ind Heavy Tank Regt	Feb 44	375	21	4	—	—	—	—	—	—	—	21

Tank Brigades	Date	Troops	Tanks	A Cars	Lorries	Tank Bns	Motor Rifle Bns	T-26	BT	T-28	T-35	T-60, T-70	T-34	KV	IS-2
Ind Tank Bde	1938	2,745	201	28	482	4	1	201	—	—	—	—	—	—	—
Light Tank Bde	1938		267	28		4	1	267	—	—	—	—	—	—	—
Light Tank Bde	1938		278	28		4	1	—	278	—	—	—	—	—	—
Heavy Tank Bde	1938		183	25		3	1	—	47	136	—	—	—	—	—
Heavy Tank Bde	1938		148	25		3	1	—	54	32	62	—	—	—	—
Ind Tank Bde	Aug 41		93	—		3	1	—	—	—	—	64*	22	7	—
Ind Tank Bde	Sept 41		67	—		2	1	—	—	—	—	38*	22	7	—
Cavalry Tank Bde	Dec 41	1,471	46	—		2	1	—	—	—	—	26*	20	—	—
Infantry Tank Bde	Dec 41	1,471	46	—		2	1	—	—	—	—	20*	16	10	—
Tank Bde	Feb 42	282	27	—		2	—	—	—	—	—	—	17	10	—
Tank Bde	Apr 42	1,152	46	3	123	2	—	—	—	—	—	16	20	10	—
Tank Bde	July 42	1,038	53	3	110	2	1	—	—	—	—	21	32	—	—
Tank Bde	Oct 43	1,264	65	3	125	3	1	—	—	—	—	21	44	—	—
Tank Bde	Nov 43	1,354	65	3	125	3	1	—	—	—	—	—	65	—	—
Guards Heavy Tank Bde	Dec 44	1,666	65	3	125	3	1	—	—	—	—	—	—	—	65

*Actual equipment consisted of whatever light tanks were available

the USA and Britain devoted a significant fraction of their armoured vehicle production to armoured infantry carriers. The main factor inhibiting Soviet production of armoured infantry carriers was the limitation imposed by attrition of tanks on the Eastern Front. Although the USSR out-produced Germany three-fold in tanks and a significant portion of German tanks were committed to other theatres especially after 1944, the disparity in the front lines was never so great. This was mainly due to the severe losses in tanks suffered by the Red Army, notably during the first two years of fighting. Through greater tactical and operational skill, the Wehrmacht was able to exact a disproportionate kill rate against Soviet tanks until 1943. Although the Germans would maintain a narrowing, but still significant tactical edge over Soviet tank units throughout most of the war, by 1944 the growing operational and strategic skill of the Soviet Army combined with its expanding inventory severely reduced the Germans' attrition

GERMAN : SOVIET ARMOURED VEHICLE COMBAT LOSS RATIO, 1941–44

Period	Ratio	Period	Ratio
6/41-2/42	1:5.0	12/43-6/44	1:1.4
3/42-5/42	1:6.6	7/44	1:4.0
6/42-10/42	1:7.9	8/44	1:2.0
11/42-3/43	1:1.3	9/44	1:1.0
4/43-8/43	1:5.7	10/44-11/44	1:1.3
9/43-11/43	1:2.5		

GERMAN : SOVIET ARMOURED VEHICLE STRENGTH COMPARISON

	Germany (Total)	Germany (E. Front)	USSR (Total)
6/41	5,639	3,671	28,800
3/42	5,087	1,503	6,690
5/42	5,847	3,981	8,190
11/42	7,798	3,133	6,940
3/43	5,625	2,374	9,200
8/43	7,703	2,555	8,200
6/44	9,148	4,740	13,600
9/44	10,563	4,186	13,400
10/44	11,005	4,917	13,900
11/44	12,236	5,202	16,000
12/44	13,175	4,785	17,000
1/45	13,362	4,881	16,200

Figures include tanks and self-propelled guns and do not include armoured troop carriers or armoured cars.

Mechanized Brigades	Date	Troops	Tanks	Tank Regts	Motor Rifle Bns	T-70	T-34	BA-64
Mechanized Bde	Sept 42	4,000	39	1	3	16	23	12
Mechanized Bde	1943	3,740	39	1	3	—	39	10
Mechanized Bde	1944	3,790	41	1	3	—	41	9

Mechanized Artillery Units	Date	Troops	Batteries	HQ Tank	SU-76	SU-85	SU-100	SU-122	SU-152, ISU-152, ISU-122
SP Artillery Regt	Jan 43		6	—	17	—	—	8	—
Light SP Artillery Regt	May 43		4	—	21	—	—	—	—
Light SP Artillery Regt	May 43		3	—	12	—	—	—	—
Med SP Artillery Regt	May 43		4	T-34	—	—	—	16	—
Heavy SP Artillery Regt	May 43		4	KV	—	—	—	—	12
Heavy SP Artillery Regt	Aug 43		4	KV	—	—	—	—	21
Ind SP Artillery Regt	Aug 43		3	—	13	—	—	—	—
Tank Destroyer Bn	Aug 43		3	T-34	—	16	—	—	—
Tank Destroyer Bn	1944		3	T-34	—	21	—	—	—
Tank Destroyer Bn	1945		3	T-34	—	—	21	—	—
Guards Heavy SP Arty Bde	Dec 44	1,804	12	—	3	—	—	—	65
Guards SP Arty Bde	Dec 44	1,492	12	—	3	—	65	—	—

Tank and Mechanized Corps	Date	Troops	Tank Bdes	Motor Rifle Bdes	Tanks (Total)	BT, T-26	T-60, T-70	T-34	KV	BM-13	SU-76	SU-85	SU-152, ISU-152	IS-2
Tank Corps	1938	12,710	2	1	660									
Tank Division	June 40	11,343	2*	1*	375	102	—	210	63	—	—	—	—	—
Tank Corps	Mar 42	5,603	3	1	100	—	40	40	20	—	—	—	—	—
Tank Corps	July 42	7,800	3	1	168	—	70	98	8	—	—	—	—	—
Tank Corps	1943	10,977	3	1	208	—	—	208	1	8	12	16	21	—
Tank Corps	1944	12,010	3	1	207	—	—	207	—	8	21	21	21	—
Tank Corps	1945	11,788	3	1	207	—	—	207	—	8	21	21	21	21
Motorized Division	Nov 39				275									
Mechanized Corps	June 40	36,080	2**	1	1,031									
Mechanized Corps	Sept 42	13,559	1	3	175	—	75	100	—	8	—	—	—	—
Mechanized Corps	1943	15,018	1	3	204	—	42	162	—	8	17	8	—	—
Mechanized Corps	1944	16,442	1	3	197	—	21	176	—	8	12	16	21	—
Mechanized Corps	1945	16,318	1	3	183	—	—	183	—	8	21	21	21	—

*In the 1940 Tank Division these were tank and motor rifle regiments, not brigades.
**In the 1940 Mechanized Corps these were tank and motorized divisions, not brigades.

advantage. In order to maintain and expand its tank inventory, the Soviets could not seriously contemplate any significant armoured infantry carrier production since it would have detracted from the more important tank production. Instead, expedients were used such as tank hand-holds to permit tanks to carry infantry into battle. On occasions, this proved to be very costly as artillery and machine-gun fire could so easily strip the tanks of infantry. Although the Soviets made no major efforts to build armoured infantry vehicles in the pre-war years, it is unlikely that a lack of appreciation of the tactical utility of armoured infantry carriers was even a subsidiary feature in the lack of such production during the war. Immediately after the war, the Soviet Army began a major investment in armoured infantry vehicles such as the BTR-152 and BTR-60.

Another important factor in the Soviet Union's ability to outpace Germany in armoured vehicle production was its good

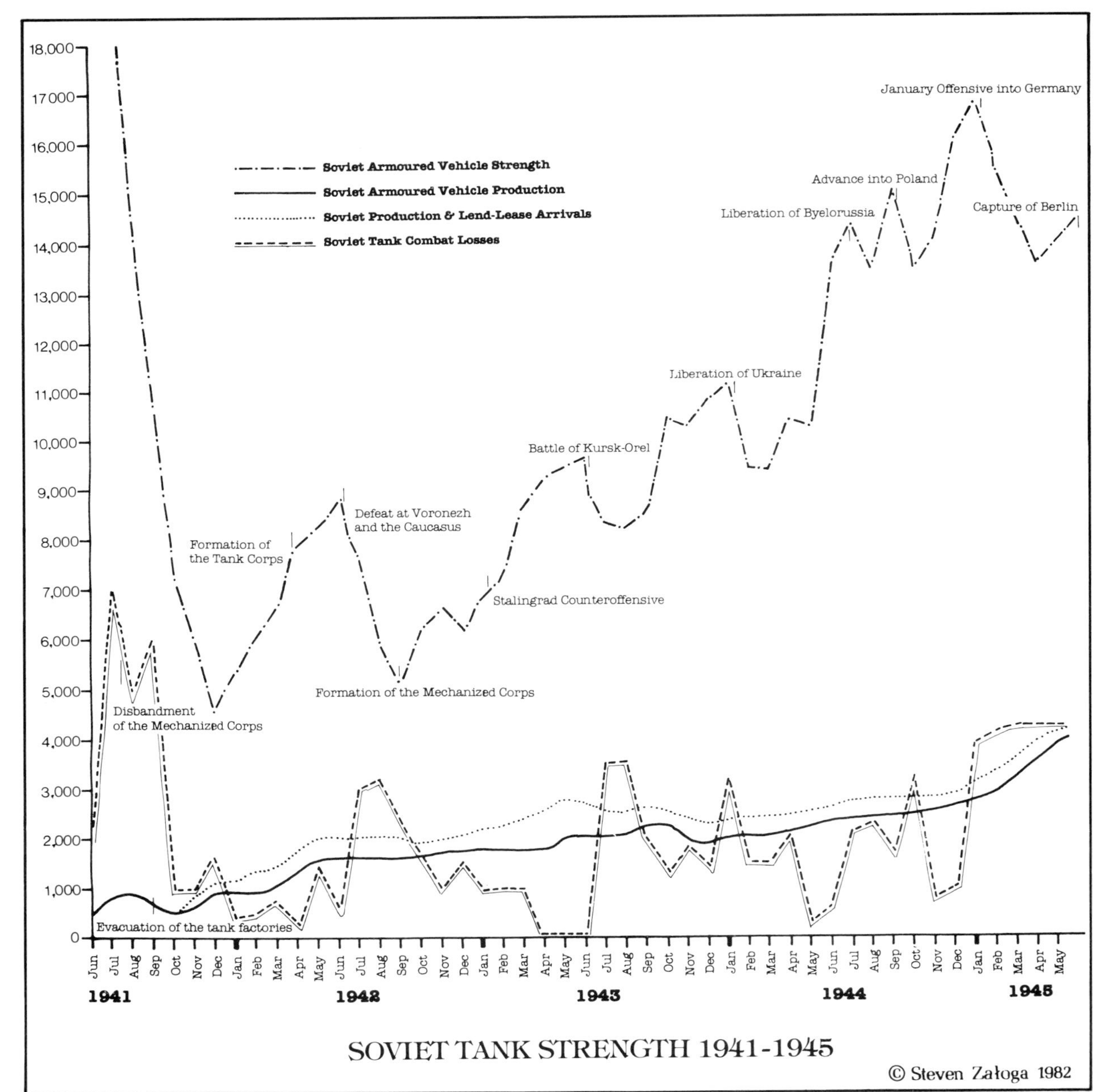

fortune in starting the war with two excellent tank designs, the T-34 and KV. By contrast, the Germans were obliged to develop new tanks to meet the Soviet threat and to modernize older designs, and this cut into potential production. Selection of heavy and complicated designs like the Panther and Tiger further exacerbated the problem. In 1944, Germany was forced to commit a significant portion of its tank strength to France to combat the US and British Armies which further diluted German tank strength. For example, in June 1944, there were about 2,000 armoured vehicles in western France compared to about 2,900 on the Eastern Front. The accompanying charts provide a numerical picture of the shifting tides of war for the Soviet and German tank forces on the Eastern Front. Lacking detailed Soviet accounts of overall tank strengths or losses, these charts are based to a large measure on German Intelligence estimates prepared by General Gehlen's Fremde Heere Ost (IIc). Gaps exist in the historical records, so in some cases estimates have had to be introduced. Some caution should be used in interpreting the charts. For example, the figures showing the relative ratio between Soviet and German tank strength on the Eastern Front should be interpreted with caution. The Soviet figures incorporate all Soviet armoured vehicles including those in RVGK reserve and those stationed in the Middle and Far East. Throughout the war, more than 2,000 Soviet armoured vehicles were stationed either in the Far East or Middle East. By contrast, the German figures refer only to vehicles operational at the front, in repair with units at the front, or in transit to the front. It does not include the sort of reserves held in Germany, which are comparable to the Soviet figures. In short, the disparity in strength between Soviet and German units at the front were never so great as it would seem from a casual glance at these figures. It is interesting to note that German

SOVIET ARMOURED VEHICLE PRODUCTION IN THE SECOND WORLD WAR

Type	1940	1941	1942	1943	1944	1945
Obsolete types	125					
T-26 variants	1,549					
BT-8	706					
T-28	12					
T-40		41	181			
T-50		48	15			
T-60		1,818	4,474			
T-70			4,883	3,343		
T-80				120		
T-34	117	3,014	12,553	15,712	3,723	
T-34-85				100	11,000	18,330
T-44						200
KV-1	141	1,121	1,753			
KV-2	102	232				
KV-1S			780	452		
KV-85				130		
IS-2				102	2,252	1,500
SU-76*			26	1,928	7,155	3,562
SU-122			25	630	493	
SU-85				750	1,300	
SU-100					500	1,175
SU-152				704		
ISU-122/ISU-152				35	2,510	1,530

*SU-76 figures include small number of ZSU-37 production; 1945 figures refer only to first six months.

PERFORMANCE OF SOVIET ARMOURED VEHICLE GUNS

Designation	20mm TNSh	45mm Models 32, 34, 38	76.2mm Model 27/32	76.2mm L-11	76.2mm F-34	85mm ZiS-S-53, D-5	100mm D-10	122mm M-30	122mm A-19, D-25	152mm ML-20
Barrel length	L/107	L/46	L/16.5	L/30.5	L/42.5	L/54.6	L/56	L/22.7	L/46.3	L/28.8
Armour piercing (HE) round		BR-240	BR-350	BR-350	BR-350A	BR-365	BR-412	—	BR-471B	BR-540
weight (kg)	0.96	1.4	6.3	6.3	6.3	9.02	15.6	—	24.9	48.7
initial muzzle vel (m/s)	815	760	387	612	655	792	1000	—	800	600
penetration at 500m (mm)	22	42	35	62	69	111	195	—	145	124
penetration at 1,000m (mm)	—	38	30	56	61	102	185	—	145	124
Armour piercing (DS) round	—	BR-240P	—	—	BR-350P	BR-365P	—	—	—	—
weight (kg)	—	0.85	—	—	3.0	4.9	—	—	—	—
initial muzzle vel (m/s)	—	1.070	—	—	965	1,200	—	—	—	—
penetration at 500m (mm)	—	80	—	—	92	138	—	—	—	—
penetration at 1,000m (mm)	—	50	—	—	60	100	—	—	—	—
HEAT round	—	—	—	—	BR-353A	—	—	BP-460A	BP-460A	—
weight (kg)	—	—	—	—	3.94	—	—	13.2	13.2	—
initial muzzle vel (m/s)	—	—	—	—	325	—	—	335	550	—
penetration, any range (mm)	—	—	—	—	75	—	—	200	200	—
High explosive round	—	—	F-534	F-534	F-534	—	F-412	F-460	F-460	OF-530
weight (kg)	—	—	6.23	6.23	6.23	—	15.8	22.6	22.6	40.0
initial muzzle vel (m/s)	—	—	387	610	680	—	900	515	800	655
HE-fragmentation round	—	O-240	OF-350	OF-350	OF-350	O-365K	—	OF-471	OF-471	OF-540
weight (kg)	—	2.1	6.21	6.21	6.21	9.2	—	24.9	24.9	43.7
initial muzzle vel (m/s)	—	750	387	610	680	792	—	515	800	655

Weight refers to projectile and not entire round; penetration performance is against vertical steel armour plate.

△311

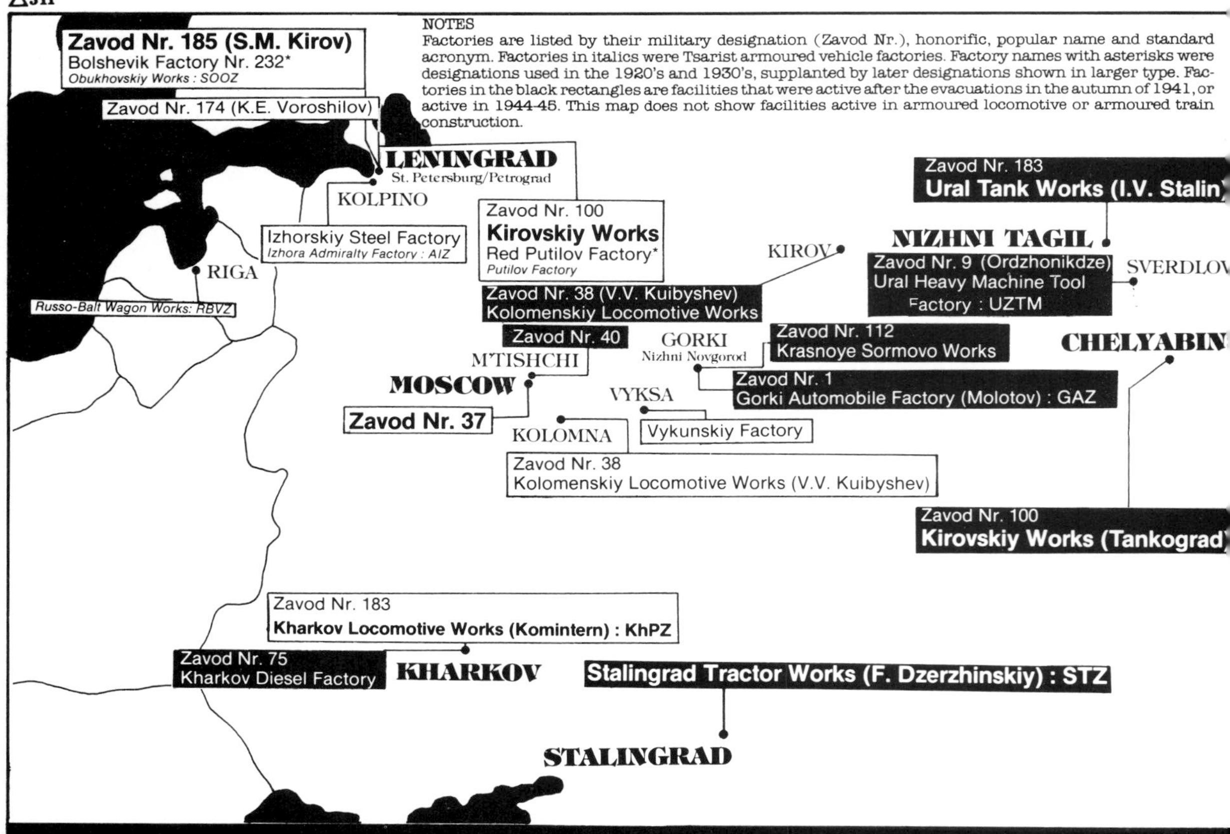

NOTES
Factories are listed by their military designation (Zavod Nr.), honorific, popular name and standard acronym. Factories in italics were Tsarist armoured vehicle factories. Factory names with asterisks were designations used in the 1920's and 1930's, supplanted by later designations shown in larger type. Factories in the black rectangles are facilities that were active after the evacuations in the autumn of 1941, or active in 1944-45. This map does not show facilities active in armoured locomotive or armoured train construction.
Zavod Nr. 185 (S.M. Kirov)
Bolshevik Factory Nr. 232*
Obukhovskiy Works : SOOZ
Zavod Nr. 174 (K.E. Voroshilov)
LENINGRAD
St. Petersburg/Petrograd
KOLPINO
Izhorskiy Steel Factory
Izhora Admiralty Factory : AIZ
RIGA
Russo-Balt Wagon Works: RBVZ
Zavod Nr. 100
Kirovskiy Works
Red Putilov Factory*
Putilov Factory
Zavod Nr. 38 (V.V. Kuibyshev)
Kolomenskiy Locomotive Works
KIROV
Zavod Nr. 183
Ural Tank Works (I.V. Stalin)
NIZHNI TAGIL
Zavod Nr. 9 (Ordzhonikdze)
Ural Heavy Machine Tool
Factory : UZTM
SVERDLOV
Zavod Nr. 40
M'TISHCHI
MOSCOW
Zavod Nr. 37
GORKI
Nizhni Novgorod
Zavod Nr. 112
Krasnoye Sormovo Works
Zavod Nr. 1
Gorki Automobile Factory (Molotov) : GAZ
CHELYABIN
VYKSA
Vykunskiy Factory
KOLOMNA
Zavod Nr. 38
Kolomenskiy Locomotive Works (V.V. Kuibyshev)
Zavod Nr. 100
Kirovskiy Works (Tankograd)
Zavod Nr. 183
Kharkov Locomotive Works (Komintern) : KhPZ
Zavod Nr. 75
Kharkov Diesel Factory
KHARKOV
Stalingrad Tractor Works (F. Dzerzhinskiy) : STZ
STALINGRAD
TSARIST & SOVIET ARMOURED VEHICLE FACTORIES
1916-1945

311. The crew of a T-34-85 Model 1944 of the 63rd Guards Tank Brigade being greeted by Czech civilians during the Soviet entry into Prague in May 1945; the castle of Prague can be seen in the background. (CTK via Jiri Hornat)

SOVIET ARMOURED VEHICLE RADIOS

Designation	RSMK	71-TK-1	71-TK-2	71-TK-3	9R	10R
Period	1930s	1938-39	1939-40	1940-41	1942-45	1942-45
Type	AM	AM	AM	AM	AM	AM
Frequency (megacycles/s)	2.5-12.0	4-5.6	4-5.6	4-5.6	4-5.6	3.75-6
CW range (km)	193	48	64	48	48	48
Voice range (km)	96	28	32	28	24	24
Power output (watts)	50		20		5	20
Power requirement (V)	12	12	12	12	12	12
Antenna length (m)	3.9	3.9	1.2	3.9	0.9-6.0	3.9

SOVIET ARMOURED CORPS ORDER OF BATTLE, 1942–45

Tank Corps	Tank Brigades	Motor Rifle Brigade	Guards Status
1 TK	89, 117, 159 TB	44 MSB	
2 TK	26, 99, 169 TB	58 MSB	8 GvTK
3 TK	50, 51, 103 TB	57 MSB	9 GvTK
4 TK	45, 69, 102 TB	4 MSB	5 GvTK
5 TK	24, 41, 70 TB	5 MSB	
6 TK	22, 112, 200 TB	6 MSB	11 GvTK
7 TK	3 Gv, 62, 87 TB	7 MSB	3 GvTK
8 TK	25, 34, 93 TB		
9 TK	23, 95, 108 TB	8 MSB	
10 TK	178, 183, 186 TB	11 MSB	
11 TK	20, 36, 65 TB	12 MSB	
12 TK	30, 97, 106 TB	13 MSB	6 GvTK
13 TK	3, 39, 135 TB		13 MK, 4 GvMK
14 TK	136, 138, 139 TB	21 MSB	
15 TK	88, 113, 195 TB	52 MSB	7 GvTK
16 TK	107, 109, 164 TB	15 MSB	12 GvTK
17 TK	66, 67, 174 TB	31 MSB	4 GvTK
18 TK	110, 170, 181 TB	32 MSB	
19 TK	79, 101, 202 TB	26 MSB	
20 TK	8 Gv, 80, 155 TB	7 GvMSB	
21 TK	64, 198, 199 TB		
22 TK	173, 176, 182 TB	22 MSB	5 MK
23 TK	3, 39, 135 TB	56 MSB	
24 TK	132, 54, 130 TB	24 MSB	2 GvTK
25 TK	111, 162, 175 TB	20 MSB	
26 TK	216, 19, 157 TB	14 MSB	1 GvTK
27 TK	55, 158 TB		
28 TK	39, 55, 56 TB	32 MSB	4 MK, 3 GvMK
29 TK	25, 31, 32 TB	53 MSB	
30 TK	197, 243, 244 TB	30 MSB	10 GvTK
31 TK	100, 237, 242 TB	65 MSB	

Guards Tank Corps	Tank Brigades	Motor Rifle Brigade	Former Status
1 GvTK	15, 16, 17 GvTB	1 GvMSB	26 TK
2 GvTK	4, 25, 26 GvTB	4 GvMSB	24 TK
3 GvTK	3, 18, 19 GvTB	2 GvMSB	7 TK
4 GvTK	12, 13, 14 GvTB	3 GvMSB	18 TK
5 GvTK	20, 21, 22 GvTB	6 GvMSB	4 TK
6 GvTK	51, 52, 53 GvTB	22 GvMSB	12 TK
7 GvTK	54, 55, 56 GvTB	23 GvMSB	15 TK
8 GvTK	58, 59, 60 GvTB	28 GvMSB	2 TK
9 GvTK	47, 50, 65 GvTB	33 GvMSB	3 TK
10 GvTK	61, 62, 63 GvTB	29 GvMSB	30 TK
11 GvTK	40, 44, 45 GvTB	27 GvMSB	6 TK
12 GvTK	48, 49, 66 GvTB	34 GvMSB	16 TK

Mechanized Corps	Mechanized Brigades	Tank Brigades	Guards Status
1 MK	19, 35, 37 MB	219 TB	
2 MK			7 GvMK
3 MK	1, 3, 10 MB	49 TB	8 GvMK
4 MK	36, 59, 60 MB	55, 158 TP	3 GvMK
5 MK	2, 9, 45 MB	233 TB	9 GvMK
6 MK	49, 50, 54 MB		5 GvMK
7 MK	16, 64, 63 MB	41 GvTB	
8 MK	66, 67, 68 MB	116 TB	
9 MK	69, 70, 71 MB	47, 227 TP	
10 MK			
11 MK			
12 MK			
13 MK	17, 61, 62 MB	13 TB	4 GvMK

Guards Mechanized Corps	Mechanized Brigades	Tank Brigades	Former Status
1 GvMK	1, 2, 3 GvMB	9 GvTB	
2 GvMK	4, 5, 6 GvMB	37 GvTB	22 GvSD
3 GvMK	7, 8, 9 GvMB	35 GvTB	4 MK
4 GvMK	13, 14, 15 GvMB	36 GvTB	13 TK
5 GvMK	10, 11, 12 GvMB	24 GvTB	6 MK
6 GvMK	16, 17 GvMB, 49 MB	29, 56 TP	
7 GvMK	24, 25, 26 GvMB	57 GvTB	2 MK
8 GvMK	19, 20, 21 GvMB	1 GvTB	3 MK
9 GvMK	18, 30, 31 GvMB	46 GvTB	5 MK

Key

Gv	Guards
MB	Mechanized Brigade
MK	Mechanized Corps
MSB	Motor Rifle Brigade
TB	Tank Brigade
TK	Tank Corps
TP	Tank Regiment

Note. Guards status refers to later unit designation. When a tank or mechanized corps was granted the honorific Guards distinction, the unit and many of its component brigades were redesignated. Former status refers to the unit's previous designation before the Guards designation. It should also be kept in mind that some of the brigades listed here were not permanently attached, particularly in 1942, and other brigades may have served with these corps at one time or another.

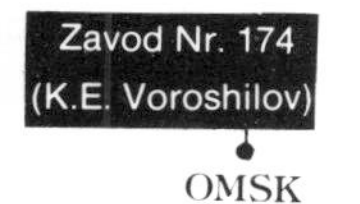

strength continued to grow throughout the war at a greater pace than Soviet strength, though never enough to catch up with the Allies. The main advantage enjoyed by the Red Army over the Wehrmacht throughout the war was not necessarily an immediate quantitative edge on the battlefield, though this did often exist. The real advantage lay in its substantial reserves of tanks. The Russians could afford to suffer staggering losses in tanks at the front, but have these redeemed by bringing forward fresh reserves.

Bibliography

During the course of research for this book, the primary archival sources used were the Lenin Library in Moscow, the National Archives in Washington DC and Suitland, MD, the Public Archives of Canada, the Public Record Office in London, the library of the Patton Armor Museum at Fort Knox and the library of the Royal Armoured Corps Museum at Bovington. The principal record groups used at the National Archives were RG 165, the US Army Military Intelligence Division records which were useful for their reports by military attachés in the USSR and neighbouring states; RG 160, the Adjutant General's records for their information on Lend-Lease; the microfilm records of the German Fremde Heere Ost IIc (T-78) for Intelligence reports on the Soviet Army during the Second World War; and RG242 for its collection of captured Soviet Army manuals. The main collections investigated at the Public Record Office were WO 277/8 and WO 193/580 regarding Lend-Lease shipments to Britain. The main records consulted in the Public Archives of Canada were RG 24 dealing with Canadian Lend-Lease affairs.

The following bibliography lists some of the books consulted during the course of research. Several categories of book have been omitted from the list for lack of space, namely campaign histories of the Soviet Army in the Second World War and general studies of tank development. For those interested in a bibliography of Soviet books dealing with the War, the authors highly recommend the Parrish study listed below. In the case of articles or books consulted in the form of translations by the American JPRS (Joint Publications Research Service) or FSTC (Foreign Science and Technology Center), a note has been appended to the list here, though the original source is indicated.

Alexandrov, V. *The Tukachevsky Affair*. Prentice-Hall Inc., 1964

Amann, R., *et al. The Technological Level of Soviet Industry*. Yale, 1977

Amnon, S. 'Red Army Doctrine and Training on the Eve of the Second World War'. In *Soviet Studies*, vol. 27, Nr. 2

Antonov, A. S., *et al. Tank*. Voenizdat, Moscow, 1954

'Les Autochenilles du Tsar de Russie'. In *L'Enthousiaste*, September 1978

Babadzhanyan, A. 'Marshal brontankovykh voisk Ya.N. Fedorenko'. In *Voyenno-istoricheskiy zhurnal*, October 1976

– (ed.). *Tanki i tankoviye voiska*. Voenizdat, Moscow, 1970

Babushkin, A. V. *Ognem raziashchie*. DOSAAF, 1975

Bagishev, A. 'Primenie tankov nerosredstvenoi podderzhki pekhoti v nastupateinikh operatsiyakh VOV'. In *Voyenno-istoricheskiy zhurnal*, June 1962

Bagramyan, I. Kh. (ed.). *Velikaya Otechestvenaya* . . . Molodaya Gvardiya, 1975

– *et al. Velikaya Otechestvenaya voina*. 5 vols., Planeta, 1975–80

Bajtos, I. 'The Russian T-60 Light Tank'. In *AFV-G2*, vol. 6, Nr. 8

Bakyrevich, Yu. 'Pod Indeksom BA-27'. In *Za Ruliom*, December 1977

– 'Stalnaya Trybuna Vozhdya'. In *Modelist Konstruktor*

Balcerzak, J., *et al. Technika Wojskowa LWP 1943–77*. WMON, 1973

Barker, A. J., and Walter, J. *Russian Infantry Weapons of WW2*. Arms and Armour Press, 1971

Barmine, A. *One Who Survived*. Putnam's, N.Y., 1945

Beaumont, J. *Comrades in Arms: British Aid to Russia 1941–45*. Davis-Poynter, 1980

Beskurnikov, A. 'Artilleriya blizhnego boya (SU-100)'. In *Modelist Konstruktor*, May 1971

– 'Artilleriya v tankovom (ISU-122)'. In *Modelist Konstruktor*, May 1973

– 'Boyevie amfibii (T-37)'. In *Modelist Konstruktor*, March 1980

– 'Bronya diya Pekhoti (T-26)'. In *Modelist Konstruktor*

– 'Boyevoi, osobii, bronyevoi (bronyepoyezd Kozma Minin)'. In *Modelist Konstruktor*, May 1980

– 'BT-5'. In *Modelist Konstruktor*

– 'Byt li tanku na pole (T-44)'. In *Modelist Konstruktor*, November 1978

– 'Legkaya Samokhodnaya (SU-76M)'. In *Modelist Konstruktor*, May 1975
– 'Legkie, no grazhnie (T-60)'. In *Modelist Konstruktor*, February
– 'Linkori tankovikh atak (KV)'. In *Modelist Konstruktor*
– 'Na Poligonakh i v boyakh (KV-85)'. In *Modelist Konstruktor*, September
– 'Na pyedestale . . .'. In *Modelist Konstruktor*, September 1973
– 'Ognem i kolesami (BA-64B)'. In *Modelist Konstruktor*, 1982
– 'Pervaya bronya (T-26)'. In *Modelist Konstruktor*, September 1981
– 'Poyedinok broni i snarda'. In *Modelist Konstruktor*
– 'Tank, obognavshiy vremya (T-34)'. In *Modelist Konstruktor*, May 1977
– 'Tank proriva (IS-3)'. In *Modelist Konstruktor*
– 'Tanki vykhodyat v boi (T-18)'. In *Modelist Konstruktor*, July
– 'Ural protiv Rheinmetalla (SU-85)'. In *Modelist Konstruktor*
Bialer, S. (ed.). *Stalin and His Generals*. Pegasus, 1965
Bilik, S. T. *Bronirovannie mashiny Sovetskoi Armii*. VABTV
Birykov, G., and Melnikov, G. *Anti-Tank Warfare*. Progress, 1972
Bolotin, D. N. *50 Years of Soviet Small Arms* (FSTC 1870–75). Military Historical Museum of Artillery, Engineer and Communication Troops of Leningrad, 1967
Brereton, J. M. 'The T-34/76'. In *Armour in Profile*, Nr. 9. Profile, 1967
– and Feist, U. *Russian Tanks 1915–1968*. Feist, 1970
Bronetankovye i mekhanizirovannye voiska Sovetskoi Armii. Voenizdat, Moscow, 1958
Ceskoslovehske Tankove Vojsko v SSSR. Nase Vojsko, 1978
Chalmayev, V. *Malyshev*. Molodaya Gvardiya, 1978
Chamberlain, P., Doyle, H., and Jentz, T. *Encyclopedia of German Tanks of World War Two*. Arms and Armour Press, 1978
Chamberlain, P., and Ellis, C. *Soviet Combat Tanks 1939–1945*. Almark, 1970
Champagne, J. P. *Les véhicules blindes a l'Armée Belge*. Everling, 1974
Chinn, G. M. *The Machine Gun*. vol. II, part VII: Soviet Machine Guns. Department of the Navy, 1952
Chudodeyev, Yu. V. *Soviet Volunteers in China 1925–45*. Progress, 1980
Condoide, M. *Russian American Trade*. Ohio State, 1946
Conquest, R. *The Great Terror*. MacMillan, 1969.
Cuny, J. 'Les chars Komsomolets'. In *L'Enthousiaste*, January 1981
Deborin, G. A. *Itogi i uroki otyechestvyennoi voinu*. Mysl, 1970
DeMouche, L. F. 'The First Russian Tank'. In *AFV News*, vol. 4, Nr. 1
'Dni i nochi tankograda'. In *Pravda*, 15 February 1975
Dupuy, T. N., and Martell, P. *Great Battles on the Eastern Front*. Bobbs-Merrill, 1982
Dyer, D. P. 'The SU-76'. In *Bellona Series*, Nr. 35. MAP, 1972
Dynin, I. 'Armour of Victory'. In *Soviet Military Review*, May 1978
Encyklopedia Techniki Wojskowej. WMON, 1978
Engineering Analysis of the Russian T34/85 Tank. Chrysler Corpn., 1951
Erickson, J. *The Road to Stalingrad*. Harper and Row, 1975
– *The Soviet High Command 1918–1941*. MacMillan, London, 1962; St. Martin's, Toronto, 1962
Fedoroff, B. T. *Dictionary of Russian Ammunition and Weapons*. Picatinny Arsenal, 1955
Feist, U. *Soviet Panzers in Action*. Squadron, 1973
'Flame-throwing Tanks in Action'. In *Tekhnika i Vooruzheniye*, August 1973 trans. JPRS
Galkin, F. I. *Tanki vozrashcaiutsia v boi*. Voenizdat, Moscow, 1964
Galkowski, W. *Rodowod katiuszy*. WMON, 1972
Garbuz, G. I. *Protivotankovaya oborona motostrelkovogo bataliona*. Voenizdat, Moscow, 1969
Gardner, M. *A History of the Soviet Army*. Praeger, 1966
Generals Balck and Mellenthin on Tactics. BDM Corpn., 1980
German Defense Tactics against Russian Breakthroughs. Dept. of the Army, 1951
Goff, J. 'The 1940 Soviet Tank Divisions: Geographic Order of Battle Analysis'. In *History, Numbers and War*, Winter 1978–79

– 'The Soviet Mechanized Corps on 22 June 1941'. In *AFV News*, vol. 17, Nr. 4
Gogolyev, L. *Avtomobili v boyevom stroyu.* Molodaya Gvardiya, 1981
Golubovich, V. 'Sosdaniye strategicheskikh rezervov'. In *Voyenno-istoricheskiy zhurnal*, April 1977
Golushko, I. M. *Tanki ozhivali vnov.* Voenizdat, Moscow, 1974
Govan, G. G. *The Tank Builders: A history of early Soviet armor Research and Development.* US Army Russian Institute, 1979
Grabin, V. G. 'Oruzhiya Pobyedi'. In *Oktyabr*, October 1978
Gribkov, A. I., *et al. Istoriya ordena Lenina Leningradskogo voyennogo okruga.* Voenizdat, Moscow, 1974
Grushevoi, K. S., *et al. Voyennie paradi na Krasnoi Plushadi.* Voenizdat, Moscow, 1981
Gvardii Katyusha. Lenizdat, 1978
Handbook on the Soviet and Satellite Armies, DA-PAM Nr. 30-50-1. US Army, 1953
Handbook on the USSR Military Forces, TM Nr. 30-430. War Dept., 1945
Hoffman, G. F. 'The United States' Contribution to Soviet Tank Technology'
ID Guide: Weapons and Equipment of East European Communist Armies, USAREUR PAM Nr. 30-60-1. HQ/USAREUR, 1973
Istoriya BT i MV Sovetskoi Armii. VABTV, 1953.
Istoriya Moskovskogo avtozavoda im. I. A. Likacheva. Mysl, 1966
Istoriya VOV Sovetskogo Soyuza 1941–45. vols. 1–6, Voyenizdat, Moscow, 1961–65
Istoriya vtoroy mirovoy voiny 1939–1945. Voyenizdat, Moscow, 1973–
Ivanov, V. D. (ed.) *50 let sovetskikh vooruzhennikh sil.* Voenizdat, Moscow, 1967
– *Oruzhie Pobedi.* Molodaya Gvardiya, 1975
Jones, K. M. 'Degtaryev machine-guns'. In *Military Modelling*, October 1974
Kharitonov, N. 'Armoured Train No. 50-67'. In *Soviet Military Review*
Khrushchev, N. *Khrushchev Remembers.* Penguin, 1971
Kireev, N. *Tankovye voiska Sovetskoi Armii.* Znanie RSFSR, 1974
Korolkov, N. P. *Tanki v boiu.* Voenizdat, Moscow, 1959
Korniushin, P., and Korolkov, I. *Sovetskie tankisti.* Voenizdat, Moscow, 1954
Korzhikin, Yu. 'Lyzhzya bedet cherez front (NKL-26)'. In *Modelist Konstruktor*
Kostyuchenko, S. A. *Istoriya Kirovskogo Zavoda 1917–1945.* Mysl, 1966
Kosyrev, E. A., *et al. Tanki.* DOSAAF, 1973
Kotin, Zh. Ya. 'Ogon, manevr i bronya'. In *Voyenniy Vestnik*, September 1977
Kovalyev, I. V. *Transport v VOV 1941–45.* Nauka, 1981
Kravchenko, G. S. *Voyennaya Ekonomika SSSR.* Voyenizdat, Moscow, 1963
– *Ekonomika SSSR v godi VOV.* Ekonomika, 1970
Kriegswehrmacht der UdSSR Januar 1942. OKH-FHO IIc, 1942
Krupchenko, I. 'Noviy trud o tankovikh voiskakh'. In *Voyenno-istoricheskiy zhurnal*, February 1973
Krupchenko, I. E. *Sovetskie tankovie voiska 1941–45.* Voenizdat, Moscow, 1973
Kucherenko, I. E. *Stroitelstvo i boyevoe primenenie sovetskikh tankovikh voisk v godi VOV.* Voenizdat, Moscow, 1979
Kumanyev, G. A. *Na sluzhie fronta i tyla 1938–45.* Nauka, 1976
Kurkotkin, S. K. (ed.) *Tyl sovetskikh vooruzhennykh sil v VOV.* Voenizdat, Moscow, 1977
Kuzmichev, A. P. *Sovetskaya Gvardiya.* Voenizdat, Moscow, 1969
Latykhin, A. N., *et al. Bog Voini.* Molodaya Gvardiya, 1979
Lee, M. O. 'The Transport Glider KT (A-40T)'. In *AFV News.* vol. 3, Nr. 6
Liddell Hart, B. H. *The Tanks, 1914–1939.* vol. 1. Praeger, 1959
Lundstrom, J. 'Prelude to Disaster: The Soviet Army – June 1941'. In *Panzerfaust*, Nr. 58
– 'The Soviet Mechanized Corps 1941'. In Panzerfaust, Nr. 55
Mackintosh, M. *Juggernaut: The Russian Forces 1918–1966.* MacMillan, 1967
Magid, A. *Korabely delaiut tanki.* Znanie, 1973
Magnuski, J. 'Aerosanie'. In *Wojskowy Przeglad Techniczny*, March 1977
– *Ciezki dzialo sambobiezne ISU, TBU 64.* WMON, 1980
– *Czolg ciezki IS, TBU 31.* WMON, 1974
– *Czolg sredni T-34, TBU 1.* WMON, 1970
– *Dzialo Pancerne SU-85, TBU 8.* WMON, 1971
– 'Lekki czolg radziecki BT-7'. In *Modelarz*, November 1967
– *Lekki dzialo samobiezne SU-76, TBU 43.* WMON, 1976
– 'Najslynniejszy czolg II wojny swiatowej'. In *Za wolnosc i lud*, 1978
– *Radzieckie dziala samobiezna.* WMON, 1975
– 'Radzieckie samochody pancerne w latach 1917–1945'. In *Wojskowy Przeglad Techniczny*, 1978
– *Ruchome Twierdze.* WMON, 1978
– 'Rozwoj radziecki artylerii samobieznej'. In *Wojskowy Techniczny*, February–March 1973
– 'The SU-122 Medium SP Gun'. In *AFV News*, vol. 13, Nr. 5

– *Uwaga T-34!*. WMON, 1977
– *Von Tankograd nach Berlin*. Militarverlag dDDR, 1980
– *Wozy Bojowe*. WMON, 1964
– and Zaloga, S. 'The Monsters of Leningrad'. In *Airfix Annual for Military Modellers*. PSL, 1978
– and Zaloga, S. 'The T-50 Infantry Tank'. In *Airfix Magazine*, September 1979
Makushin, N. 'Razvitiye oboronnoi promyshlennosti urala v 1937–1941'. In *Voenno-istoricheskiy zhurnal*, March 1977
Mashini, atavshie pamiatnikami. DOSAAF, 1977
Maslov, P. 'Formirovaniye i podgotovka tankovikh reservov'. In *Voenno-istoricheskiy zhurnal*, January 1972
Mazarrasa de, J. *Los Carros de Combate en España*. Ed. San Martin, 1977
Melnikov, P. E. *Krasnogorskiy Bastion*. Lenizdat, 1982
Meretskov, K. *Serving The People*. Progress, 1971
Miller, Jr., M. J. *Red Armor in Combat*. Grenadier, 1969
Milsom, J. 'Russian Armoured Cars'. In *AFV Profile*, Nr. 60. Profile, 1973
– 'Russian BT Series'. In *AFV Profile*, Nr. 37. Profile, 1971
– *Russian Tanks, 1900–1970*. Arms & Armour Press, 1970
– and Zaloga, S. *Russian Tanks of World War 2*. PSL, 1977
Miranovich, G. 'At the Armored Vehicle Proving Grounds'. In *Krasnaya Zvezda*, trans. JPRS
Mitrofanov, A. N. *Ogon, bronya, manevr*. DOSAAF, 1978
'Der mittlere Panzer T-28'. In *Modelbau Heute*, August 1980
Mostovenko, V. D. 'K voprosu o razvitii sovetskikh tankov'. In *Voenno-istoricheskiy zhurnal*, July 1965
– 'Perviye tanki nashei strani'. In *Krasnaya Zvezda*, 8 August 1967
– 'Razvitiye sovetskikh tankov v gody VOV'. In *Voenno-istoricheskiy zhurnal*, September 1961
– 'Samie moshchiye tanki'. In *Znanenosets*, May 1975
– 'Tanki, vremya konstruktor'. In *Krasnaya Zvezda*, 30 June 1965
– *Tanki*. Voyenizdat, Moscow, 1958
Muikku, E. 'Klimi Mallina'. In *IPMS-Mallari*, Nr. 28
– 'T-34'. In *IPMS-Mallari*
Nikulin, L. *Tukhachevskiy*. Voenizdat, Moscow, 1964
Norman, M. 'Russian KV and IS'. In *AFV Profile*, Nr. 17. Profile, 1971
Nove, A. *An Economic History of the USSR*. Penguin, 1972
O'Ballance, E. *The Red Army*. Faber and Faber, 1964
O legendarnikh kayushakh. Molodaya Gvardiya, 1975
Offord, E. F. 'SU-85 and SU-100 Tank Destroyer'. In *Armour in Profile*, Nr. 21. Profile, 1968
Orgill, D. *T-34: Russian Armor*. Ballantine, New York, 1971
Orientiernngsheft Russland, Stand 1.2.1939. OKH/Wehrmacht, 1939
Orlov, V. 'Glavniy konstruktor tankov'. In *Znanie-sila*, February 1978
Oruzhie slavy. Voenizdat, Moscow, 1975
Parrish, M. *The USSR in World War II: An Annotated Bibliography*. Garland, 1981
Pataj, S. *Artyleria Ladowa*. WMON, 1975
Perotkin, I. (ed.). *The Battle of Kursk*. Progress, 1974
Perret, B. 'Forgotten Armoured Engagements'. In *Military Modelling*, Nr. 1, July 1979
– and Lord, A. *The Czar's British Squadron*. William Kimber, 1981
Pictorial History of the Russian Tanks of World War 2: T-34 and Stalin. Koku-Fan, 1978
Pobedonostsev, Yu. A. *Pervye starty*. DOSAAF, 1972
Popov, N. 'Razvitiye samokhodnoi artillerii'. In *Voyenno-istoricheskiy zhurnal*, January 1977
Pozdyshev, S. *Zheleznodorozhnie voiska Sovetskoi Armii*. Voenizdat, Moscow, 1959
Preliminary Report No 1/0, Russian KV/1. Royal Military College of Science, 1944
Preliminary Report No 2/0, Russian T/34. Royal Military College of Science, 1944
Proriv podgotovitelnoi oborony strelkovimi soyedineniyami. Po opytu VOV 1941–45. Voenizdat, Moscow, 1957
Pustovoitenko, N. *Po Mestam boevoi slavi Odessi*. Mayak, 1976
Radzievskiy, A. I. *Tankoviy udar*. Voenizdat, Moscow, 1977
Ramspacher, E. *Chars et Blindes Français*. Lavauzille, 1979
Reznichenko, G. I. *Mashini, stavshiye pamiatnikami*. DOSAAF, 1977
Roland, P. 'Soviet Self-propelled Artillery, 1921–1945'. In *Military Journal*, vol. 1, Nr. 1
Roschin, I. *Narod-Frontu*. DOSAAF, 1974
Rosenlof, K. 'The KV-1 (Appliqué)'. In *NYAS Newsletter*, Nr. 1
– and Zaloga, S. 'The BA-64 Light Armored Car'. In *IPMS Quarterly*, vol. 12, Nr. 5
Rotmistrov, P. A. *Tanki na voine*. DOSAAF, 1966
– *Vremia i tanki*. Voenizdat, Moscow, 1972

Russian Combat Methods in World War II, DA-PAM Nr. 20-230. US Army, 1950
Ryzhakoye, A. 'K voprosu o stroitelstve bronetankovikh voisk Krasnoi Armii v 30-e gody'. In *Voenno-istoricheskiy zhurnal*, August 1968
Scheibert, H. *Stalins Giganten – KW-I un KW-II*. Podzun-Pallas, 1978
Scoon, R. 'To Russia With Love'. In *Old Motor*, vol. 9, Nr. 1
Scott, H. F., and Scott, W. F. *The Armed Forces of the USSR*. Westview, 1979
Selivokhin, V. M. *Tank*. Voenizdat, Moscow, 1962
von Senger und Etterlin, F. M. *Der sowjetische mittlere Kampfpanzer der Baureihe T-34 bis T-62*. J. H. Lehmans, 1970
Sergeyev, L. 'Legendarnaya tridsatchetverka'. In *Krasnaya Zvezda*, 28 January 1982
Shavrov, V. B. *Istoriya konstruktsiy samoletov v SSSR 1938–1950*. Mashinstroyenie, 1978
Shimkevich, L. 'Naval Artillery'. In *Soviet Military Review*, July 1980
Shmakov, V. A. *Vishli na front katyushi*. Mosk. Rabochii, 1982
Shmelev, I. 'Komponovka'. In *Tekhnika Molodezhi*, April 1979
– 'Latniki XX veka'. In *Tekhnika Molodezhi*, June 1979
– 'Perviye'. In *Tekhnika Molodezhi*, February 1979
– 'Semya tanketki rastet'. In *Tekhnika Molodezhi*, July 1979
– 'Tolko po rovnomu mestu'. In *Tekhnika Molodezhi*, March 1979
– 'Ognemetnie tanki'. In *Tekhnika Molodezhi*
– 'Uchitivaya boyevoi opit'. In *Tekhnika Molodezhi*, May 1979
Shtemenko, S. M. *The Last Six Months*. Doubleday, 1977
Shugurov, L. M., and Shirshov, V. P. *Avtomobili strani sovetov*. DOSAAF, 1980
Sidorenko, A. 'Razvitiye vooruzheniya sukhoputnykh voisk v 1945–1953'. In *Voenno-istoricheskiy zhurnal*, March 1973
Sloan, J. 'Soviet Units in World War II: New Data from Soviet Sources'. In *History, Numbers and War*, vol. I, Nr. 3
Small Unit Actions during the German Campaign in Russia, DA-PAM Nr. 20-269. US Army, 1953
Solovyov, B. *The Turning-Point of World War II*. Progress, 1982
Sovetskaya Voennaya Entsiklopediya, vols. 1–9. Voenizdat, Moscow, 1976–80
'Sovetske tanky'. In *Voienska Tekhnika*, November 1977
Sovetskie tankovie voiska 1941–45. Voenizdat, Moscow, 1973
Sovetskiye voorzhenniye sily: istoriya stroitelstva. Voenizdat, Moscow, 1978
The Soviet Army, DA-PAM Nr. 30-2. US Army, 1949
Soviet Projectile Identification Guide TM 30-240. US Army, 1953
'Soviet Tank Repairs in World War II'. In *Strategy and Tactics*, Nov–Dec 1980
Spielberger, W. *Armor on the Eastern Front*. Aero, 1968
Statistical Abstract of Industrial Output in the Soviet Union, 1913–55. National Bureau of Economic Research, 1956
Sutton, A. C. *Western Technology and Soviet Economic Development, 1930–45*. Hoover Institute, 1971
Syropyatov, V. 'Razvitiye tanktekhnichesko obespecheniya v gody voiny'. In *Voenno-istoricheskiy zhurnal*, September 1978
Tank. Voenizdat, Moscow, 1954
Tanki. DOSAAF, 1973
Tanks of Other Nations: USSR. RAC Bovington, 1970
Terekhov, P. V. *Boyevie deistviya tankov na severo-zapade v 1944*. Voenizdat, Moscow, 1965
Truppen-Ubersicht und Kriegsgliederungen Rote Armee. Stand: August 1944. OKH/FHO IIc, 1944
Tsigankov, I. S., and Sosulin, E. A. *Orudiye, minomet, boyevaya mashina*. Voenizdat, Moscow, 1980
Ubersicht uber seit kriegbeginn neuaufgetretene verbande der Roten Armee, 1941–1945. OKH/FHO IIc, 1945
Ubersicht uber seit kriegsbeginn zerschlagene und aufgeloste verbande der Roten Armee, 1941–1945. OKH/FHO IIc, 1945
Vannikov, V. L. 'The USSR defence Industry on the Eve of the War'. In *Voprosi Istoriy*, October 1968–January 1969
Vishniakov, V. A. *Tank na pedestale*. Voenizdat, Moscow, 1970
Voprosy strategii i operativnogo iskusstva v sovetskikh voyennikh trudakh, 1917–1940. Voenizdat, Moscow, 1965
Voprosy taktiki v sovetskikh trudakh, 1917–1940. Voenizdat, Moscow, 1970
Vozneseskiy, N. *Voennaya Ekonomika SSSR v VOV*. Ekonomika, 1948
Vseobecny Popis Tanku a Jeho Bojova a Technicka Charakteristika T-34-85. CSA, 1953
White, B. T. *British Tanks and Fighting Vehicles, 1914–45*. Ian Allen, 1970
Whiting, T. E., *et al. The US Army in World War II, Statistics-Lend Lease*. US Army, 1952
Yakovlyev, N. D. *Ob artillerii i nemnogo o sebe*. Voenizdat, Moscow, 1981
Yeremenko, A. *The Arduous Beginning*. Progress, 1966

Yevtyushiy, N. I. *Razvitiye aerosannogo transporta v SSSR*. Izd. Akad. Nauk, 1959
Yuvenalev, I. 'Aerosan v boyakh za rodinu'. In *Modelist Konstruktor*
– 'Aerosan NKL-16/42'. In *Modelist Konstruktor*, March 1981
Zaloga, S. 'Another Look at the IS-2'. In *AFV News*, vol. 11, Nr. 5
– 'Armour in China, 1920–45'. In *Military Modelling Annual*, 1982
– 'Armour of the Spanish Civil War'. In *Modelworld*, vol. 2, Nr. 3
– 'The Factory Tanks of Odessa'. In *AFV News*, vol. 14, Nr. 4
– *Modern Soviet Armour*. Arms & Armour Press, 1979
– 'Organization of the Soviet Armoured Force, 1939–1945'. In *AFV News*, vol. 16, Nr. 2
– 'Russian Heavy Tanks JS-1 and JS-2'. In *AFV News*, vol. 6, Nr. 3
– 'Soviet AFV Production'. In *AFV News*, vol. 13, Nr. 1
– 'Soviet Anti-tank Guns in World War II'. In *Tankette*, vol. 9, Nr. 1
– 'Soviet Armoured Trains, 1920–41'. In *AFV News*, vol. 17, Nr. 2
– 'Soviet Artillery Tractors, 1940–45'. In *AFV News*, vol. 13, Nr. 1
– 'Soviet Heavy Tanks in World War II'. In *Flight Plan*, vol. 3, Nr. 2
– 'Soviet Rocket Artillery'. In *Military Journal*, vol. 1, Nr. 2, 4
– 'Soviet Tank Markings, 1930–45'. In *AFV News*, vol. 9, Nr. 6; vol. 10, Nr. 1
– 'SU-76'. In *AFV News*, vol. 6, Nr. 6
– 'The T-34 Series'. In *Flight Plan*, vol. 1, Nr. 4
– and Grandsen, J. *Blitzkrieg 1939–40*. Arms & Armour Press, 1981
– and Grandsen, J. *Eastern Front 1941–45*. Arms & Armour Press, 1983
– and Grandsen, J. 'Pre-war Soviet AFV Markings'. In *Military Modelling*, December 1982
– and Grandsen, J. 'Soviet Fast Tanks'. In *Military Modelling*, January, February 1982
– and Grandsen, J. *Soviet Heavy Tanks*. Osprey, 1981
– and Grandsen, J. *The T-34 Tank*. Osprey, 1980
– and Grandsen, J. *The T-34 in Action*. Squadron, 1981
– and Kamiat, B. 'The Putilov-Garford Armored Car'. In *NYAS Newsletter*, Nr. 1
– and Rosenlof, K. 'Armour of the Russo-Finnish Wars, 1940–44'. In *Airfix Magazine*, May 1976
Zakharov, M. 'Kommunisticheskaya partiya i tekhnicheskoye perevooruzheniye armii i flota v gody predvoyennikh pyatiletok'. In *Voenno-istoricheskiy zhurnal*, February 1971
Zgorniak, M. *Sytuacja militarna Europy w okresie kryzysu politycnego 1938*. PWN, 1978
'Zhozef Kotin'. In *Voyenny Vestnik*, September 1977
Zhukov, G. K. *The Memoirs of Marshal Zhukov*. Delacorte, 1971
Zinich, M. S. 'Stankostroyeniye i tyzheloye mashinostroyeniye SSSR v 1941–45'. In *Voprosy Istoriy*, May 1973

Index

312 The crew of a Russian M4A2 (76mm) rest aboard their tank after having joined up with the US 82nd Airborne Division at Grabow, Germany on 3 May 1945. This is believed to be a tank of the 64th Guards Tank Brigade which fought at Gdansk earlier in the year. (US Army)

победе!